CALCULUS FROM THE GROUND UP

Calculus from the Ground Up

Copyright © 2018 Jonathan Bartlett all rights reserved.

Published in the United States by BP Learning in Broken Arrow, Oklahoma.

Library of Congress Control Number: 2018905879

ISBN: 978-1-944918-02-6

For author inquiries please send email to info@bplearning.net.

Bookstore bulk order discounts available. Please contact info@bplearning.net for more information.

For more information, please see www.bplearning.net.

1st printing

Calculus from the Ground Up

By
Jonathan
Bartlett

To Michael Bartlett, my Dad, who first sparked my interest in Calculus, and to Sue Rankin, who made sure I learned it well.

Contents

Chapter 1

Introduction

There are already a million books on calculus available. Why write the million and first? I began writing this book because most books on calculus miss the heart of calculus.

When I was younger I did well in mathematics, but I never enjoyed doing math. Math always seemed boring and dry. You have a formula, you stick some numbers in, and you get a result. Sometimes the problems might be slightly more interesting, but at the end of the day, it was just plugging numbers into equations and getting answers. I was good at it, but I did not enjoy it.

Calculus, however, is a different animal.

The community that I often tutor with, Classical Conversations, employs the *classical* method of education. Most people have never heard of this method. At its core, it is very simple. All learning, for any subject, is divided into three stages. In the first stage, called the *grammar* stage, the student learns the vocabulary, the facts, the pieces of the puzzle for the subject they are studying. In the second stage, called the *logic* stage, the student learns how to put the bits that they learned in the grammar stage into a form that can be used to solve problems or answer questions. The last stage, called the *rhetoric* stage, the student learns how to invent—how to create new ideas out of the old ones that they have learned, and how to convince others that their ideas are true.

I used to coach basketball, and I used this method in coaching. First, I taught the grammar stage—how to dribble, pass, and shoot. Then, I taught the logic stage—how to move the ball around the court and make a shot. This usually culminated in them learning one or two basketball plays, such as the famous "give and go" play. If I had coached older players, I would have gone on to the rhetoric stage—how to look at the opposing team and create a strategy to beat them.

Mathematics is like this, too. First, in the grammar stage, we learn to count, add, subtract, multiply, and divide. Then, in the logic stage, we learn all of the great formulas—the distance formula, the quadratic formula, various formulas for the areas of various shapes, and the basic methods for solving equations. There is a little rhetoric there, but not much. Geometry sometimes ventures slightly into the rhetoric stage with formal proofs, but the students are usually too young, and the material is, frankly, uninteresting to most students.

This is why I like calculus so much. Calculus is the gateway to the rhetoric stage of mathematics. If you have suffered through formula after boring formula, tired of the mere memorization, calculus is your chance to be *creative* with math. Sure, it still has formulas and things to memorize. Yes, it is math and requires an amount of rigor, with both correct and incorrect answers. However, rather than simply take someone else's formula and memorize it "because the book said so," you will learn to *create your own*, and to understand where the other formulas are coming from.

In physics, for example, you learn the equation to find the position of a falling body after a certain period of time. The equation is $p(t) = p_0 + v_0 t + \frac{1}{2}at^2$. In physics, you just have to memorize that equation. In calculus, however, you will learn how you could have easily come up with that equation on your own. To be certain, there is much beyond calculus in mathematics. But calculus is the gateway which leads you there.

Most calculus textbooks I have encountered are mostly about teaching the list of topics that are needed to pass a standardized test on calculus. While testing and standards have their place, the goal of this book is not to teach to a test or make sure you will have met someone else's standard. My goal with this book is to focus on *how math is invented*, and invite you to be a part of that process. I want to train more than your skills in applying formulas, I want to train your *intuitions* so that they will be well tuned to look at problems from a variety of perspectives and find solutions.

It is not all excitement—there will be hard work and some drudgery. But at the end, you will have made mathematics your servant, and the opaqueness of the subject will fade to a transparency that you did not know was available.

1.1   The Focus of This Book

There are two sides to Mathematics that often get rolled into one: the abstract logic of what you are trying to do, and the concrete practicalities that get in the way.

To understand the distinction, let's say I am trying to find how fast I can get from my house to the theater downtown. Let's say that there are two steps—first take the bus downtown, then take a separate bus to the theater. Let's say the bus going downtown is a 30 minute ride, and the bus to the theater is a 5 minute ride. That sounds like an easy problem, right?

$$30 \text{ minutes } + 5 \text{ minutes } = 35 \text{ minutes}$$

Well, abstractly, yes—if you add the two numbers together, it takes 35 minutes. However, it is only an easy problem *given certain assumptions*. For instance, the simple addition depended on both buses being there at the time I wanted them to be. Let's say I wanted to be at the theater at 6:00 PM. What time do I need to leave? Using our abstract solution, I need to leave at 5:25. But what happens if the bus to the theater doesnt pick up at 5:55? How does that affect my timing?

Therefore, to make a more correct description of my calculations, I need to say, "if for any time I want to leave there is a bus which leaves at that time, and if this is true for both bus stops, then I can add the times the two buses take together to arrive at a total time." Now, if you count the letters in that sentence, I actually spend more time talking about the preconditions that make my abstract logic true than I do about the logic itself. If I had gone even further and included the entire bus schedule in listing the times of day for which my equation would work, then I would have totally obscured the logic of what I was trying to accomplish.

This, I think, more than anything, is what obscures higher-level math. This is why people think math is hard. So much time and effort is spent on describing the preconditions that are required to be true in order to for an operation to be valid, that there is almost no time left for actually talking about the basic logic behind what that operation is supposed to be doing or accomplishing.

I find, however, that if someone understands the basic, underlying logic of an operation, they will also intuitively understand the limits of it, even if they can't directly articulate it. For instance, if you do a lot of reading, you will come to a very usable understanding of how sentences are put together. You will know the rules of grammar *implicitly*, even if no one tells you them explicitly. You may not know how to describe the grammar you are using, but because you have an intuitive grasp on how the language works, you are able to follow the rules without knowing them exactly.

Therefore, this book will not spend a lot of time on formulating the precise limitations of every operation. We will cover some of the more practically important ones, but my hope is that the intuitive understanding you gain will render these details unneeded for the most part. These details are not unimportant, but their place of importance is not here.[1] It is editors, not writers, who must be well-versed in the grammatical rules, and here we are focused on being writers and creators of math, not editors. Editing is an important function, but it is not the focus of this book. This book aims at getting you to intuitively understand how to work with equations and get them to do your bidding.

You should also note that if you ever get bogged down reading other mathematics books and papers, keep in mind that a lot of the long definitions that they give are a lot like our example of the bus schedule. The core idea may actually be simple and straightforward (and often beautiful), but the descriptions of these ideas will likely dedicate a lot of space and thought into determining the precise conditions under which these ideas can be applied. The trick for someone reading such a book or paper is to be able to separate out the core idea and intuition from all of the extraneous details which, while technically true and perhaps necessary, oftentimes interfere from a good understanding of the subject.

If you are an instructor, you should also take a moment right now and read Appendix A, as it details many of the ways which make this book unique from a teaching perspective.

1.2 What You Should Already Know

This book assumes that the student will already have completed courses in algebra, geometry, and trigonometry, although the required geometry and trigonometry is kept to a minimum. The student should be able to manipulate equations, graph equations, analyze triangles, and know the basic formulas such as the formula for a line, area formulas, the quadrative formula, the distance formula, Pythagorean theorem, exponents, logarithms, etc. The student should be familiar with trigonometry functions such as sin, cos, *tan*, as well as understand the inverse functions such as arcsin, arccos, arctan, etc. Finally, the student should have an understanding of the concept of a function, and how functions work within mathematics. These ideas will not be given much or any explanation in the book, save for a brief overview in the first part of the book. Additionally, Appendix H contains many of the rules from Algebra and Trigonometry, and can be used for reference if you are fuzzy on the rules.

1.3 How This Book is Organized

First of all, this book is written in a very conversational style. I teach calculus every year, and this book is based on what I tell my students in class. It is conversational because my goal is to draw insights out of students, and I find that speaking to them, asking them questions, and pointing to the deep insights are the best ways to engage with them. The book is written in the way that I would talk to my class, and I hope that it helps you to better connect with the material.

---

[1]My hope is that this approach will lead to an increase in the number of people conversant in the calculus without a large decrease in the rigor of the practice of mathematics. Hopefully the intuitions gained will help you both (a) apply calculus in the right circumstances, and (b) have a general sense of when you may be outside of the boundaries where it is applicable. I don't want to diminish in any way the role that the editors play in mathematics. Mathematics is wonderful precisely because there is a group of people who break it down into its most basic propositions and rebuild it to be sure that everything holds together. This is unlike other disciplines, such as biology, where many practitioners have difficulty even understanding the difference between an assumption and a conclusion, and there doesn't seem to be anyone in the field even capable of realizing the situation that they are in. My goal is to land somewhere in the middle, such as in the engineering fields, where not everyone has the skills (or desire) to deduce everything from first principles, but recognizes that such things are important, and could probably at least envision how it might be done, and respect those that actually do it.

Each chapter will have important new terms printed in bold print. At the end of each chapter is a review of the lessons learned, and then an application section which contains problems to be solved.

The first part of this book focuses on the basic fundamentals of mathematics that calculus makes heavy use of—lines, variables, functions, graphs, and basic thinking skills. The first part ends with an overview of what calculus is and the main insights driving it. The second part of the book focuses on the derivative, which is one of the two main operations of calculus. The third part of the book focuses on the integral—the other main operation of calculus. The fourth part of the book deals with some more philosophical (but very practical!) concepts concerning infinity and related ideas. Finally, the fifth part introduces you to some variations on the core calculus ideas.

One thing the reader should be aware of is that, as the text progresses, each time a particular type of problem is solved, it receives less and less explanation than the previous time. The first time a type of problem is given, there is usually a large amount of detailed explanation of every step. I try to state even the obvious, because the obvious is not obvious to everyone.

The next time through, while it is all still explained, some of the steps may be condensed into one, or the steps are not given the same amount of detail. By the third time through, the student is expected to be somewhat familiar with the process, and not need copious explanations of each point. If a student is having difficulties understanding the second or third example of a concept, they should go back and re-read the previous example to see if the step that they are stuck on receives more explanation.

As for exact or approximate answers, many of the numerical answers in the solution guide are approximate. There is no hard and fast rule for deciding whether or not something should be approximated or kept in an exact form, but generally I try to keep solutions exact until keeping it exact becomes more unwieldy than useful. This usually means that if I just have fractions, I will keep them as fractions, but if I have complex formulas involving roots or other strange functions (i.e., sin, cos, ln, etc.), I will move to decimal approximations. When rounding, the solution guide rounds to four decimal points. Depending on when and how you round, the final digit for rounded answers may differ from the solution guide. If you approximated slightly differently than I did, it is not a big issue. The goal here is to understand how calculus works, not get stressed out over how many decimal points you have in your solution.

Now, if the answer is looking for an *equation* instead of a number (and we will be building a lot of equations in this course), the solution should be exact, because we want precisely the right equation. However, if your equation is in a slightly different form than ours, that is alright.

For instance, if my answer was $\frac{1+x}{x}$, I could also express that as $\frac{1}{x} + 1$. Both of those are equivalent, so they are both considered correct. The solution guide tries to give a fairly clean-looking solution (i.e., putting constants before variables in multiplied terms, simplifying terms, etc.), but if you didn't do all of the clean-up steps, that is okay. Write the equations the way that you learned to do it in whatever Algebra book you learned from.

There is a balance between wasting time trying to get an equation into the simplest form and having an unnecessarily complicated answer. I try to hit this balance well, but there may be a few occasions where your answer is off only because you simplified it in a different way. If you are self-studying, this is fine. If you are in a class, I'm sure your professor will let you know what his rules for simplification are.

In any case, enough of the introduction—let's get started!

Part I

Preliminaries

This part begins with a general philosophical framework for understanding how to approach mathematics problems. Next, there is a short refresher for several of the foundational tools that undergird calculus, focusing on lines, graphs, and functions. Having a solid grasp of these concepts will enable you to understand the concepts behind calculus much more readily. The section ends with a high-level overview of where calculus will lead us.

Chapter 2

A General Method for Solving Mathematics Problems

A lot of people get confused in mathematics because they view it as a whole list of equations and formulas to be memorized. However, memorizing equations and formulas is merely scratching at the surface of mathematics. It is no surprise that someone who has merely committed such things to memory finds mathematics tedious and boring.

In this chapter I will present the outline for a general method for solving harder problems in mathematics. When one is used to simply having a list of formulas and applying the formulas, it might be surprising to think about a *general* method for solving problems. And, to be honest, this method does not lead you directly to the answers. Instead, what it does is to prepare your mind to discover them. If the question is simple and you know the formula, then this method is overkill. However, if it is a difficult problem and you are stuck, this formula will help you out. While we won't refer back to these steps specifically in the rest of the book, I think that you will find these concepts in play as we discover the concepts behind calculus.

2.1   The Process

2.1.1   Step 0: Write it Down

Before we get to the *real* steps, you should be sure that you actually *write the problem down*. This may seem obvious, but many people are tempted to skip this step because it seems repetitive. Writing the problem down, however, makes sure that you really know what the problem is asking. I nearly failed my college statistics class because I was continually answering the wrong question and leaving out important parts of the question. Writing down the question as it is posed helps prevent you from taking too many mental shortcuts, and it also prevents you from missing key details that will help you solve the problem. Writing the problem down ensures that the question itself goes all the way through your mind to your hand.

2.1.2   Step 1: Find Out What the Problem Means

I like to tell people that "step 1 of math is philosophy." What I mean by that is that problems are not just numbers that we plug into an equation that someone else gave us. Numbers only work when they are given *meanings*, and the important first step is to grasp what is *meant* by the question.[1]

This is the job of philosophy. Philosophy asks the question of meaning—it tries to take something that is ambiguously worded and convert it into something definite. I encourage you, if you ever get the chance, to read the works of Plato. It isn't that Plato's ideas are perfect or even great. It is that the main character in Plato's writings, Socrates, is able to assist the people he talks with in making their ideas more clear, definite, and rational by asking good questions about the *meanings* of the words they use.

Socrates always forced the people he talked with to articulate clear meanings of the words they used. He asked tough questions about these terms to force the person he was talking with to see all the details and implications about the terms they were using—both so they could make better and more exacting use of their own terminology, and so they could see if there was any vagueness or contradiction in the terms they were using.

Mathematics is the same way. When presented with a problem, the first step is to know what you are talking about. You must ask yourself questions about the meaning of the problem in order that you may know just what it is you are trying to find. If your *conception* of the problem is vague or contradictory, then you will have little success in finding the answer. If, instead, you can formulate a very precise meaning for the problem, the way forward to the solution becomes much easier.

When finding the meaning of the problem, there are two general categories I like to use: knowledge and ignorance. In order to do mathematics well, you must be able to be very specific about both your knowledge and your ignorance. Think about Algebra—in Algebra, we are very specific about our ignorance—we mark it with an x. If I say, "three times some number is twelve" then I can convert that into an equation by marking my ignorance ("some number") with an x and saying $3x = 12$. Because I marked my ignorance explicitly, I can then solve that and say $x = 4$.

We might be ignorant in more than one area. If this happens, then we simply add more letters (x, y, z, a, b, c, etc.), each one representing a *specific* ignorance. If you confuse the things that you are ignorant about, you will get the math wrong.

Oftentimes we have more than one similar quantity. These are often differentiated with subscripts. For instance, if I talk about the distance that Bob and Jill each travelled, I can either give each distance its own letter, such as x for Bob's distance and y for Jill's, or I can use a single letter for distance, and use a subscript for each one. In that case, I could use d_{Bob} for Bob's distance, and d_{Jill} for Jill's distance. Sometimes mathematicians shorten their subscripts, so that d_B is Bob's distance, and d_J is Jill's distance. Or, they can try to abstract away Bob and Jill and replace them with numbers, such that d_0 is Bob's distance and d_1 is Jill's distance.[2]

In all of these cases, we are being explicit about our ignorance, and using **variables** to represent what our ignorance is in equations.

In addition to being precise about our ignorance, understanding the meaning of the problem means being precise about our *knowledge*. This entails a number of things. First, we need to write down any relationships that the problem itself gives us, and we should try to write them down in the form of equations, if the problem is specific enough to do that. After that, we should write down any other facts that we know relating to the problem.

---

[1]It is usually wrongfully thought that physics is developed primarily by experiment. It isn't that experiments aren't important, but if you are a physicist, it is unlikely that what you do all day is experiment after experiment. Some do this, but the primary tool for the physicist is actually philosophy. Einstein developed his equations while he was a patent clerk. They don't give patent clerks fancy labs, or even any labs at all. He developed the equations for relativity by simply *thinking* about what it meant if matter and energy were equivalent. How would the world look if this were true? Unfortunately, in the sciences today, philosophy is all but forgotten. But philosophy is about training your mind to think clearly about tough questions that may be presented ambiguously. Learning the methods of philosophy train our mind to think clearly when others are thinking mindlessly.

[2]Also note that some mathematicians start counting at zero and some start counting at 1. So, one mathematician may use d_0 and d_1 while another mathematician may use d_1 and d_2.

If we are dealing with triangles, what are some facts we know? Well, we know that all the angles will add up to 180 degrees (or π radians). If the triangle is a right triangle, we know that we can use the pythagorean theorem. If the triangle is not a right triangle, we know that we can draw a line and convert our single triangle into two right triangles that are easier to manage. We also know the equation for the are of the triangle, and various rules about triangles such as those for similar triangles.

If we are dealing with circles, we know another set of facts. We know the equations for the area and the circumference. You might remember the formula for the arc length of a circle. You might remember the equation for a graph of a circle.

In any problem, you should certainly list all of the facts defined in the problem. But if you are stuck, sometimes just listing through all the facts that you know that are related to the facts and relationships listed in the problem is helpful. Looking through them will help you realize connections and relationships you hadn't thought of before.

Learning and doing math is not about numbers so much as it is about learning truths about the world that can be related to each other. Numbers, formulas, and equations are merely the vehicles which allow us to do that.

The best type of relationship to know for mathematics are equations, and they should be written as such where possible. But even if you don't know how to express a relationship as an equation, at least write down the relationships that you know.

2.1.3 Step 2: Converting Questions into Answers

The thing I find most amazing about mathematics is that it allows us to convert precisely worded questions into answers using the internal logic of the question itself. Think about this. Normally, when we have a question, we have to *go out* to find the answer. We have to look in a book, or study the world, or ask someone. But, in mathematics, the goal is to ask the question in a precise enough way that *the question can be transformed into the answer.*

This is a useful skill for your whole life. It means that many of the things we think about, if we learn to be precise enough in how we approach the question, the question itself tells us what the answer is. Mathematics is merely practice for this kind of thinking.[3]

To convert a question into a fixed numerical answer (i.e., we want to know the specific value of x), we need to at least have the same number of equations as we do unknown values. We don't always need a fixed answer—sometimes we are just looking to discover a new relationship. In any case, the number of equations gives us the maximum number of variables that can be reduced. You can't always use equations to reduce your variable count—sometimes two equations are both telling you the exact same thing, so they don't actually count as independent equations. But, at most, you can reduce the number of unknowns by at most the number of equations you have at your disposal.

We can often convert our questions into answers by simply making substitutions. Let's say we have the two equations:

$$y = x + 5$$

$$xy = 6$$

Here, we have an equality between y and $x + 5$, which means that anywhere I see y I can replace it with

---

[3]A great book that will give you a large amount of practical advice for adding precision to questions is the book *How to Measure Anything: Finding the Value of "Intangibles" in Business* by Douglas Hubbard. He shows how nearly anything, no matter how abstract, can be converted into a measurable quantity.

$x + 5$. So, if we replace y with $(x + 5)$ in the second equation, we will get a new equation:

$$x(x + 5) = 6$$

Note that it is usually preferable when doing substitutions to actually put parentheses around your substitution when you first do it, so it is clear that the order of operations gets properly applied. Since y was a single unit in the original equation, the thing it replaces comes in as a single unit, and the parentheses make sure that happens correctly.

If we simplify this new equation, we have the following equation:

$$x^2 + 5x = 6$$

This looks a lot like something—what is it? It looks almost like a quadratic equation. In fact, if we manipulate it just a bit, it becomes a quadratic equation:

$$x^2 + 5x - 6 = 0$$

At this point, we can go back to Step 1 and ask what the equation *means*. If we have a quadratic, do we know of any special formulas related to this? In fact, we can use the quadratic formula to get an answer (actually, a set of two answers) directly:[4]

$$x = \frac{-b \pm \sqrt{b^2 - 4ac}}{2a}$$

$$x = \frac{-5 \pm \sqrt{5^2 - 4 \cdot 1 \cdot (-6)}}{2 \cdot 1}$$

$$x = \frac{-5 \pm \sqrt{25 + 24}}{2}$$

$$x = \frac{-5 \pm \sqrt{49}}{2}$$

$$x = \frac{-5 \pm 7}{2}$$

Thus, x can be either 1 or -6.

So, not only can we convert our questions into answers, sometimes what we will do is convert our questions into *new* questions which we have to go back to step 1 and think about all over again.

2.1.4   Step 3: Convert Our Steps Into a Formula

This step is often not necessary, but this is what really makes math helpful. Solving a problem once is good. Solving a problem in such a way that you have a formula for the rest of your life is better. In life (whether in business, the sciences, or even construction) you will often face the same quantitative problems repeatedly. You could solve them each time. Or, even better, you can come up with a formula so that you only have to solve them once, and then never have to solve them again. From then on out you can just plug and chug your numbers.

To convert a series of steps into a formula, what you need to do is the following:

1. Figure out which parts of your formula are fixed and which parts will vary from time to time that you use it.

---

[4]If you don't remember the quadratic formula, you should probably review it and other formulas in Appendix H. The quadratic formula is used quite a bit in this book.

2. Replace the parts that will vary each time (but still stay constant within a particular usage) with a variable to represent them. These are not variables in the typical sense because they do not vary within the problem. Instead, I call these **constant variables** because in some ways they act like variables (they *vary* each time you use the formula), but, within the equation, they act like constants. This distinction has probably not been important in your mathematics career previously, but, as we will see in the future, in calculus constants and variables get treated differently.

3. Next, perform the steps just like you did before, but using your constant variables as stand-ins for the real numbers.

4. At the end, you will get a formula for doing the same process over and over again.

If you aren't quite sure about this step, it should become clearer in the examples in the next section.

2.2 Applying the Method

In this section, we will look at a few applications of the method to simple problems. These are problems that you could probably solve well enough without these steps, but seeing them worked on simple problems will help put your mind in the right place to use the steps in harder problems.

2.2.1 Bob and Jill's Travels

Bob and Jill both leave a point going opposite directions. They each travel at a different, but steady, speed for three hours—Bob is traveling at 25 miles per hour and Jill is traveling at 30. After three hours, how far apart are they?

Step 1 for this is to find out what the problem means:

1. What are we looking for? We are looking for the total distance they traveled. We will call that distance x and thus name what it is we are ignorant of.

2. Bob and Jill *leave a point*. Stated another way, that means their starting distance apart is zero.

3. Bob and Jill are going in opposite directions. If they were going at angles to each other it would be more difficult, but since they are going in opposite directions, that means that the total distance between them is just the distances they each travelled *added together*.

4. Since we don't know the individual distances that Jill and Bob traveled, we will represent their travels by other variables—d_J and d_B.

5. Bob and Jill are traveling at a *speed*. What is a speed? Speed is $\frac{\text{distance}}{\text{time}}$.

6. What is the relationship between speed and distance? Distance is simply speed multiplied by the amount of time spent.

7. How long were they traveling? The question itself gives that answer—three hours.

8. How fast are they traveling? Again, this is answered by the question—Bob is traveling at 25 miles per hour and Jill is traveling at 30.

We can convert several of these into equations. We can convert 1, 2, 3 & 4 into a simple equation like this:

$$x = d_B + d_J$$

We don't yet know d_J and d_B, but that's okay. Points 5, 6, 7, and 8 allow us to write equations for these:

$$d_B = 25\frac{\text{miles}}{\text{hour}} \cdot 3 \text{ hours} = 75 \text{ miles}$$

$$d_J = 30\frac{\text{miles}}{\text{hour}} \cdot 3 \text{ hours} = 90 \text{ miles}$$

In step 2, we convert our question into an answer using the internal logic of the question itself. We have three unknowns (x, d_J, and d_B) but we also have three equations (two of which we just solved). Therefore, we can plug our answers into the final equation and get the results we want:

$$x = d_B + d_J$$
$$= 75 \text{ miles} + 90 \text{ miles}$$
$$= 165 \text{ miles}$$

So, the total distance between them is 165 miles.

Now, step 3 says that we should convert this into an equation. That way, if we have a similar problem in the future, rather than having to go through the entire mental process that we just did, we can just have an equation that we can plug the numbers into and find the result.

As mentioned the way to do this is with constant variables to stand in for the givens in our problem. What were we given? We were given the amount of time (we'll call that t), Bob's speed (we'll call that s_B), and Jill's speed (we'll call that s_J). So, we can rewrite our equations using these variables:

$$x = d_B + d_J$$
$$d_B = s_B \cdot t$$
$$d_J = s_J \cdot t$$

Even though we don't have specific valuese for these anymore, we can substitute them just as we did before. We will put the *formula* for d_B in place of d_B in the equation, and the same for d_J. That will give us the following:

$$x = s_B \cdot t + s_J \cdot t$$

While not required, we can actually simplify this a bit by factoring out t from the right hand side.

$$x = t(s_B + s_J)$$

And now we have a simple equation that we can use for *any* similar problem.

2.2.2   Adding Consecutive Odd Numbers

What three consecutive odd integers add up to 111?

In order to solve this problem, we need to do a few things. The first is to express our ignorance. What don't we know? We don't know *any* of the three numbers. So, let's give each number its own letter to express our ignorance—x, y, and z. However, now that we've expressed our ignorance *precisely*, the problem statement allows us to make this into an equation:

$$x + y + z = 111$$

That is three unknowns but only one equation. To solve it, we need at least three equations. However, we have not finished asking about the meaning of the problem.

The problem says, "consecutive odd integers." What do we know about odd integers? Well, half of the integers are odd. Specifically, every other number is odd.

Additionally, it says they are consecutive, which means one right after another. So, how do you get from one specific odd number to the very next one? You add two! Therefore, if we designate x as our first number, that means that we can get to the next one (y) by just adding two to x. We can write that down as an equation:

$$y = x + 2$$

What about z? Since it is also a consecutive odd integer, we know it has to be two more than y. That's enough for an equation as well.

$$z = y + 2$$

Now we have three equations for three variables. We can move on to step 2, which is converting our question into an answer. We can take our original equation and substitute for z:

$$x + y + (2 + y) = 111$$

Now we can substitute for y:

$$x + (2 + x) + (2 + (2 + x)) = 111$$

By regrouping and rearranging a bit, we can convert this into:

$$x + x + x + 2 + 2 + 2 = 111$$
$$3x + 6 = 111$$

And now we are in a position to solve it:

$$3x + 6 = 111$$
$$3x = 111 - 6$$
$$3x = 105$$
$$x = \frac{105}{3}$$
$$x = 35$$

And, we can then determine that y is 37 and z is 39.

In this case, Step 3 is even easier, because the only constant that needs to be transformed into a constant variable is the final value. We can use v for this. Then, we can go back and do a similar transformation:

$$x + y + z = v$$
$$x + y + (2 + y) = v$$
$$x + (2 + x) + (2 + (2 + x)) = v$$
$$3x + 6 = v$$

Now we have an equation that will solve any similar question. If I ask, "what three consecutive odd integers add up to 237" you can simply substitute that in to get the first one (x):

$$3x + 6 = 237$$
$$3x = 231$$
$$x = 77$$

As a side note, this assumes that the given value v actually *can* be achieved by adding three consecutive odd integers. If your result is an even number or a decimal, then that result can't be achieved by adding three consecutive odd integers.

2.3 Additional Tips

Many students have trouble knowing what to do when they get stuck or have a hard time getting answers correct. The following tips are not an exhaustive, but should help you if you keep them in mind while solving problems.

2.3.1 Don't Solve the Problem Immediately

Sometimes, for very simple problems, you can solve the problem immediately. However, this is almost always a bad idea when dealing with new concepts. The problem with solving a problem immediately is that you haven't taken time to *understand* the problem. Remember, Step 1 of math is philosophy. Take time to understand the problem before attempting to solve it.

2.3.2 Don't Skip Steps

My children, when they have difficulties with math, is almost always because they skipped steps. Getting impatient and trying to skip steps hurts you in two ways. In the first way, it makes it more likely that you are going to do the problem wrong. When you *write down* each step, it makes you more deliberate about what you are doing, and you can more easily catch your mistakes. Additionally, other people can help you see any mistakes you may be making. In the longer term, the problem-solving steps help ingrain in your mind the pattern of the problem. Skipping steps, especially when you are first learning, prevents the pattern of the problem from being imprinted on your mind.

2.3.3 Draw the Problem

If a problem involves anything that is remotely drawable, you should do it. Because you are now thinking about it both visually and analytically, it will help you involve more of your mind in the problem-solving activity. When you can see the problem, sometimes the solutions, or at least the direction of the solution, becomes more apparent.

2.3.4 Focus on the Next Step

Don't think you have to solve the whole problem in one bite. You can actually iterate back-and-forth between Step 1 and Step 2 as many times as you need. Apply one step, then look at the problem again anew. Does the problem look different now? Are there any avenues that have opened up? Should you press forward or go back to the drawing board?

If you don't force yourself to do the whole thing at once, but just do the next step that is before you, oftentimes you can reach a solution that you hadn't thought of before.

2.3.5 Ask "What If"

Another important task in problem-solving is asking "what if" questions. In geometry or trigonometry, you might think, "what if we drew a line here?" How would that change the way we looked at the problem? What if we drew a line that created a right triangle?

You can also think about equivalencies that you know. Sine and cosine are related. What happens if you transform a sine function into a cosine function—does that lead you closer to a solution?

Sometimes, you get an equation or problem that *almost* looks like something you've seen before. You might then ask yourself, is there something that I can do to this problem that makes it easier to solve?

Along the same lines, while we are used to trying to *reduce* the number of variables, sometimes adding one in makes a problem more similar to a problem we know how to solve.

When you first start doing mathematics, your ability to ask these questions is limited. However, as you learn more and more mathematics, your ability to ask good "what if" questions increases. Geometry and trigonometry are the best introduction to this type of thinking.

A good example of this will be seen in Section 4.7.

2.3.6 Think Through a Simplified Example

Sometimes, if you are having trouble figuring something out, it helps to think through a simplified version of the problem. What is it that is making the problem hard? Can you solve the problem without that obstacle? If so, how can you then modify your thinking to include the obstacle?

Oftentimes thinking through the simple pieces are what allow us to eventually discover the solutions to the hard problems.

2.4 Conclusion

Many think that philosophy is very divorced from mathematics, because math deals in hard numbers while the philosophers gaze at their navels. Such thinking could not be more wrong. Philosophy, at its core, provides the basic tools of thought. Some of these are so ingrained in us that we cannot see life through any other lens. This doesn't mean that philosophy is useless, it just means that it has been so useful that we cannot imagine life without it.

Philosophy asks two main types of questions—questions about *what it means* for something to be true, and *how we can know* if something is true. Philosophy allows us to build up mathematical principles by understanding the meaning of each term. In order to build equations, we must know what a thing really is at the deepest level. That is philosophy.

An equation is nothing more than an equivalency between two ideas.[5] To know that two things are equivalent requires the ability to understand philosophically what they mean. Otherwise, we wouldn't be able to tell that they were equal. Once we know they are equal, we can use the rules of mathematics (which were themselves derived from philosophy) to manipulate them and deduce further truths.

For my own classes, in nearly every example I do with students, I make them answer the philosophical questions first: what does the question mean? This prevents you from using equations that don't apply, and

---

[5]Technically, this can be any relationship, not just equality. Inequalities are equations, too. But the general idea still applies.

will be of the most general help to you in the future. Having a habit of tackling the problem of meaning first helps you to think for yourself. In life, you often have to rely on experts. Experts are great, but oftentimes the questions that they are answering are not the same as the questions that you are asking. Knowing how to dive into the meanings of questions will help you know if the answers you are getting match the questions you are asking, and if the expert is applying the right solution to the problem.

Chapter 3

Basic Tools: Lines

For any journey into the woods, you need to make sure that your backpack has the basic tools that you will need. These first chapters make sure that some of the most important concepts from previous years are at the forefront of your mind while you go through this book.

3.1 The Line

The humble line is a powerful tool of mathematics. A **line** is a straight path through space (whether in two, three, or more dimensions), that extends infinitely in both directions. When we refer to a line in this book, we always mean a straight line. A curved line will simply be referred to as a curve. Sometimes the word line refers only to the part of the line that is between two endpoints, but that is more properly called a **line segment**.

Innumerable theorems, formulas, and equations are based on the properties of a line, and calculus is no exception. Therefore, a review of lines is important.

Out of all of the possible lines in a graph, in order to specify a specific line, you only need two points from the line. It doesn't matter if you are working in one, two, or three dimensions (or more), any two points will uniquely determine a line. As long as the two points are not the same, you can draw one and only one line that connects and includes them. Such a line does not stop at the given points, but extends infinitely in both directions. The two points are used merely to point you to the one line among the infinite possible lines you could be referring to. Any two, distinct points on the line will do the job of defining your line.

3.2 The Equation of a Line

In two dimensions, lines follow a simple, standard equation:

$$y = mx + b \tag{3.1}$$

This equation has four components:

x This is a variable that corresponds to the horizontal component of a location on the line's graph.

y This is a variable that corresponds to the vertical component of a location on the line's graph.

m This is a constant that represents the slope of the line. The slope is how many units the graph goes up
   for every unit that it goes to the right, often described as "rise over run" (i.e., $\frac{rise}{run}$).

b This is a constant that represents how much the line is shifted up or down from the origin (a positive
   number means that it is shifted up, a negative number means that it is shifted down, and zero means
   that it actually crosses the origin).

Here is the graph of the equation $y = 3x + 1$:

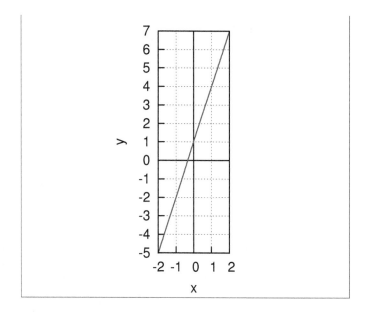

If you take this equation, and match each term to the corresponding value in the standard line equation
(Equation 3.1), then you will see that *m* is 3 and *b* is 1. *b* tells you where the line will intersect with the
y-axis. Since *b* is 1, then the graph is shifted up 1 unit from the origin, which means that it crosses the
y-axis at 1. Check the graph to verify this.

Now, the slope (*m*) is 3. This means that line will go *up* three units for every one unit that it goes to the
right. If the slope is positive, the line will slant to the right, if the slope is negative, the line will slant to the
left, and if the slope is zero the line will be flat.

Slopes are often represented as ratios, even when they don't need to be, to help readers understand that the
slope corresponds to a ratio between the changes in the *y* direction and the changes in the *x* direction. In
this case, the slope is 3, which, if expressed as a ratio, is $\frac{3}{1}$. For every 3 units the *y* value changes, the *x*
value changes 1. The slope can also just be a real number, which can be read as rising that many units for
every one unit to the right that it moves.

Let's look at another example:

$$y + 1 = \frac{1}{2}(x - 3)$$

This equation doesn't look like the standard line equation, but nonetheless it does in fact give a line. However,
in order to get it to match up to Equation 3.1 you will need to manipulate it a little bit. The first thing to
do is to distribute the coefficient $\frac{1}{2}$ over the $(x - 3)$ term. Doing that will give you

$$y + 1 = \frac{1}{2}x - \frac{3}{2}$$

This is closer, but there is a constant on the left hand side of the equation that we need to move to the right in order to match Equation 3.1. Therefore, we will subtract 1 (which is also $\frac{2}{2}$) from both sides of the equation, yielding:

$$y = \frac{1}{2}x - \frac{5}{2}$$

This equation now corresponds with the equation of the line. It has a slope of $\frac{1}{2}$, which means that for every 1 unit of change of the y value, it will change 2 units of the x value. b is set to $-\frac{5}{2}$, which means that it intercepts the y-axis at -2.5. Pull out a sheet of graph paper and see if you can draw this line simply from the information given.

3.3   Determining a Line From Two Points

Earlier we said that a line can be determined from any two points. We can intuitively think about this by thinking of a piece of graph paper with two dots drawn on it. If we take a ruler, there is only one way to connect those dots in a straight line. In addition, when we make the straight line, there are infinitely many possible points on that line. If we had chosen *any* two points on that line, using the ruler to connect them would give us the *exact same* straight line.

Now, when we look at the graph paper and think about what it means to connect two points into a line, we are thinking intuitively and geometrically. That is, we are using our common sense to better understand what we see. However, it is important in mathematics to be able to translate our intuitions into a form that is more usable—one that we can calculate with. It would be great if we could take the *idea* that a line is created by two points and convert it into a *formula* that allows us to convert the two points into an equation for a line.

Formulas like this, which take intuitive ideas and convert them into algebraic form that we can then use for manipulation and calculation, are called **analytic forms** (also known as **closed forms**), because they give us a reliable way of analyzing the situation which involves more precision and less intuition. Analytic forms allow us to not only make our ideas clear and exact, but also to create formulas which can make our ideas usable and teachable. Additionally, analytic forms are much easier to implement on a computer as well for future automation.

In this case, can we take the *idea* that a line is formed from any two points, and convert it into an *equation* for a line? How would we do that?

Well, if you look back at Equation 3.1, the term m refers to the slope. What is a slope? What does that word mean? Going back to the previous section, a slope is a *ratio* of the change in the y direction to the change in the x direction. This is often expressed as "rise over run", or $\frac{rise}{run}$. Since this is a *ratio*, it means it doesn't matter how far apart any two points in the line are, the *ratio* of the changes will remain the same no matter which points you pick. Therefore, if we have any two points, we can determine their slope simply by calculating the ratio of the differences in the y and x values of the points.

For instance, let's say that we have two points: P_0 and P_1. P_0 is located at the coordinates $(2, 3)$ and P_1 is located at the coordinates $(4, 6)$. To determine the slope, we just need to make a ratio out the changes in y compared to the changes in x. Therefore, given two points, P_0 and P_1, the slope between them is:

$$m = \frac{y_1 - y_0}{x_1 - x_0} \tag{3.2}$$

In this equation, y_0 is the y coordinate of P_0, x_0 is the x coordinate of P_0, y_1 is the y coordinate of P_1, and x_1 is the x coordinate of P_1.

In this case, using the points given above, that means:

$$m = \frac{6 - 3}{4 - 2}$$

which gives

$$m = \frac{3}{2}$$

So, for every rise of three our graph makes, it goes over two.

Now our equation is half complete. As it stands, we have:

$$y = \frac{3}{2}x + b$$

Now we just need to figure out b and our equation will be complete.

To solve this, all we need to do is plug in an *actual* value for x and y and solve for b. In this case, we have two points, P_0 and P_1, and if we use the x and y coordinates for either of these points, we can solve for b. Let's use P_0, which is $(2, 3)$. Substituting for x and y in the equation, we get:

$$3 = (\frac{3}{2})(2) + b$$

$$3 = \frac{6}{2} + b$$

$$3 = 3 + b$$

Now, subtracting 3 from both sides yields us

$$0 = b$$

So now we know that b is 0, which means the equation will cross through the origin. So, using the values for m and b that we have discovered, the equation for the line is:

$$y = \frac{3}{2}x + 0$$

Or, more simply:

$$y = \frac{3}{2}x$$

3.4 Converting the Line Intuition into an Analytic Form

Going further, we can actually present a complete analytic equation for the line in terms of its two points. Usually, it is easier to solve for the equation of a line as we did in the previous section. Nonetheless, having a fully analytic version of the equation is helpful in many cases. For example, if we wanted to write a computer program to calculate the equation of a line from two points, then having a fully analytic version would be helpful, as computers lack intuition altogether.

To see how we can develop this, remember we already have an equation for m (Equation 3.2). Now we just need to rearrange the basic line equation to solve for b:

$$b = y - mx \tag{3.3}$$

Since we used a specific point (P_0), we can substitute the specific x and y values, giving:

$$b = y_0 - mx_0$$

If we substitute in the equation of the slope, we get:

$$b = y_0 - \frac{y_1 - y_0}{x_1 - x_0} x_0 \tag{3.4}$$

So, combining Equations 3.1, 3.2, and 3.4, we can put them all together to get this monstrosity:

$$y = \frac{y_1 - y_0}{x_1 - x_0} x + y_0 - \frac{y_1 - y_0}{x_1 - x_0} x_0 \tag{3.5}$$

This is a fully analytic equation, because you can find the final answer simply by substituting into the formula and calculating. No intuition needed, just plug and chug. However, if you were to use such a formula, it doesn't necessarily aid your *understanding* of *how* the different parts relate together.

The final goal of most mathematics is often finding the analytic form of the equation. However, in *learning* mathematics, a more important goal is the intuitive sense of how the different pieces relate to each other, and, secondarily, how to *produce* an analytic equation from the more intuitive understandings.

Equation 3.6 is a shorter form of Equation 3.5. Equation 3.6 is more likely to appear in textbooks, but the goal of Equation 3.5 was to show you how you could develop the equation yourself from the basic principles of what a line is.

$$y - y_0 = \frac{y_1 - y_0}{x_1 - x_0}(x - x_0) \tag{3.6}$$

As an exercise, you should try rearranging Equation 3.5 in order to make it look like equation3.6.

—   Example 3.1

Given the two points $(7, 2)$ and $(2, 5)$, find the equation of the line that goes between these points.

To find the answer to this problem, we can use either solve it a step at a time (solving for m then solving for b) or we can do it directly with Equation 3.5 or Equation 3.6. Let's use Equation 3.5. We start with the equation:

$$y = \frac{y_1 - y_0}{x_1 - x_0}x + y_0 - \frac{y_1 - y_0}{x_1 - x_0}x_0$$

Now, we will simply substitute in our two points. It doesn't matter which point we use as Point 0 or Point 1, as long as we are consistent.[a] So, if we take $(7, 2)$ for P_0 then we will use 7 for x_0 and 2 for y_0. That means that $(2, 5)$ will be P_1 so we will use 2 for x_1 and 5 for y_1.

Substituting these into our equation, we get:

$$y = \frac{y_1 - y_0}{x_1 - x_0}x + y_0 - \frac{y_1 - y_0}{x_1 - x_0}x_0$$

$$y = \frac{5 - 2}{2 - 7}x + 2 - \frac{5 - 2}{2 - 7}7$$

$$y = \frac{3}{-5}x + 2 - \frac{3}{-5}7$$

$$y = \frac{-3}{5}x + \frac{10}{5} - \frac{-21}{5}$$

$$y = \frac{-3}{5}x + \frac{31}{5}$$

So, using this equation, we can see that the slope is $\frac{-3}{5}$ and the y-intercept is $\frac{31}{5}$.

---

[a]If you think about the ruler example, you get the same line if you draw from the first point to the second point as you would if you draw from the second point to the first point.

You have probably messed with lines quite a bit in previous Algebra classes. Lines and slopes, though they may seem basic, are *essential* to calculus. Therefore, you should be sure that you understand every part of this chapter before proceeding to further chapters.

Review

In this chapter, we learned:

1. A line is a straight path through space, whether in 1, 2, 3, or n dimensions.

2. A line can be fully determined by any two points on the line, and can be drawn by using a ruler to connect the two points.

3. A line contains infinitely many points.

4. The standard form of the equation of the line is $y = mx + b$, where m is the slope and b is the y-intercept.

5. It is easy to draw lines when they are written in standard form.

6. Given two points (which determine a line), it is easy to calculate the equation of the line that they determine.

7. Combining all of our knowledge about lines allows us to come up with an analytic description of how to determine a line from points, where all you have to do is plug in point coordinates and it spits out the resulting equation.

Exercises

1. Write out the standard equation for a line (Equation 3.1) five times.

2. What does m refer to on the standard equation for a line?

3. What does b refer to on the standard equation for a line?

4. Draw the line given by the equation $y = 5x - 3$.

5. Draw the line given by the equation $y = \frac{1}{3}x + 1$.

6. Draw the line given by the equation $y = 2.3x + 4.1$.

7. Draw the line given by the equation $5y = 3x + 10$.

8. Draw the line given by the equation $y + x = 2$.

9. Determine the equation of the line given by the point $(2, -1)$ and the slope $\frac{1}{5}$.

10. Determine the equation of the line given by the points $(1, 1)$ and $(2, 3)$.

11. Determine the equation of the line given by the points $(4, 5)$ and $(-3, 2)$.

12. Give an analytic equation for determining the equation of a line given a single point (x_0 and y_0) and the slope (m).

Chapter 4

Basic Tools: Variables and Functions

This section introduces a lot of ideas and a lot of vocabulary. Please pay special attention to the terms that are introduced, as they will be important for understanding later concepts.

4.1 Variable Relationships

In all of advanced mathematics, you will be dealing with variables and functions. A **variable** is a stand-in for a value. Sometimes a variable stands for an unknown value that must be solved for. For instance, if I have x dollars in my pocket, there is only one value for x, even though we don't know what it is.

Other times, a variable represents a continuum of possible values that can be used. For instance, let's say that someone has an investment scheme which will double your money. We can then create an equation where x represents the amount of money you invest, and y represents the amount of money you will have at the end of the investment period. Since the money doubles, we can represent this by saying

$$y = 2x$$

In this case, x doesn't represent a single quantity, but any amount you want. The equation only tells you, based on the amount of money you put in (x) how much money you will get out (y). In this case, x is referred to as an **independent variable** because you get to choose how much money you invest. y (the amount of money you receive) is referred to as a **dependent variable** because its value *depends* on the value you invest. Variables are called **co-dependent** if their values depend on each other.

Now, there is no real reason that we use x and y specifically to represent these quantities, except for tradition and convention. Mathematicians often use letters to refer to quantities because they are much easier to write in equations. When you are used to reading such variable names, using short, standardized variable names also makes the equations easier to read. For equations of two variables, the independent variable usually uses the letter x and, when graphed, it takes the horizontal axis. The dependent variable usually uses the letter y and takes the vertical axis.

These are known as **conventions**. A convention is a standard practice, but not a strict rule. The goal of a convention is to aid communication by standardizing the way that things are written and drawn. Knowing that the horizontal axis is usually the independent variable allows you to look at most graphs and understand which axis is dependent on which other axis. There are occasions when the convention is not followed, but the convention is there to help you more quickly understand what is happening in the most common cases.

4.2   Functions of Variables

Now, in the equation $y = 2x$, we say that y is an **explicit function** of x. This means that y is wholly dependent on the value given in x, and is not dependent on anything else. A **function** can be thought of as a machine that takes in one or more values, and produces a value (usually only one) as an output.

In the case of $y = 2x$, we can say that y is a function of x, because the *only* thing on the left-hand side of the equation is y, and *everything* on the right-hand side of the equation can be written as a function of x (meaning that everything on the right hand side depends only on the value of x, and not the value of anything else).

Functions *are not equations.* They are *parts* of equations. A function will take up at most one side of an equation. If one side of the equation is a single variable, and the other side of the equation does not have that variable, we can say that the solitary variable is a function of the variables on the other side of the equation. That is, the other side of the equation can be thought of as a machine, which, when provided the values of the other variables, produces the lone variable.

Now, prior to calculus, most of the graphs that you have seen are, in fact, functions, so we should take a moment to think about what it would mean for something to not be a function. Let's take, for instance, the graph of a circle:

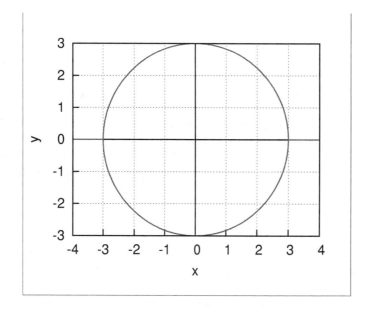

Notice that for nearly every value of x, there are actually *two* potential values of y! This means that the value of y is not entirely based on the value of x. For y to have a definite value, you also need to know something about the value of y! In this case, x and y are **co-dependent variables**, meaning that neither one of them is fully independent of the other. The circle was not a function, because for any valid x, there was more than one possible value of y. Generalizing this, we can say that y can be represented as an explicit function of x if, for every valid value of x, there is *exactly one* value of y.

Given a graph, an easy way to figure out if a graph is a function of x or not is to use the **vertical line test**. The vertical line test simply says that if there is *any* vertical line that we can draw that will intersect with the graph more than once, the graph cannot be a true function of the independent variable.

Sometimes you can get around this by prefering certain values over others. For instance, we can solve for y

as follows:

$$x^2 + y^2 = 9 \qquad \text{Equation for a circle of radius 3}$$

$$y^2 = 9 - x^2 \qquad \text{Get the } y \text{ by itself}$$

$$y = \sqrt{9 - x^2} \qquad \text{Square root both sides}$$

However, the square root has two possible values—positive and negative, so it is not a function. But we can consider this a function if we choose to take only the positive or negative square root. Whether or not this is appropriate depends on the problem at hand.

Additionally, sometimes you can treat expressions that yield multiple values as an **improper function**. That is, it may behave enough like a function at any given point so that we can pretend it is a function for most purposes. In other words, if you zoom in on the graph close enough, the zoomed-in part of the graph looks like a function. This allows you to treat it like a function in most instances.

4.3 Implicit Functions

Now, in some cases, even if y is a function of x, sometimes the function is defined *implicitly* rather than *explicitly*. For example, take a look at the following equation:

$$xy = y + x$$

In this equation, the xs and ys are mixed together on the same side of the equation. This doesn't necessarily mean that it can't be written as a function. In this case, it definitely can ($y = \frac{x}{x-1}$). However, sometimes solving for a variable so that it is on one side only is tedious and doesn't need to be done. In such cases, these equations can be left as **implicit functions**. An implicit function is one where y *can be written* as a function of x, but the equation itself doesn't separate out the ys and the xs. Therefore, we can tell from the vertical line test that this is the graph of a function, but we would have to do more work to actually figure out what that function is.

4.4 Naming Functions

Functions, like variables, can be given names. Usually, if there is only one function under consideration, its conventional name is f. Just as when we have multiple variables, they get named x, y, and z, names of multiple functions are often called f, g, and h. Sometimes they are given longer, more descriptive names (think about sin and cos), but usually in mathematics the single-letter names dominate discussions.

Functions are denoted with a **parameter list**—a list of variables that the function will use to generate its value. That is $f(x)$ means that the function f will determine its value based on a single parameter—the value given for x. The function $g(x, y)$ means that the function g will determine its value based on *two* parameters—both x and y. In these examples, we say that f is a function of x, and g is a function of x and y.

So how are these function names used?

Function names are used for a variety of reasons. Sometimes they are used to represent an *unknown* process, just like variable names are used to represent unknown values. Sometimes function names are used to abstract away certain pieces or ideas of a function. One can say, "for any $f(x)$ the following is true..." and then talk in general terms about what is true about functions of x. When we have $f(x)$ we may just mean "any expression we want, as long as it is a function of x."

Let's say that I tell you that I have a formula to determine how much money I should put into savings each year that is based on one variable—my income. Let's say that x represents my income, and y represents the amount of money I put into savings that year based on that income. Now, I have only told you that the amount of money I save is based on my income. I haven't told you exactly what the formula is that I use. Perhaps I put 10% into savings. Perhaps I put all money over \$50,000 into savings. I haven't told you. All you know at the moment is that it is based entirely on my salary. In other words, you know that the amount of money I am saving is a *function of* my salary that year. Therefore, since we know that y (the amount of money I put into savings) is a function of x (my salary), and we don't know *what* the function is, we can't write out the function. However, we *can* wite the following:

$$y = f(x)$$

This is usually read as "f of x." What this says is that there is some function, called f, which takes one **parameter**, called x. The result of the function, whatever it is, is what we put into y.

The goal of any mathematical formula is communication, whether there is a lot or a little to communicate. We might *want* to communicate the whole equation which relates my savings to my salary, but we might only *know* that, whatever it is, it is determinable based on my income (x). Therefore, $y = f(x)$ gives the reader that much information. It says that y is in fact a function of x, but without specifying what that function is. In other words, when we say that $y = f(x)$ we know that the *only* variable that y depends on is x—there are no other variables to consider.

Now, let's say that I tell you that I use the first \$10,000 of my salary for expenses, and from the rest of it I save half. What is the equation that relates these now? Well, the amount saved is 50% (0.5) of the salary (x) after \$10,000 is taken away.

This means that:

$$y = 0.5(x - 10,000)$$

However, we earlier said that $y = f(x)$. Therefore, substituting $f(x)$ for y in the equation above, that must mean that:

$$f(x) = 0.5(x - 10000)$$

So, while previously we only knew vaguely that f is a function of x, now we know exactly what $f(x)$ means. Just like solving for a variable, we can also solve for a function.

We'll get back to this equation in a moment. But first, let's talk about something else—salary. Let's say that I have another equation which relates my salary to the year. That is, this equation tells me what my salary will be based on the year, with year 0 being the year when I joined the workforce. So, in this equation, the independent variable is the year, and the dependent variable is the salary. Using common conventions, y will represent the dependent variable (salary), and x will represent the independent variable (year).

That means, again, that y is a function of x. However, to distinguish this function from the previous one, we will call the function $g(x)$. Therefore, $y = g(x)$. Now, let's say that I tell you that my salary started at \$15,000 on year zero, and then increased by \$1,000 every year after. This gives the equation:

$$y = 15000 + 1000x$$

Therefore,

$$g(x) = 15000 + 1000x$$

So now, we have two functions. $f(x)$ takes x as my salary, and yields how much I've saved based on my salary. $g(x)$ takes x as a year, and yields how large my salary is based on what year it is. Now, this can be very confusing, because in each of these functions, x refers to a different quantity. In $f(x)$, x refers to my salary, and in $g(x)$, x refers to the year.

When you use functions, the x referred to in the function is a **local variable**, meaning that its value is taken from the parameter given to it, which is not necessarily the same thing as x in the rest of the equation. So, for instance, if I have $g(3)$, then this yields a value where I take the number 3 and substitute it for every occurrence of x in the definition of the function. So, $g(3)$ becomes $15000 + 1000 \cdot 3$, or 18000.

Now, let's say that I know that Phil moved to New York the year after I made \$19,000. How would we figure out what year Phil moved? Well, let's say that x represents the year that Phil moved. That means in year $x - 1$ I made \$19,000. Therefore, we can write an equation saying:

$$g(x - 1) = 19000$$

So what does $g(x - 1)$ mean? It means that when we use $g(x)$, we will replace every occurrence of x in the definition of $g(x)$ with $x - 1$.

So, the definition of $g(x)$ is:

$$g(x) = 15000 + 1000x$$

So $g(x - 1)$ becomes:

$$g(x - 1) = 15000 + 1000(x - 1)$$

So since we are sending in $x - 1$ as the parameter of the function g, we replace all of gs local xs with the value given. Having to temporarily translate in your head what x means in this specific instance can be tedious at first, but with practice it can be done well and with ease.

So, to solve our full equation we do these steps:

$$g(x) = 15000 + 1000x \qquad \text{the original function}$$

$$g(x-1) = 15000 + 1000(x-1) \qquad \text{substituting in } x-1 \text{ as the parameter}$$

$$g(x-1) = 19000 \qquad \text{this is a given quantity}$$

$$15000 + 1000(x-1) = 19000 \qquad \text{set our two definitions of } g(x-1) \text{ equal to each other}$$

$$15000 + 1000x - 1000 = 19000 \qquad \text{multiply through}$$

$$14000 + 1000x = 19000 \qquad \text{simplify}$$

$$1000x = 19000 - 14000 \qquad \text{subtract 14000 from both sides}$$

$$1000x = 5000 \qquad \text{simplify}$$

$$x = 5 \qquad \text{divide both sides by 1000}$$

Therefore, we know that Phil moved on year 5.

4.5   Combining Functions

Now, one thing that you may have noticed about functions $f(x)$ and $g(x)$ in the previous example, is that for $f(x)$ took in a salary as an independent variable, and gave out a savings amount as a dependent variable. However, in $g(x)$ the salary is the dependent variable, while the year number is the independent variable. Now, if we can put in a year number to $g(x)$ and get a salary out, and we can put a salary into $f(x)$ and get a savings amount out, shouldn't it then be possible to create a function where we put in a year number, and get out the amount I am putting into savings?

This type of tying two functions together is called **function composition**. This is normally written out like this:

$$h(x) = f(g(x))$$

where $h(x)$ is our new function created by wiring the output of $g(x)$ into the input of $f(x)$. To see how this works, let us first expand the innermost function, $g(x)$. This will give us:

$$h(x) = f(15000 + 1000x)$$

So now, we can use $15000 + 1000x$ as the input for $f(x)$. If we expand the definition of $f(x)$, this will give us:

$$f(x) = 0.5(x - 10000)$$

$$h(x) = f(15000 + 1000x)$$

$$h(x) = 0.5((15000 + 1000x) - 10000)$$

$$h(x) = 0.5(1000x + 5000)$$

$$h(x) = 500x + 2500$$

So now we have an explicit, analytic function which takes the year number, and tells you how much money I am going to put into savings. So, for year 11, it would give $h(11) = 500 \cdot 11 + 2500 = 5500 + 2500 = 8000$. Therefore, in year number 11 I would put \$8,000 into my savings account.

There is no limit to the number of functions that can be chained together to generate new functions. In addition, composing functions is not the only way to combine two functions.

Let's say, for instance, that I always pay my Jack $3 per hour more for a job than I pay Jim for the same job. Therefore, if $f(x)$ is the amount of money I pay Jim for x hours of work, and $g(x)$ is the amount of money that I pay Jack for x hours of work, I can show the relationship between their two payments by saying:

$$g(x) = f(x) + 3x$$

Now lets say that they work together as a crew for the same number of hours. If we say that $h(x)$ is the amount of money that the crew makes for x hours (i.e., Jim's pay plus Jack's pay), then we can say:

$$h(x) = f(x) + g(x)$$

Now, since we know the definition of $g(x)$, we can determine that:

$$h(x) = f(x) + g(x)$$
$$g(x) = f(x) + 3x$$
$$h(x) = f(x) + f(x) + 3x$$
$$h(x) = 2 \cdot f(x) + 3x$$

So, as you can see, functions can be combined in a variety of ways. So far, we've just dealt with concrete examples of functions. However, in calculus, you will need to be able to think of them abstractly.

In other words, in the example above, you could easily see the relationships of money to pay, and understand that two people being paid means that we add their payments together. However, often times in mathematics, you have to be able to manipulate the equations without having clear, concrete meanings for each term. These types of abstract manipulations are called **formal manipulations** because they deal only with the algebraic forms, and not on the underlying concrete understandings.

Just to make sure you understand the concept, let's look at a function which we will assign no concrete meaning to make sure that you understand the concept.

Let's say that we have two functions:

$$f(x) = x^2 + 2x + 3$$
$$g(x) = 2x + 3$$

Given that, let's find $h(x)$ where

$$h(x) = f(g(x))$$

If we substitute the inner value first, we will get:

$$h(x) = f(2x + 3)$$

Then, if we use $2x + 3$ as the parameter for $f(x)$, then, rewriting we will get:

$$h(x) = (2x + 3)^2 + 2(2x + 3) + 3$$

Expanding and distributing terms, we will get:

$$h(x) = 4x^2 + 12x + 9 + 4x + 6 + 3$$

Collecting terms together, we will get:

$$h(x) = 4x^2 + 16x + 18$$

4.6   Inverse Functions

Inverse functions are what you get when you try to run a function in reverse. For instance, if I have a function that multiplies by 2, the inverse of that function would be a function that divides by 2. An inverse function takes the output of a particular function and gives you back the input.

Inverse functions are usually identified by adding a −1 in small letters next to the function name. Thus, given the function:

$$f(x) = 2x$$

The inverse of that function would be written as:

$$f^{-1}(x) = \frac{x}{2}$$

Therefore, we know that any value we put in for x in $f(x)$, we will get that number back if we put the result of $f(x)$ into $f^{-1}(x)$. In other words the inverse function is a function for which, for any valid x, $f^{-1}(f(x)) = x$.

With the example above, we can see that if we put 2 in to $f(x)$ we will get 4. If we put 4 into $f^{-1}(x)$ we will get 2 (our original number) back.

Inverse functions are not always so easy, though. If the original function is a little more complex, it might not be so easy to see what its inverse would be. The way that you solve for an inverse function is fairly straightforward. First, use y as the result of the function. Second, manipulate the function using algebra so that x is alone on one side of the equation. The other side of the equation, if you substitute x in for y, becomes the value of the inverse function.

—   Example 4.1

Let's say that we have $f(x) = 2e^{x+1}$. What is $f^{-1}(x)$?

So, first, we will set this equal to y, so that $y = 2e^{x+1}$. Now, we will use algebra to get the x all by itself on one side of the equation:

$$y = 2e^{x+1} \qquad\qquad \text{our initial equation}$$

$$\frac{y}{2} = e^{x+1} \qquad\qquad \text{divide both sides by 2}$$

$$\ln\frac{y}{2} = x + 1 \qquad\qquad \text{take the natural log of both sides}$$

$$\ln\frac{y}{2} - 1 = x \qquad\qquad \text{subtract 1 from both sides}$$

Now that x is by itself, to get the inverse function we just use the side of the equation that has y, but we substitute in the variable x for y, giving us:

$$f^{-1}(x) = \ln\frac{x}{2} - 1$$

One problem for inverse functions is that, for most functions, their inverse is not a true function. Remember that a function produces a single value from its inputs. However, if the graph of your original function goes both up and down, then the inverse of that function will have *multiple* values for a given x value.

For instance, take the function $f(x) = x^2$. This is a true function—for any given x there is exactly one result. What is the inverse? The inverse of this function is $f^{-1}(x) = \sqrt{x}$. However, square roots can be positive or negative, so this is more accurately presented as $f^{-1}(x) = \pm\sqrt{x}$. Thus, for a given x value, there might be as many as two distinct values.

With higher exponents, there are more possible values in the inverse function. Some functions, such as sin and cos, have inverses which have infinitely many results for any given value. For these, the inverse functions are usually given a pre-defined fixed range of possible results.

For the most part, this is not a terrible situation, but it is good to keep in mind that even if $f(x)$ is a true function, $f^{-1}(x)$ might not be, or it may have to be used with special qualifications.

4.7 Inventing Functions and the Magic of Substitution

In section 4.5 we looked at how to use functions, analyze them, and combine them into new functions. In this section, we will look at how to take an existing equation and *invent* new functions to help us look at equations under new lights.

Let's look at the following equation:

$$\sin^2(x) + 4\cdot\sin(x) + 4 = 0$$

How might this be solved?

In order to solve this, I want you to think about different types of equations you have encountered in your time doing mathematics. Does it remind you of anything, even if it isn't exact? If you notice, the first term is squared, the second term is to the first power, and the third term is a constant. What sort of equation kind of looks like that?

If you said "quadratic equation," you would be correct. If you didn't, take a close look, and see if you can at least see the resemblance between a quadratic equation and the equation above. For a reminder, the basic form of a quadratic equation is

$$ax^2 + bx + c = 0 \tag{4.1}$$

where a, b, and c are constants. To solve such an equation for x, you use the quadratic formula. For reference, the quadratic formula is:

$$x = \frac{-b \pm \sqrt{b^2 - 4ac}}{2a} \tag{4.2}$$

Now, there is one problem—the equation doesn't exactly match the quadratic equation. Each time we are supposed to have an x, we have a $\sin(x)$ instead. So what do we do?

Once you recognize that every place where we wanted to have x that we instead have $\sin(x)$, then we can create a function to *convert* one to the other.

So, what we wanted was x, but what we got instead was $\sin(x)$. Therefore, we will create a new variable, u. We will then say that:

$$u = \sin(x)$$

Now, we have decided, using our own creative power, that we want to have a new variable u to be equal to $\sin(x)$. Now, every place where we have $\sin(x)$, we can replace it with u, based on our definition.

So, replacing $\sin(x)$ with u gives us this equation:

$$u^2 + 4u + 4 = 0$$

This now actually *is* a quadratic equation! The only difference is that it uses the variable u instead of x. However, the rules of algebra are the same no matter what we name our variables.

Therefore, using the quadratic formula, we can find the answer:

$$u = \frac{-4 \pm \sqrt{4^2 - 4 \cdot 1 \cdot 4}}{2 \cdot 1}$$

$$= \frac{-4 \pm \sqrt{16 - 16}}{2}$$

$$= \frac{-4}{2}$$

$$= -2$$

So, we have established that $u = -2$. Are we finished? Not quite. Remember that the oiginal problem was to find x, not u. However, when we did the transformation, we also built an equation that relates x and u, namely $u = \sin(x)$. Therefore, since they are equivalent, we can substitute the other way as well, putting $\sin(x)$ back in for u and solve the equation:

$$u = -2$$

$$u = \sin(x)$$

$$\sin(x) = -2 \qquad\qquad \text{since both of these are equal to } u \text{ they are equal to each other}$$

Now, the inverse operation of $\sin(x)$ is $\arcsin(x)$ (also known as $\sin^{-1}(x)$). If we apply that to both sides, it will undo the $\sin(x)$ on the left:

$$\arcsin(\sin(x)) = \arcsin(-2)$$
$$x = \arcsin(-2) \qquad \text{since arcsin is the inverse of sin, we just get } x$$
$$x \approx 1.57$$

So, let's go back through our steps. First, we thought about if our strange equation was related in any way to a more standard equation that we already knew. Once we figured out that it was similar to a quadratic equation, we then looked for a way to transform the equation into a form that we could use the quadratic formula for. We found out that the big problem standing in our way was that the equation was using $\sin(x)$ instead of x in each term. Therefore, we decided to make a substitution, substituting u (which was a function of x) for $\sin(x)$. This gave us the form that we wanted in order to solve it using the quadratic formula. After we solved for u, we then needed to get back to x. We used our original equation relating u and x to get our answer for u in terms of x. Then, we solved for x.

It sounds like a lot of steps, but, in brief, we invented a new variable which we could substitute for another variable in the equation to make it solvable. You have to be careful when doing that, however, because you have to make sure that the substitution actually can replace all of the instances of x in the equation. If you don't, then you have just *increased* the number of variables in your equation. That isn't necessarily wrong, but it usually is counterproductive.

For instance, if the equation had instead been $\sin^2(x) + 4x + 4 = 0$, then the substitution would not have worked. You would have wound up with $u^2 + 4x + 4 = 0$, which is still not in a solvable form. We just have more variables.

Inventing variables to substitute for functions in an equation is a very powerful tool, but you do have to be sure you are using it right.

4.8 Multiple Variables

A function can be a function of more than one variable. For instance, the distance a person travels when moving depends on both their speed and the amount of time they spend traveling. Therefore, we can write a function to represent this:

$$d(\text{speed}, \text{time}) = \text{speed} \cdot \text{time}$$

This indicates that the function $d()$ (i.e., distance) is based on two parameters—speed and time. Therefore, in this function, *both* speed and time are independent variables, and the distance travelled is the dependent variable.

Often times, in functions of two variables, x and y are both the independent variables, and z becomes the dependent variable. These can be represented by graphs in three dimensions. So, for instance take the function $f(x, y) = 3xy$. If we want the value of $f(4, 5)$, we would get $3 \cdot 4 \cdot 5 = 60$. So, our dependent variable (which we would likely graph as z) would be 60.

Note that functions can *also* have more than one dependent variable.

4.9   Logarithms and the Natural Log Function

At this point in your mathematical education, you should be familiar with logarithms and what they are used for. Nonetheless, many people have forgotten about logarithms by the time they enter calculus. Logarithsm are the inverse of exponents. That is, $\log_a(b)$ tells me what value I need to raise a to in order to get b. a is considered the **base** of the logarithm. So, $\log_2(8)$ (which is read as "log base 2 of 8") is 3 because $2^3 = 8$.

Two special logarithms are $\log_{10}(x)$ and $\log_e(x)$, where e is Euler's number, which is approximately 2.71828. If you see $\log(x)$ without any base listed, that usually refers to $\log_{10}(x)$. However, even more important, is $\ln(x)$, which is an abbreviation for $\log_e(x)$. In calculus (and in the many other places), $\ln(x)$ is the most widely used logarithm because it simplifies many calculus operations. This is known as the **natural logarithm** because it is easier to define and manipulate than other logarithms. In calculus (and really anywhere), if there is no specific reason to use another base of a logarithm, the natural logarithm is an easy choice to use.

If you do not remember your exponent rules, they are listed in Appendix H.1.4. One of the most important facts about logarithms is that they can be used to convert exponentiation into multiplication.

For instance, let's say I have the equation $z = x^y$, but the exponent is giving me trouble (for whatever reason). I can take the natural log of both sides, which would give me the equation $\ln(z) = \ln(x^y)$. The logarithm rules in Appendix H.1.4 say that an exponent that is *inside* the logarithm can be moved outside the logarithm as a multiplier. Therefore, the new equation is $\ln(z) = y\ln(x)$. Thus, by using logarithms, we converted a problem involving exponents into a problem involving multiplication. This has many uses in calculus and beyond.

Review

In this chapter, we learned:

1. Variables can either refer to a single unknown value, or to a range of possible values that can be used in a function or equation.

2. Independent variables are the variables which other variables (dependent variables) are determined by. It is considered "free" because the person using the equation usually gets to choose the value. The dependent variables are determined by the values set in the independent variables.

3. Independent variables are usually plotted on the horizontal (x) axis, while dependent variables are usually plotted on the vertical (y) axis.

4. Variables are co-dependent if their values depend on each other.

5. Many commonly-used variable and function names have no particular meaning, but are instead used beause of historic conventions. Following the conventions makes it easier to quickly grasp what is being written.

6. A function is a set of math operations that yield a value given the value of an independent variable or variables.

7. A function is defined implicitly if it is given as the result of an equation of both x and y where the dependent variable is not alone on one side of the equation.

8. True functions have one value for each set of inputs.

9. The vertical line test tells us graphically if a function is a true function—if any vertical line crosses more than one point on the graph, the function is not a true function.

10. Functions can be used as inputs to other functions.

11. Functions can be combined together to produce new functions.

12. An inverse function runs a function in reverse—given the result of a function, what operations do we need to perform to get back the original value?

13. Inverse functions are written as $f^{-1}(x)$ to denote the inverse function of $f(x)$.

14. Inverse functions are often not true functions.

15. In an equation, you can introduce a new variable to represent a function.

16. Introducing variables for functions can decrease the complexity of a function and make it easier to solve.

17. When you substitute a variable for a function, you have to remember to substitute it back at the end.

18. Functions can have more than one independent variable.

19. Functions can have more than one dependent variable.

20. The logarithm function is the inverse of exponentiation.

21. The natural logarithm is the logarithm using Euler's number (e) as the base, and is the "default" logarithm to use in calculus.

22. Logarithms can be used to convert problems involving exponentiation into problems involving multiplication.

Exercises

1. If $f(x) = 3x + 5$, what is $f(7)$?

2. If $f(b) = b^2 + 2$ what is $f(9)$?

3. If $f(x) = 2^x + x$ what is $f(3)$?

4. if $f(n) = 2n - 7$ what is $f(q + 5)$

5. If $f(x) = x^2 + 3x$, what is $f(z + 1)$?

6. If $h(x) = \frac{x^4}{9}$, what is $h(3)$?

7. If $f(x, y) = 3x + 4y$, what is $f(5, 6)$?

8. If $f(x) = x^2 + 5x$ and $g(x) = 5x - 9$, what is $f(g(x))$ in terms of x?

9. What is the inverse of the function $f(x) = x + 1$?

10. What is the inverse of the function $f(x) = 5x$?

11. What is the inverse of the function $g(x) = \frac{x}{5}$?

12. What is the inverse of the function $g(x) = (x + 1)^3$?

13. What is the inverse of the function $f(x) = \ln(x^2)$?

14. Convert the implicit function $xy = x + 1$ into an explicit function of x.

15. Convert the implicit function $x + y = 3y$ into an explicit function of x.

16. Convert the implicit function $x + y = 3y$ into an explicit function of y.

17. Solve the following equation for x: $\tan^2(x) + 6\tan(x) + 3 = 0$. Use radians when doing calculations.

18. If $f(x) = 3x$, $g(x) = x^2$ and $h(x) = f(g(x))$, what is $h(x)$ in terms of x?

19. What is the value of $h(5)$ in the previous exercise?

20. If $f(x) = \sin(x) + 4$, $g(x) = 2\cos(x) - 6$, and $h(x) = f(x) + g(x)$, what is $h(x)$ in terms of x?

21. Take the equation $y = 2x + 3$. Let's say we have a function $f(x) = 2x$. Rewrite the equation using $f(x)$.

22. Take the equation $y = 6x + 5$. Let's say we have a function $f(x) = 3x$. Rewrite the equation using $f(x)$.

23. Take the equation $y = 2x$. Let's say we have a function $f(x) = x - 1$. Rewrite the equation using $f(x)$.

Chapter 5

Basic Tools: Graphs

Most people misunderstand mathematics, and think that *manipulating symbols* is the primary art of mathematics, but that is not true. To be certain, manipulating symbols is very important, and helps you think more concretely about abstract problems. Manipulating symbols helps you think about problems in their basic, logical relationships, and helps you solve problems for which you may lack the ability to imagine what the result might be.

However, mathematics is, more generally, about the ability to use reason to manipulate the things that we know so that we can determine the things that we don't know. Sometimes that comes to us in terms of symbols and numbers, but sometimes it comes to us in different ways, such as with a graph.

Many times in life you will never have an equation for a function. Many functions are known only by their graphs. If you are in business, you may have a graph of sales. You don't know what equation governs this graph, or even if there is one. You are given the bare graph itself. Equations may be approximated for it, but what we really know is the graph itself.

In science, one of the main tasks is to take a set of data and infer what sort of relationship is occurring. The primary way to understand that, is to understand what the graphs of different functions look like.

Graphs are very important in calculus, specifically, because many of the concepts are easiest to understand when looking at a graph.

Therefore, this chapter will give a quick overview of graphing in mathematics.

5.1   Thinking About Graphs

What *is* a graph? A graph simply visually shows the relationship between values. The most common graphs are two-dimensional, showing the relationship between two values. Usually, those values are x and y, with x (or whatever the independent variable is) being represented on the horizontal axis, and y (or whatever the dependent variable is) being represented on the vertical axis. This is not technically required, but following this convention helps people understand the graph at a glance.

The axes of a graph are essentially number lines, oriented so that they each are in a separate dimension of space, and they intersect at the zero points. These are known as Cartesian graphs, because they implement the coordinate space invented by the mathematician and philosopher Reneé Descartes. This revolutionized the world of mathematics by providing a systematic link between algebra and geometry. Using this system, you could describe geometric shapes using equations. This may seem obvious to you now, but in the 17th century it was revolutionary.[1]

Since then, there have been other ways developed for graphing, such as polar graphs, which you probably have run into. This book's primary focus is on cartesian graphs, though the methods we develop can be adapted to other graphing systems.

5.2   Graph Shifting

Below is a graph of the equation $y = x^2$.

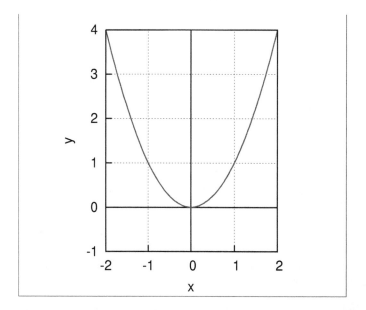

Notice that this graph has a vertex right at the origin and is symmetrical around the y-axis. Now, we can play with this graph a bit as well.

Let's say we wanted to shift the graph a bit. Let's say we wanted to move the graph to the left one unit. How would we do that? It would look like this:

---

[1]With most true ideas, it is revolutionary when discovered, but afterwards it seems so obvious that we wonder why no one ever noticed it before.

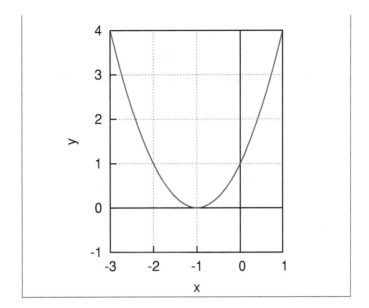

It is actually be the exact same graph—the same shape, the same everything, just shifted over. So how do we convert the equation for the original graph, $y = x^2$, so that it moves over by one unit?

If you look at the new graph, what is the difference in the relationship between x and y? The x value, if you added one to it, would be the same as the x value in the previous equation. Therefore, if we take our equation, and add 1 to every instance of x, the y values will match up.

Therefore, the new equation is $y = (x + 1)^2$. This can also be written as $y = x^2 + 2x + 1$, but it is the same equation.

The same thing can be done if you shift the graph up or down. If we shift the graph up, we can look at how this will affect the equation as well. What would it look like to shift the graph up two units?

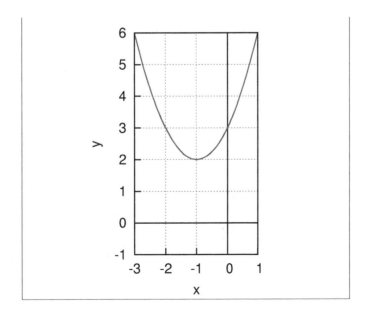

Now, how would we accomplish that? Well, each resulting value

In general, any shift can be accomplished by replacing all occurrences of x with $(x - x\_shift\_amount)$ and all occurrences of y with $(y - y\_shift\_amount)$. So, if we had the equation $y^3 x^2 = x^5 + 3y - 2$, we can move this equation down two units (-2) and to the right three units ($+3$) by replacing every occurrence of x with $(x - 3)$ and every occurrency of y with $(y - -2)$, which would simplify as $(y + 2)$.

Therefore, the shifted equation will be $(y + 2)^3 (x - 3)^2 = (x - 3)^5 + 3(y + 2) - 2$.

5.3   Inverse Functions and Graphs

The inverse of a function can be thought of in graphical terms as well. The graph of a function can be used to match x values to y values. To make an inverse graph, all you have to do is re-label the x and y axes.

For instance, here is the function $y = 2x - 1$:

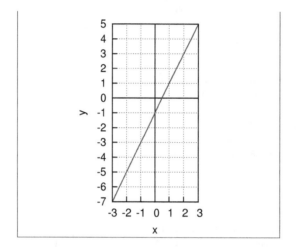

A basic graph of the inverse function can be had just by relabeling the x and y axes with each other's labels, like this (note that the graph is the same, but the labels are different):

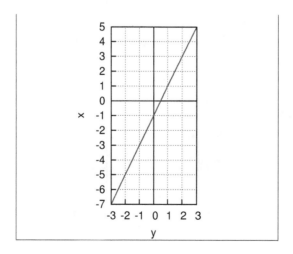

However, we normally have our x axis as our horizontal axis. Therefore, we can fix this by reflecting the graph over the line $y = x$, like this:

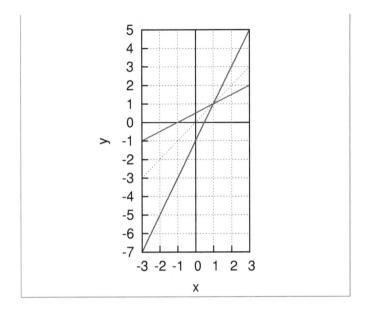

So, interestingly, if we know a function only from its graph, we can also find the inverse function from the graph as well, merely by reflecting over the line $y = x$.

5.4 Graphs of Common Functions

Throughout life we will see all sorts of data—data in our job, data about our home (i.e., interest rates, home valuations, etc.), data about our investments, etc. Therefore, it is important to be able to *recognize* a function in a graph when you see it. This will help you to be able to reason about the data that you see, and perhaps even make educated guesses about data you don't see.

5.4.1 Polynomials

A **polynomial** is an equation in which x is raised to various integer powers. The largest power in a polynomial is known as its **degree**. So, if the largest power is x^5, then the equation is a fifth degree polynomial.

Polynomials always have a fixed number of humps. Usually, the number of humps in a polynomial is one less than the degree of the polynomial. A second-degree polynomial will likely have one hump, a third degree will likely have two humps, and an eight degree will likely have seven humps.

Below is the graph of the polynomial $y = x^4 - 5x^3 + 5x^2 + 5x - 6$:

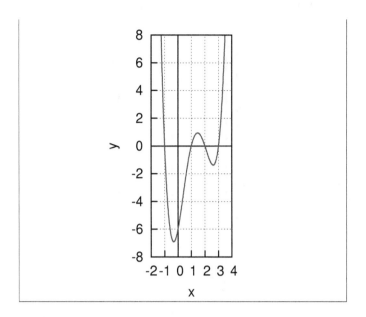

As you can see, it is a fourth degree polynomial, and it has three humps. However, polynomials can also have fewer humps, as two humps can come together to cancel each other out.

A line is technically a polynomial itself, of degree 1 (a normal line) or 0 (a horizontal line—i.e., a constant function).

5.4.2   The Exponential Function

Another important function is the **exponential function**. An exponential function is one that is made by taking some constant value and raising it to the x power.

For instance, below is the graph of $y = 2^x$:

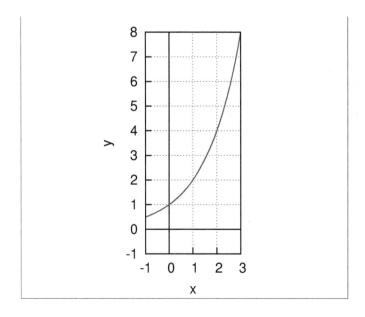

Exponential functions are used anywhere where the effects of something compound continuously. For instance, returns on interest-bearing bank accounts are expressed as exponential functions since the added interest itself generates interest. They are also used for the physical process of radioactive decay, since the effects of radioactivity themselves limit the amount of radioactivity available.

If an exponential function has a number greater than 1 as its constant, the value will get bigger forever, getting bigger faster and faster. If an exponential function has a number greater than 0 but less than 1 as its constant, the value will get smaller forever (but never hit zero). This is known as an **exponential decay function**, and can also happen if the exponent is multiplied by a negative number ($y = 2^{-x}$ and $y = 0.5^x$ graph as the same function). Numbers less than zero are essentially non-sensical (though they can be modeled using imaginary numbers), and the value 1 itself is a constant function, because 1 raised to any power is still 1.

Here are the graphs of $y = 2^x$, $y = 1^x$, and $y = 0.5^x$ superimposed over each other:

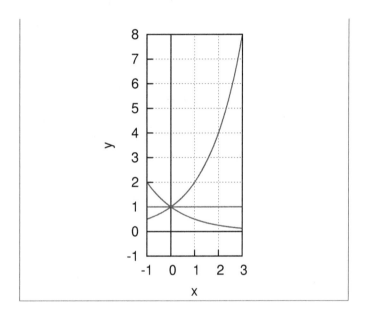

Some typical modifications to an exponential graph include:

- Multiplying by a constant factor—this is the same as simply making the y values that many times larger.

- Multiplying the exponent by a constant factor—this makes the graph get steep twice as fast.

If a negative number is multiplied by the exponent, then the graph is known as an *exponential decay* function.

5.4.3 Trigonometric Functions

Trigonometric functions are characterized by repeating forever.

As an example, below is the graph of $y = \sin(x)$:

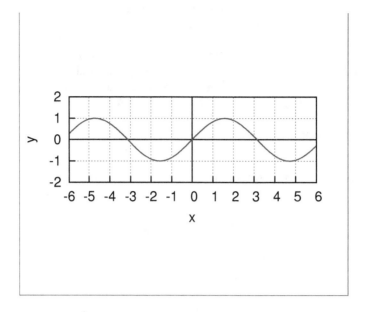

Unlike polynomials, which have a finite, fixed number of humps, this graph has an *infinite* number of humps. They just keep going on and on and on. In graphs that have repetitive elements, the number of units it takes before the graph repeats is known as the **period**.

The cosine function is exactly like the sine function, except that it is shifted over by a quarter of a period:

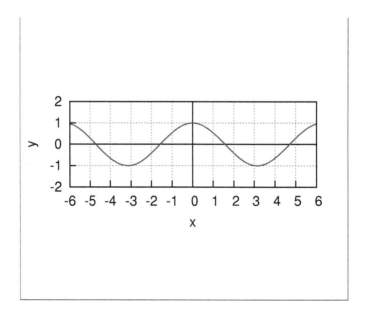

Sines and cosines are important not only in trigonometry, but also in sound production. If you play a sine wave through a speaker, you get a pure tone. If you have ever looked at a graphed sound wave, it is actually just a large set of sine wives on top of each other.

The tangent function is a little more strange, because it has vertical asymptotes at every period:

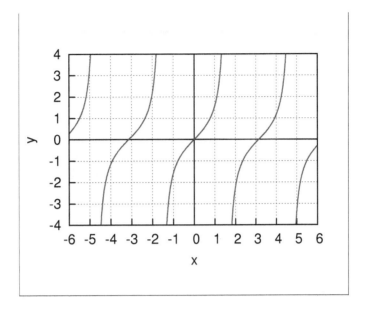

5.5   Combining graphs

Since graphs simply represent functions, composing functions together into a new function will also generate a new graph.

Being able to recognize combined graphs is important, but it takes a lot of familiarity with what graphs look like, and how the composition of functions affects their graph. However, once you understand it, it is much easier to transition between equations and mental images of what those equations mean.

The classic combined function is the exponential decay of a sine wave. If you imagine plucking a guitar string, what happens? First it plays a tone, but that tone gets quiter and quieter as time goes on. The tone is represented by a sine function, but the decrease in volume is represented by an exponential decay function. By multiplying the exponential decay by the sine function, you get a quieter and quieter result.

The general form of an exponential decay of a sine wave is shown in the graph below (the actual equation is $y = 10\sin(x)1.1^{-x}$):

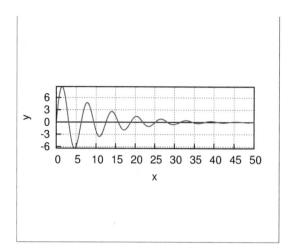

As you can see, it takes the same form as a wave function, but narrows as time passes.

5.6   A Warning About Educational Graphs

Most graphs you have experienced in your mathematics training until now have probably been smooth, continuous graphs—**smooth** meaning that the graph doesn't have any jagged edges, and **continuous** meaning that you could draw the whole graph without picking up your pencil. They will generally continue that way in this book. There are several reasons for this. The first is that smooth, continuous functions are easier to think about and analyze. The second is that smooth, continuous functions pop up a lot in real life. The third is that even some discontinuous functions can be reasonably approximated by continuous functions. In calculus, we will see that, to even perform the operations of calculus, it is a requirement that the graphs be smooth and continuous, at least over the parts of the graph we are interested in.

Example graphs of discontinuous functions are below. They aren't graphs of anything in particular, they are here just so you can get a feel for one might look like.

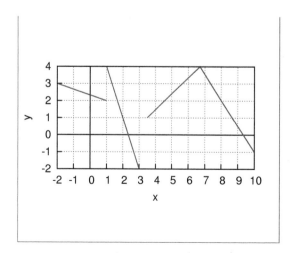

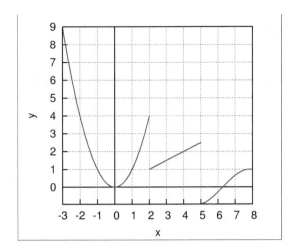

In all, discontinuous functions are harder to work with, and require higher levels of math to do so. That's why almost all lower math focuses on them. However, there is a tendency among people to think that because *all* they ever worked with in school are smooth, continuous functions, that this must be a general truism of life. They assume that all features of life and the world must be smooth and continuous. I just wanted to point out that not all of life is necessarily like that.

There is an interesting verse in the Bible that deals with this. It says that the scoffers will say, "For ever since the fathers fell asleep, all continues just as it was from the beginning of creation" (2 Peter 3:4). In other words, the scoffers view the whole world as being a continuous function from beginning to end. They have forgotten the important discontinuities that have existed in the world.

It is wise to recognize that every inquiry has limits. As we will see in future chapters, we can only use calculus if we have a smooth continuous graph. That doesn't mean that the world must provide us with smooth and continuous functions.

Sometimes people will assume the smooth and continuous nature of things to be true because it makes calculations easier, and they don't have a specific reason to believe otherwise, or they have reason to believe that the discontinuities won't have significant impact on their results. This is fair enough. A wise person, however, even when employing such means, recognizes the limitations of the approach.

I often give my classes a problem like the following: "If a car reaches a stop light going west at 20 miles per hour, where was the car two hours ago?" The answer seems simple enough—it was 40 miles to the east, right? But the question actually doesn't say—we have no idea what the car was doing for the last two hours. We were assuming continuities that didn't exist. Now, in math class, that is pretty reasonable. All of our questions are done assuming that nothing surprising is happening. But we have to remember that, when we want to apply this to the real world, sometimes surprising things do happen.

We won't cover this topic much more in this book, but I did want you to recognize that the real world doesn't always operate like it does in educational manuals and models.

Review

In this section, we learned:

1. Graphs enable us to think about a problem visually as well as analytically.

2. Graphs can enable us to think about functions for which we don't have formulas.

3. Understanding the graphs of various functions can help us infer the underlying formulas for data that we find in various endeavors in life.

4. In a two-dimensional graph, the independent variable (usually x) is usually plotted on the horizontal axis, while the dependent variable (usually y) is usually plotted on the vertical axis.

5. A graph can be shifted by subtracting the amount of shift from every instance of the variable that is shifted.

6. An inverse function can be found by merely swapping the x and y axes.

7. Equivalently, an inverse function can be plotted by mirroring a graph over the line $y = x$.

8. Knowing the graphs of common functions will help you to be able to visually understand equations simply by looking at their formulas.

9. The number of humps in a polynomial is at most one less than the number of degrees of the polynomial.

10. Exponential functions are the result of repeated compounding of results.

11. Trigonometric functions often appear when thing have cycles that repeat over and over again.

12. Graphs from combined functions are more difficult to interpret, but experience with them will help.

13. A smooth graph is one without sharp corners—all curves are gradual to some degree.

14. A continuous graph is one which you can draw without picking up your pencil.

15. While much of mathematics focuses on smooth, continuous functions because they are easier to analyze, don't be fooled into thinking that reality must always be this way.

Exercises

1. What is the most number of humps that the following polynomial can have?
$y = x^4 - 10x^3 + 35x^2 - 50x + 24$

2. What is the most number of humps that the following polynomial can have?
$y = 49x^3 - 4x^6 - 14x^5 + 56x^4 - 196x^2 - 36x + 144 + x^7$

3. What is the most number of humps that the following polynomial can have?
$y = 3x + 4$

4. What is the equation of the following graph if shifted to the left five units and down one?
$y = x^2 + 2x - 3$

5. What is the equation of the following graph if shifted up two units and to the left three units?
$5y = x\sin(x)$

6. Draw the graph of $y = 5x$ on graph paper. Now draw the inverse of this function.

7. Draw the graph of $y = x^2$ on graph paper. Now draw the inverse of this function.

8. Draw graphs of the following functions from $x = -6$ to $x = 6$: $\sin(x)$, $\cos(x)$, and $\ln(x)$. Draw 2^x from $-3 \leq x \leq 3$.

Chapter 6

Calculus: The Big Picture

Calculus is one of my favorite mathematical subjects—its beauty and power are unparalleled in mathematics. Calculus allows you to take an equation that you know, and be able to derive *new equations* from it that tell you *more information* about the original function. If you took physics in high school, you were probably taught a number of equations for how things move. You may have wondered where these came from. Most equations in physics are based on small observations, which then, using calculus, are used to build large-scale equations from them. It allows you to take equations for how things are that we can observe and measure, and transform them into new equations for things that are much more difficult to quantify and measure.

Calculus has two primary operations that it uses to develop these new equations: the **derivative** (used to find slopes) and the **integral** (used to find areas). On their own, they might not seem all that helpful, but as we progress we will see how these two small tools can be used to build and solve all sorts of interesting equations, and solve all sorts of interesting problems.

This chapter is an attempt to walk you through the *ideas* behind the calculus without getting too deep into the mechanics. If, at the end, you understand the *idea* of the derivative and the integral, but have no idea how you would calculate one, that is fine, because that is precisely the goal of the chapter. We will cover the general *methods* to calculate derivatives and integrals in later chapters.

Also, this chapter is very loose on both terminology and the symbols we use. We will actually use terms and symbols slightly differently later in the course (especially the integral); the goal here is merely to introduce you to the general concept as easily and intuitively as possible.

6.1   The Integral: The Equation of Area

The first operation we will look at is the **integral**. Although we will learn a better way of imagining the integral in Chapter 17, in this chapter we will think of an integral as a technique for finding the area under a curve. Essentially, an integral takes an equation and gives us a new equation which tells us how to find the area bounded by the graph of the equation with the x and y axis and a particular value of x.

Take, for instance, the graph below:

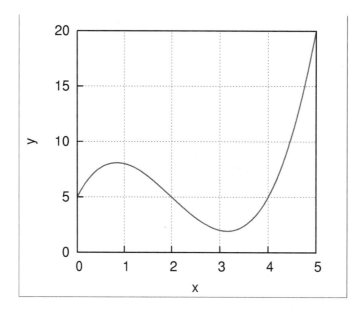

This is the graph of an equation. The actual equation is unimportant, but for concreteness I'll let you know that the equation is:

$$y = x^3 - 6x^2 + 8x + 5 \qquad (6.1)$$

What is most important is that we have a curve that is generated by an equation.

Let's say that we want to know the area bounded by the curve, the x-axis, the y-axis, and a specific x value. An *integral* would be a new equation which, when given a paricular x value, would give us the area bounded by that region.

So, if we wanted to know the area bounded by $x = 4$, that would be the area of the shaded region below:

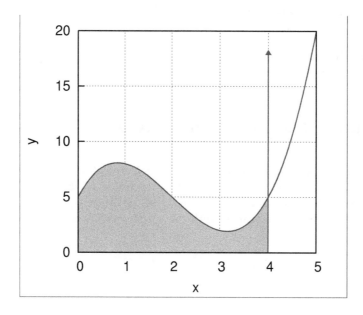

The integral is an equation that tells us, for whatever x value we want to place the boundary at, what the area under the curve is. If we wanted to know the area of the equation up to the value of $x = 6$, we could give the integral the x value of 6, and it would give us this value.

In this case, using techniques you won't learn until much later, the integral of our curve is the following equation:

$$\text{area} = \frac{x^4}{4} - 2x^3 + 4x^2 + 5x \tag{6.2}$$

So, if we want to know the area under the curve for Equation 6.1 bounded by $x = 4$, we can evaluate Equation 6.2 with x as 4 and get the answer. If you actually put that value in, you will find that the area of the shaded region is 20.

In later chapters we will develop some general rules for understanding how to compute integrals directly from equations, and you will be able to determine integrals for equations like these with no problem whatsoever. In this chapter, however, I want to show a few integrals which can be computed just from the basics of geometry, without any special rules from calculus.

As a simple example, let's take an equation for a constant, $y = 2$. Let's look at a graph of this equation:

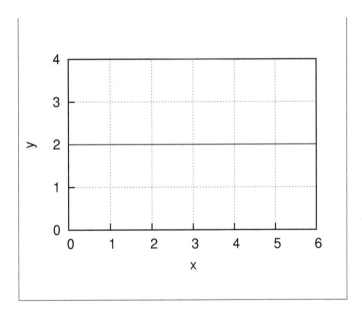

Now, at any point along the graph, we can figure out the area of the region bounded by the graph, the x-axis, the y-axis, and whatever x value we want. For instance, let's look at the area where $x = 4$.

The shaded region below is the region we are wanting to find the area of:

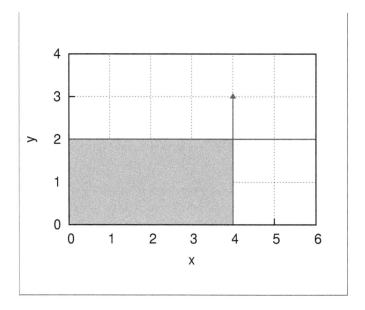

Now, this forms a simple rectangle. The area of a rectangle is *width·height*. Since the top line of the graph is $y = 2$ then the height is always going to be 2, and since we are marking the right boundary at $x = 4$, then the width will be 4. Therefore, the area of the rectangle formed will be $4·2 = 8$.

Likewise, if we want to know the area under the graph at $x = 6$ we would follow the same procedure. The height will be 2 (because the y value is fixed at 2), and the width will be 6, because the boundary is 6 units over on the x-axis from the origin. Therefore, the area of this rectangle will be $6·2 = 12$.

Now, is it possible to develop a general equation which, for any given x boundary, we will know the area under the $y = 2$ line?

Since $y = 2$ forms a straight line, and the boundary at any given x will be a straight line perpindicular to the $y = 2$ line, the bounded region will *always* form a rectangle. Since $y = 2$, the height will *always* be 2. That is half of the equation of the area of a rectangle. What about the width? The width will always be our x-value. Therefore, the area bounded by the equation and a given x value will always be:

$$\text{area} = 2·x \tag{6.3}$$

As we mentioned earlier, this new equation is known as an *integral*. If we wanted to graph this new equation, we would set the vertical axis to be the value of the area. However, if we used the variable y to represent this, it would cause confusion, because it is a *different* y than the one in our original equation. In order to avoid confusion, we want to distinguish between the previous y value and the vertical axis on our graph. Therefore, we will use the variable A_0 for the vertical axis, since this equation is the area under the previous graph.

$$A_0 = 2x \tag{6.4}$$

A graph of the equation looks like this:

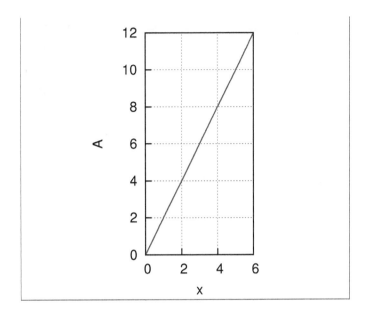

So the integral of $y = 2$ winds up being $A_0 = 2x$. But notice that this new equation is still an equation just like any other. We can, in fact, find the area under this new line as well!

Let's look at the shape generated when we shade the area bounded by the graph and $x = 3$:

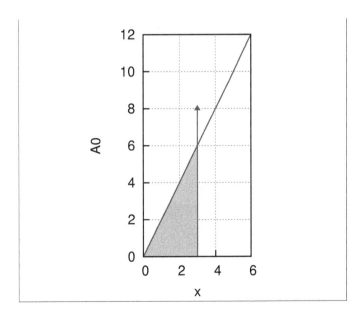

What shape is it? It's a triangle. If you remember, the area of a triangle is

$$\frac{1}{2} \cdot \text{base} \cdot \text{height} \tag{6.5}$$

So, let's say we wanted to know the area bounded by the graph and $x = 3$.

What is the base? Well, the base is simple our x-value, 3. What is the height? The height is simply the A_0-value. Since $A_0 = 2x$, and $x = 3$, then the height is 6. So the area becomes $\frac{1}{2} \cdot 3 \cdot 6$ which yields 9. So the area is 9 square units.

What if we wanted to know the general equation, like before, so we could find the area under the line for any x value? You should notice that no matter where we draw our x boundary, it will always form a triangle. The triangle will have a base that will be the x value. Also, no matter where we draw our x boundary, the height will be A_0 *for that value of* x. Therefore, for base = x and height = A_0, the equation will be:

$$\text{area} = \frac{1}{2} \cdot x \cdot A_0 \tag{6.6}$$

Now, this is in terms of x and A_0, but we would like the area to be entirely a function of x. Thankfully, we already have an equation that gives us the equation for A_0:

$$A_0 = 2x$$

So, if we substitute, we get:

$$\text{area} = \frac{1}{2} \cdot x \cdot 2x \tag{6.7}$$

Now, since the previous area was given as A_0, the new area will be A_1, giving us:

$$A_1 = \frac{1}{2} x \cdot 2x = x^2 \tag{6.8}$$

This equation simplifies to:

$$A_1 = x^2 \tag{6.9}$$

Therefore, for the graph of $A_0 = 2x$, the area under the graph can be determined by the equation $A_1 = x^2$.

This forms the basic parabola:

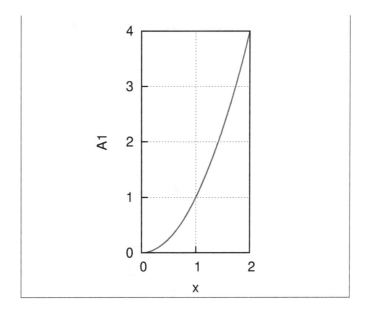

At this point, we have exhausted our ability to do integrals using basic geometry, but I hope you can see the basic idea that we can take an existing equation and create a new equation that tells us new information about the original one.

In the case of the integral, the new information is the equation for the area under curve generated by the original equation.

6.2   The Derivative: The Equation of Slopes

The integral was an equation which told us, for any x value, what the area under the curve was between $x = 0$ and the given value of x. It was a new equation that gave us information about the original equation. The **derivative** yields a new equation which gives us a different piece of information—it tells us the *slope* of the graph at any x value.

To see this more clearly, let's imagine a simple curve, say $y = x^2$.

You can see it below:

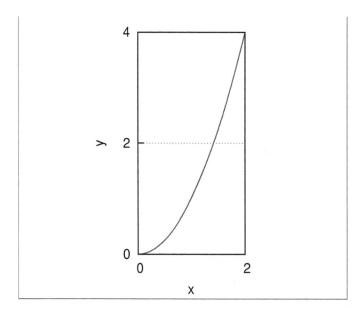

Now, at any point on that graph, you can draw a line that is tangent to that graph (meaning that it skims the graph at exactly one point in that vicinity).

Below is the tangent line that touches the graph at $x = 1$:

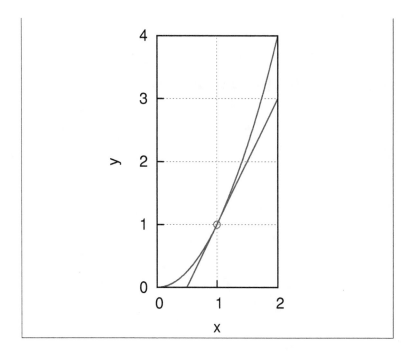

The slope of the tangent line tells us the slope at that point. In this case, the slope is 2.

Now, the derivative isn't really concerned with the whole tangent line, it just uses the slope of the tangent line in order to discover the slope of the graph at that point. If you were to magnify the region where the tangent line touches the graph, you would notice that the slope of the curve *at that point* is the same as the slope of the tangent line at that same point.

Here is the same graph, with the where the tangent line touches the graph is enlarged:

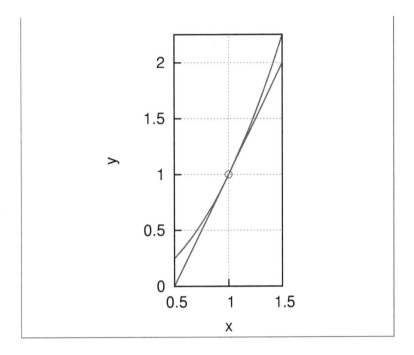

So, *at that point*, the slope is the same as the slope of the tangent line. But notice that the slope is constantly changing. If we picked some other point, it would have a different slope.

For instance, at $x = 0.25$ the slope is much shallower:

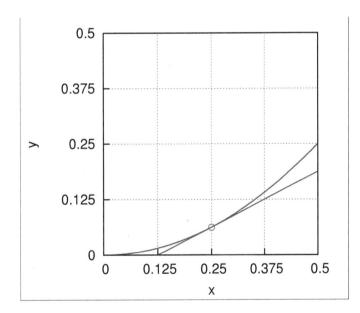

You can estimate the slope at any point of a graph by putting a ruler on the graph where it just skims the surface of the graph at a single point. This will make your ruler the tangent line.

You can then estimate the slope of the tangent by picking any two points that your ruler touches and using the slope formula to find the slope:

$$m = \frac{y_1 - y_0}{x_1 - x_0}$$

6.2.1   Calculating an Estimated Slope

But let's say we don't have a ruler handy, and we want to *calculate* the tangent line. What would we do? Well, if we only have one point, we can't calculate a line, and the tangent is only supposed to intersect the line at a single point. But, let's say that instead of getting an exact value of the slope, we just wanted to estimate it. What might we do then?

In that case, we might pick out two points that were very close to each other, and determine the slope between them. In fact, we should think that the closer that two points are to each other, the closer the slope between those points will be to the slope at that exact point.

So, let's say we wanted to estimate the slope of the point on the graph where $x = 3$. What process might we do to accomplish this? If you remember from Chapter 3, the slope formula (Equation 3.2) tells you how to determine the slope from any two points.

We know what the first point is—it is the location of the function at $x = 3$. The equation is $y = x^2$, so when $x = 3$, $y = 9$, which gives an initial point of $(3, 9)$. Now, for the second point, we will pick a point close to the original point, say $x = 3.1$. So, at $x = 3.1$, $y = 3.1^2 = 9.61$, giving us a second point of $(3.1, 9.61)$. Using the slope equation, we can see that the slope between these two points is:

$$m = \frac{y_1 - y_0}{x_1 - x_0} = \frac{9.61 - 9}{3.1 - 3} = \frac{0.61}{0.1} = 6.1$$

Therefore, at $x = 3$ we have determined that the slope is approximately 6.1. Note that the slope is *exactly* 6.1 between these two points, but it is only an *estimate* of the slope at precisely $x = 3$.

However, we can get a closer estimate by picking a second x value that is even closer to the original $x = 3$. For instance, we can look at $x = 3.01$. For that x value, $y = 3.01^2 = 9.0601$. Using the slope equation again, we can see that the slope between these two points is:

$$m = \frac{y_1 - y_0}{x_1 - x_0} = \frac{9.0601 - 9}{3.01 - 3} = \frac{0.0601}{0.01} = 6.01$$

This is a more exact answer than our previous answer, because the two points we chose were closer together. As we move the points closer and closer together, our estimated slope will become closer and closer to the true slope of the line. Now, since I know the content of the next several chapters, I will let you in on a secret—the *true* answer is simply 6. At $x = 3$, the slope of the graph is 6.

We can do similar calculations for $x = 1$. We will look at the slope between $x = 1$ and $x = 1.01$. The value of y at $x = 1$ is 1, and the value at $x = 1.01$ is 1.0201. So, using the slope formula, the slope between these two points is:

$$m = \frac{y_1 - y_0}{x_1 - x_0} = \frac{1.0201 - 1}{1.01 - 1} = \frac{0.0201}{0.01} = 2.01$$

And again, by telepathically looking into the future chapters, I can tell you that the actual value for the slope is 2.

Try doing this yourself for $x = 2$ and $x = 4$, both using 0.1 and 0.01 as the distance to the next x value.

—   Example 6.1

Find an estimated slope for the equation $y = x^2$ at $x = 2$, using both 0.1 and 0.01 as the distance to the next x value.

So, to start with, we need to find the y value at $x = 2$:

$$y = x^2 = (2)^2 = 4$$

This gives us a first point, $(2, 4)$.

For the second point, we need to do the same with a nearby x value that is 0.1 further along the x axis. So we will find the y value at $x = 2.1$:

$$y = x^2 = (2.1)^2 = 4.41$$

This gives us a second point, $(2.1, 4.41)$.

Now we can use the point-slope formula to find the slope between these two points:

$$m = \frac{y_1 - y_0}{x_1 - x_0} = \frac{4.41 - 4}{2.1 - 2} = \frac{0.41}{0.1} = 4.1$$

Therefore, an estimate of the slope at $x = 2$ is 4.1.

We can get a better estimate by picking a value even closer to $x = 2$. If we use $x = 2.01$ that will give us a better estimate. With $x = 2.01$ the y value can be calculated as follows:

$$y = x^2 = (2.01)^2 = 4.0401$$

This gives us the point $(2.01, 4.0401)$. Now we can use the point-slope formula to find the slope between these two poitns:

$$m = \frac{y_1 - y_0}{x_1 - x_0} = \frac{4.0401 - 4}{2.01 - 2} = \frac{0.0401}{0.01} = 4.01$$

Therefore, an even better estimate of the slope at $x = 2$ is 4.01.

—   Example 6.2

Find an estimated slope for the equation $y = x^2$ at $x = 4$, using both 0.1 and 0.01 as the distance to the next x value.

So, to start with, we need to find the y value at $x = 4$:

$$y = x^2 = (4)^2 = 16$$

This gives us a first point, $(4, 16)$.

For the second point, we need to do the same with a nearby x value that is 0.1 further along the x axis. So we will find the y value at $x = 4.1$:

$$y = x^2 = (4.1)^2 = 16.81$$

This gives us a second point, $(4.1, 16.81)$.

Now we can use the point-slope formula to find the slope between these two points:

$$m = \frac{y_1 - y_0}{x_1 - x_0} = \frac{16.81 - 16}{4.1 - 4} = \frac{0.81}{0.1} = 8.1$$

Therefore, an estimate of the slope at $x = 4$ is 8.1.

We can get a better estimate by picking a value even closer to $x = 4$. If we use $x = 4.01$ that will give us a better estimate. With $x = 4.01$ the y value can be calculated as follows:

$$y = x^2 = (4.01)^2 = 16.0801$$

This gives us the point $(4.01, 16.0801)$. Now we can use the point-slope formula to find the slope between these two poitns:

$$m = \frac{y_1 - y_0}{x_1 - x_0} = \frac{16.0801 - 16}{4.01 - 4} = \frac{0.0801}{0.01} = 8.01$$

Therefore, an even better estimate of the slope at $x = 4$ is 8.01.

6.2.2   Plotting Slopes on a Graph

Now that we have several slopes for the equation $y = x^2$, and since a slope is simply a number, we can actually plot the slopes themselves on a graph. It probably isn't clear *why* you would want to do this at this point, but I hope you see that since we have a slope (which is a number) for each value of x, we can easily make a new graph, where the vertical axis is the slope of the previous graph, and x represents the same value as it did on the previous graph.

We don't want to call the vertical axis y, because we don't want to confuse it with our previous usage of the variable y. Therefore, we will call the vertical axis y'. Note the mark next to the y—this mark is called the **prime**, which indicates that it s a related, but different value from our original y.

So now, let's plot these slopes on a new graph:

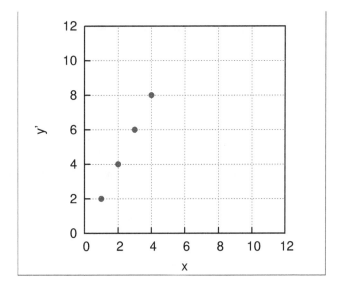

Now, do you notice something interesting about these points? They seem to form a line! In fact, they do form the line $y' = 2x$. Your estimated slopes will be slightly off, but the true values of the derivative yield $y' = 2x$.

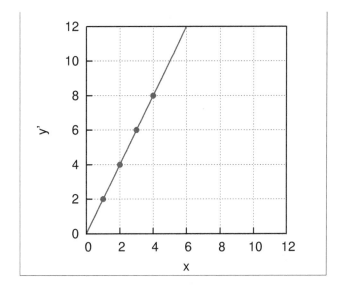

So, what we can say (using a little bit of knowledge from future chapters) is that for any point on the graph of $y = x^2$, the *slope at that point* will be given as $y' = 2x$. For example, if we wanted to know how steep the graph was at $x = 20$, we can use the equation for y' and determine that the slope of the original equation at $x = 20$ is 40.

6.2.3 The Slope of a Slope

Now, let's look more closely at the equation $y' = 2x$. Even though it is a graph of slopes from another equation ($y = x^2$), it itself has slopes. Or, more technically, since it *is* a line, it has exactly one slope for the entire graph.

Going back to chapter 3 (Equation 3.1), the equation for a line is:

$$y = mx + b$$

In this case, instead of y we have y', and there is no b because the line goes through the origin. So our equation becomes this:

$$y' = 2x + 0$$

So what is the slope of the line? The slope is m, so in the case of $y' = 2x$, the slope is 2. Since this is true for the entire line, it will be true at *any* value of x. So, at $x = 0$, the slope is 2. At $x = 3$, the slope is still 2. At $x = 25$, the slope is still 2.

To graph this second derivative, we will use y'' to designate that we have yet another meaning for the vertical axis—the slopes of y'. Since y'' is always 2 for every value of x, the equation is simply:

$$y'' = 2$$

And the graph looks like this:

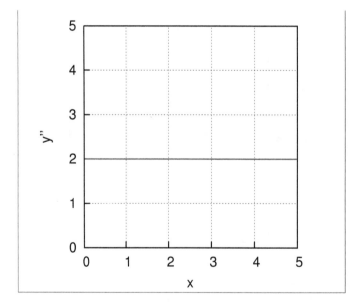

Interestingly, this is yet another line. It, too, has a slope. However, the slope on this line is zero (it never rises or falls, no matter how much it runs). Therefore, the equation for the slopes on this line is simply:

$$y''' = 0$$

So, as you can see, if you have a smooth graph, you can plot the slopes of the graph for each x value onto a new graph. The equation behind this new graph is known as the **derivative** of the previous equation. We will learn more about the derivative and what we can do with it in later chapters.

For now, just keep in mind that the derivative is an equation which represents the slopes of another equation.

Figure 6.1: Relating Integrals and Derivatives

	derivative →		derivative →	
$y = x^2$		$y' = 2x$		$y'' = 2$
	← integral		← integral	

6.3 Relating Derivatives and Integrals

Did you notice something odd about the examples in the sections on the derivative and the integral?

In the section on integrals, we started with this equation:

$$y = 2$$

When we performed the first integral, we arrived at this equation:

$$A_0 = 2x$$

When we performed the second integral, we arrived at this equation:

$$A_1 = x^2$$

When we looked at derivatives. The first equation we looked at was the same, basic equation:

$$y = x^2$$

Then, we determined that the derivative of that equation was this equation:

$$y' = 2x$$

And, again, taking another derivative, we find this equation:

$$y'' = 2$$

What you can see is the very strange fact that finding a derivative is the *very opposite* operation of finding the integral! It may seem strange that these two operations—finding the slope and finding the area under the curve—are inverses of each other. There are some caveats to this insight, and the particular equations here were picked precisely because it demonstrates it so well.

But the basic insight is true—integrals and derivatives are, for the most part, inverses of each other. Why this is the case will become more apparent as we proceed through the book.

6.4   Equations About Equations

Although the derivative and the integral are at the core of calculus, there is another insight which I want you to take away. What fascinated me about calculus when I first began it was that you could develop new equations *that would tell you about other equations.* What these new equations will do is help us to answer questions about the old equations that we might not have been able to answer before.

As an example, take the curve below.

$$y = x^3 - 15x^2 + 71x - 105$$

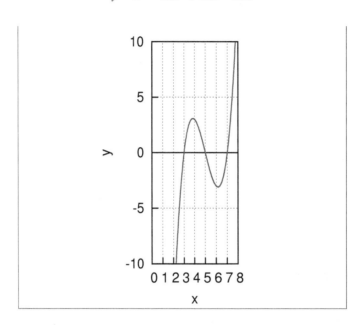

Notice that there are two humps on the equation—one going up and one going down. Normal techniques for evaluating curves sometimes help us find the zeroes (where the equation crosses the x-axis), but they don't help us at all find the top and bottom of the humps. So how would calculus help?

Well, think about what a derivative is. A derivative is an equation telling us what the *slopes* of an equation are. Is there anything unusual about the slopes of the equation at the top and bottom of the graph? Pull out your ruler, and try to make a tangent line to the graph at the top and the bottom.

If you do it correctly, you might notice that the tangent line is *flat*—it is perfectly level. What does that mean for the slope? Well, a line that doesn't move up and down has a slope of zero (it doesn't rise no matter how much run there is).

So, if you knew the derivative of the equation, you could find out the places where the *derivative* crosses the x-axis (i.e., where the derivative is zero), and it will tell you where the tops and bottoms of the primary equation are. That might not seem worthwhile, but, as we will see in future chapters, there are a lot of interesting things that you can do with that.

As for the integral, the obvious application is geometry—using the integral to find the areas for funny-shaped objects. But there are bigger applications that go much deeper—areas can be used for all sorts of operations that involve totalling.

Many equations in physics, for example, are built by applying the integral. For instance, The displacement equation, which gives the total distance traveled based on acceleration, is based on the integral. It is achieved by totalling the effects of acceleration over a period of time. What we will learn in calculus is not what these equations are specifically, but what sort of thought processes lead to them, and even how we might build our own equations to discover the answers that interest us.

As a side note, can you see why we said earlier that calculus only applies to smooth, continuous functions? Imagine a function with a break in the middle. How would you find the area under a curve if part of the curve went *missing*? Or, think about slopes. If you have a junction with a jagged edge, what slope is the junction point itself? Is it the slope coming up or going down? If you have a missing part of a curve, what is the slope of the missing section? As you can see, calculus requires smooth and continuous functions for its operations to make sense.

Review

In this chapter, we learned:

1. Calculus allows you to take existing equations and derive new equations which tell you about the original equation.

2. Calculus introduces two primary operations—the integral and the derivative.

3. The integral tells you, given a function, what the area under the curve up to a specific x value will be.

4. The derivative tells you, given a function, what the slope of the curve at a specific x value will be.

5. The symbol $\int$ is used to represent the operation to find the integral.

6. The symbol $'$ is used to represent the operation to find the derivative.

7. Since the derivative is simply the slope of a function, the slope/derivative *at a specific point* can be estimated by using a ruler and drawing a tangent line touching the graph at that point.

8. The derivative at a specific point can also be estimated by calculating the slope between the given point and a nearby point using the slope formula.

9. Using the slope estimation technique above, you can get closer and closer to the "true" value of the slope by moving the two points closer and closer together.

10. Since the result of the integral or derivative of a function is a new function, such functions themselves have integrals and derivatives.

11. Derivatives and integrals are, in essence, reverse operations of each other. That is, the derivative of the integral of a function gives you your original function.

12. Calculus works well on smooth, continuous functions. The less smooth and continuous the function, the less that calculus can help you analyze the function.

Exercises

1. Describe the integral in your own words.

2. Describe the derivative in your own words.

3. Think about the graph of $y = 6$. What is the area under the graph at $x = 3$ (i.e., the area bounded by the x-axis, y-axis, the actual graph $y = 6$, and the vertical line at the endpoint, $x = 3$).

4. Think about the graph of $y = 3x$. What is the area under the graph at $x = 2$?

5. Given the equation of the line $y = 5x + 3$, what is the slope of the line? Since that is the slope for every value of x, what would the *equation* of the derivative be?

6. Plot the equation $y = 2x^2 - 3$ on a sheet of paper from $x = -1$ to $x = 3$. Use a ruler to estimate the slope of this equation at $x = 2$.

7. Plot the equation of $y = x^3 - x^2$ on a sheet of paper from $x = 0$ to $x = 2$ (plot every 0.5 increment on the x axis). Calculate an estimation of the value of the slope at $x = 1$ by finding the slope between the point on the curve at $x = 1$ and $x = 1.1$. Calculate the slope again between the point at $x = 1$ and $x = 1.01$. What do you think the "real" slope actually is?

8. Take the equation $y = x^2 + 2x$ and calculate an estimation of the slope at $x = 3$ by finding the slope between the point on the curve at $x = 3$ and $x = 3.1$. Calculate the slope again between the point at $x = 3$ and $x = 3.01$.

9. Take the equation $y = 3x^2 - x$ and calculate an estimation of the slope at $x = 4$. In order to estimate the slope, for the second point use an x value that is 0.001 away from your real x value.

Part II

The Derivative

The derivative is the first basic tool of calculus. The derivative is an equation that yields the slope of another equation for any given value of x. The derivative can be used for a variety of purposes, including finding related rates of change as well as maximum and minimum values.

Chapter 7

The Derivative

The first core concept of calculus is the **derivative**. In chapter 6, we covered conceptually what a derivative is. This chapter will focus on taking the *concept* of what the derivative is, and using it to create a *general equation* that will help us find the derivative of any other equation.

The derivative is a beautiful tool for solving problems. However, before we can learn to use it to solve problems, we must first take the time to learn and understand the tool itself. The versatility of the derivative for solving problems will make the time taken over the next several chapters to learn it well worth the effort.

The procedure we learn in this chapter is meant to help you closely tie in your mind the concept of the derivative to its calculation. However, the procedure itself is somewhat unwieldy for more difficult equations. Therefore, in the chapters that follow, we will learn some rules that allow us to determine the derivative of most equations very quickly. Those rules, however, are premature if you don't have a good grounding in what a derivative is.

7.1   What is a Derivative?

A derivative is an equation that tells us the *slope* of some other equation for each x value. In the new equation (the derivative), the horizontal axis is the same as for the original equation, but the vertical axis contains a value that represents the *slope* of the original equation. Therefore, if I have an equation for a derivative, and it says that the value of the derivative at some given x value is $\frac{3}{4}$, that means that the slope of the original equation is $\frac{3}{4}$ for that x value.

Now that we know what a derivative *is*, we can start to think about how it can be solved. If we think back to the steps that we learned in Chapter 2, it says that we should begin by finding out what the problem *means*. Therefore, we should begin by asking, what does it mean for something to be a slope?

If you remember from Chapter 3, a slope is simply a ratio of $\frac{rise}{run}$ of a graph at a point. More technically, it is the ratio of the change in y to the change in x, as in $\frac{y \text{ change}}{x \text{ change}}$. A ratio, if you divide it out, just becomes a number like any other number, so its value can be plotted. Knowing this allows us to use the slope formula to understand how we might calculate a derivative.

7.2   The Derivative as a Slope

The method that we used in chapter 6 to plot the slope of the graph was fairly straightforward:

1. To calculate a slope, we need two points.

2. We first choose the point for which we desire the slope. This can be any x value for which we want to know the slope at that point. We will call this value x_0.

3. Using this chosen x_0, we can compute the y value at this point using the original equation. We will call this y value y_0. We now have our first point, (x_0, y_0).

4. Since a line needs two points, we need to find the next point.

5. We choose a new x value that is just a tiny bit away from the original x value in order to give us a good approximation of the slope at that point. We will call this new point x_1.

6. Using x_1, we can compute the corresponding y value using the original equation. We will call this value y_1. We now have our second point, (x_1, y_1).

7. Now, armed with two points, we can use the slope formula to tell us the slope between these two points: $m = \frac{y_1 - y_0}{x_1 - x_0}$

In the following example we will look at an example problem to illustrate the procedure. Remember that using our meanings and definitions in a concrete problem is the second step of the general problem-solving procedure we learned in Chapter 2.

—   Example 7.1

Estimate the slope of the equation $y = x^3 + 1$ at $x = 2$. For your second point for the estimation, use an x value that is 0.01 more than the original.

To do this using the procedure given above, we need to first evaluate the y value at $x = 2$. Using the equation, we find:

$$y = x^3 + 1$$
$$= (2)^3 + 1$$
$$= 9$$

So, the first point is $(2, 9)$. For the second point, we want to pick an x that is just a little further away. For this example, we are using for our next x value a number that is 0.01 away. So, since the first point has x as 2, the second point will have an x value of 2.01. What is the y value here?

$$y = x^3 + 1$$
$$= (2.01)^3 + 1$$
$$= 9.120601$$

So, our next point will be $(2.01, 9.120601)$. Now that we have the two points, we can use the point-slope formula to come up with a slope between these points:

$$m \approx \frac{y_1 - y_0}{x_1 - x_0}$$

$$\approx \frac{9.120601 - 9}{2.01 - 2}$$

$$\approx \frac{0.120601}{0.01}$$

$$\approx 12.0601$$

Therefore, the slope of the graph $y = x^3 + 1$ at $x = 2$ is approximately 12.0601.

In step three of our general procedure, we want to convert our steps into a repeatable formula that we can use. Therefore, we want to generalize this method so that we can spell it out in a formula, and so that it works for any equation where y is a function of x.

Here, again, is our trusty equation for slope:

$$m = \frac{y_1 - y_0}{x_1 - x_0} \tag{7.1}$$

Now, if y is a function of x then we can use function notation to say $y = f(x)$. In our specific case, $f(x) = x^2$. Using $f(x)$ instead of x^2 will allow us to generalize our method beyond the specific equation we are looking at, and say that this method works for any equation where y is a function of x.

So, if $y = f(x)$, then any given point on the graph can be given as $(x, f(x))$. This is true because a point is simply an x and a y value, and $y = f(x)$. Now, we can imagine a new point which is a small distance from ou x value, let's say that it is 0.01 away from our x value. The new x coordinate will be $x + 0.01$, and the new y coordinate will be $f(x + 0.01)$. Therefore, the coordinate of the second point will be $(x + 0.01, f(x + 0.01))$.

So now we have two points, $(x, f(x))$ and $(x + 0.01, f(x + 0.01))$. Therefore, we can plug these into our slope formula, and have the following equation:

$$m = \frac{f(x + 0.01) - f(x)}{x + 0.01 - x} \tag{7.2}$$

By simplifying the denominator, we can reduce this to

$$m = \frac{f(x + 0.01) - f(x)}{0.01} \tag{7.3}$$

So, if we plug in our own function into this, where $f(x) = x^2$, we get

$$m = \frac{(x + 0.01)^2 - (x)^2}{0.01}$$

If we expand out $(x + 0.01)^2$, this becomes

$$m = \frac{x^2 + 0.02x + 0.0001 - x^2}{0.01}$$

The numerator can be simplified so that the equation becomes

$$m = \frac{0.02x + 0.0001}{0.01}$$

Dividing through by the denominator yields this equation:

$$m = 2x + 0.01$$

So, for any point on the graph, the slope between that point and a point whose x value is 0.01 away from that point is given by the formula $2x + 0.01$. Therefore, for the point on the graph where $x = 3$, the slope between that point and the point on the graph where $x = 3.01$ will be 6.01. At $x = 65$, the slope between that point and the point where $x = 65.01$ will be 130.01.

— Example 7.2

Find an equation to tell the slope of the line $y = x^3 + 1$ at any given value of x, using the given point and a point 0.01 away from that point for estimation purposes.

We can use Equation 7.3 to figure this out. Since y is given in terms of a function of x where $f(x) = x^3 + 1$, we can write Equation 7.3 as follows:

$$m = \frac{f(x + 0.01) - f(x)}{0.01} \qquad \text{Equation 7.3}$$

$$= \frac{((x + 0.01)^3 + 1) - (x^3 + 1)}{0.01} \qquad \text{substituting in our } f(x)$$

$$= \frac{x^3 + 0.03x^2 + 0.0003x + 0.000001 - x^3}{0.01} \qquad \text{expanding exponents}$$

$$= \frac{0.03x^2 + 0.0003x + 0.000001}{0.01} \qquad \text{simplifying the numerator}$$

$$= 3x^2 + 0.03x + 0.0001 \qquad \text{dividing by 0.01}$$

Therefore, for any x, the slope between that point and another point 0.01 away will be given by $3x^2 + 0.03x + 0.0001$.

You should look at the relationship between this example problem and Example 7.1. See if you can use this formula to get the same answer as in Example 7.1

7.3   Generalizing to Arbitrarily Small Distances

So, we have determined what the equation is for finding slopes between a current point and a point where the x value is 0.01 away. However, we could get even closer. We could do the same equation for a point that is 0.00001 away from the original point, rather than 0.01 away.

We can use this to build a new a new version of Equation 7.3 that is even more accurate:

$$m = \frac{f(x + 0.00001) - f(x)}{0.00001}$$

This would give us even better results. The problem, however, is that no matter how close I make the second point to the first, I can always think of a closer point.

So, let us alleviate this problem by introducing a new variable, which will represent the x distance between the first point and the second point. We will call this quantity h so that it doesn't get confused with our variables.

So now, our first point will be $(x, f(x))$ (just like before), but the second point will be $(x + h, f(x + h))$, where h is the distance between the two x values. If we use the slope formula, we then get this equation:

$$m = \frac{f(x + h) - f(x)}{x + h - x}$$

If we simplify the denominator, we get this equation:

$$m = \frac{f(x + h) - f(x)}{h}$$

In calculus, we often use y' to denote the derivative of the equation, so we will simply swap y' for m:

$$y' = \frac{f(x + h) - f(x)}{h} \tag{7.4}$$

This is known as the *general formula for the derivative*. Equation 7.4 is very important and should be not only well-understood but also memorized. The notation of using y' to indicate the derivative is known as *Newton's notation* for the derivative. This is important only because later on we will be learning other notations for the derivative.

So, if we substitute in $f(x) = x^2$ into this, we get:

$$y' = \frac{(x + h)^2 - x^2}{h}$$

We can expand out $(x + h)^2$ and get:

$$y' = \frac{x^2 + 2hx + h^2 - x^2}{h}$$

The x^2 and $-x^2$ cancel each other out, giving:

$$y' = \frac{2hx + h}{h}$$

We can then divide by the denominator and get:

$$y' = 2x + h$$

Now, you can use this equation to tell you the slope of $y = x^2$ at any point, using any distance you want between the points. If I want to use 0.000001 as the distance between my x values, I just substitute that for h in the equation and I get:

$$y' = 2x + 0.000001$$

So, at $x = 4$, the slope between that point and the point with an x value 0.000001 away will be 8.000001.

If I want to use 0.00000000001 as the distance between my points, that becomes:

$$y' = 2x + 0.00000000001$$

7.4   Instantaneous Slope

So far, instead of finding the slope *at* a particular point (i.e., the slope of the tangent line that intersects with *only* that point), we have been *estimating* the slope by using two points which are very close to each other. However, what we really, really want is not a point that is nearby, which will give me an approximate tangent, but instead I want the *exact* tangent. An exact tangent will touch the graph at *exactly* one point.

Such an exact slope is also known as an **instantaneous slope** or an **instantaneous rate of change**. It is *instantaneous* because it is the slope exactly at that point or instant on the graph. It is not an estimate for the slope, but the exact slope.

So, let's revisit what we have looked at so far. For the equation $y = x^2$, we found an equation for an estimate of the slope for any two points where the second one's x value is h units away. This equation is:

$$y' = 2x + h$$

So, if we want to know the estimate of the slope at $x = 9$ and will estimate with a second point whose x value is 0.000000000001 away from the first, then we can just plug these into the equation and get:

$$y' = 2 \cdot 9 + 0.000000000001 = 18.000000000001$$

But what about finding the slope at *exactly* $x = 9$? Think about it this way—if we want to find the slope at exactly $x = 9$, how far away will the second x value be? The answer is it will be 0 units away! Therefore, we can plug in 0 to our equation and get the following:

$$\begin{aligned} y' &= 2x + h \\ &= 2 \cdot 9 + 0 \\ &= 18 \end{aligned}$$

Therefore, the *exact* slope at $x = 9$ is 18!

We can make this even more general by substituting 0 for h in the equation itself. That means that the *actual* slope at any point on the graph $y = x^2$ can be found by taking our original $y' = 2x + h$ and replacing

h with zero, giving us:

$$y' = 2x + h$$
$$y' = 2x + 0$$
$$y' = 2x$$

So we can now officially say that the derivative of $y = x^2$ is $y' = 2x$.

Now, you might call foul by saying that this contradicts what we said earlier—that we needed *two* points to make a line, and if they are zero away from each other, it is the same point! For right now, we justify this by saying that h is not actually zero, but instead is *arbitrarily close* to zero. Therefore, for our purposes, we can treat it *as if it were* zero. We will see more formal ways of understanding this in Chapters 10 and 28.

For right now, we will just say, for our purposes, that h gets close enough to zero that it acts like zero numerically, but since it is not actually zero we still have two distinct points and we don't run into a divide by zero error when h is sitting in the denominator.

7.5   The General Method

In this section we will look at a general method for performing derivatives using Equation 7.4 to find derivatives.

The basic method is as follows:

1. Write down your original equation as a function of x (so make sure that y is by itself on the left, and say "$f(x) =$" instead of "$y =$").

2. Write down Equation 7.4.

3. Expand the equation by substituting both $f(x + h)$ and $f(x)$ using the original $f(x)$ from Step 1.

4. Simplify this equation so that h is eliminated from the denominator.

5. Treat all remaining remnants of h in the equation as if they were zeroes.

6. Simplify

We are going to use these steps to find the derivative of a slightly more complicated derivative. It will wind up having a lot of terms, but the method is the same as before. Here is the starting equation:

$$y = x^3 + 3x + 10 \tag{7.5}$$

Writing in terms of a function, we have:

$$f(x) = x^3 + 3x + 10$$

Equation 7.4 says:

$$y' = \frac{f(x + h) - f(x)}{h}$$

Substituting $f(x)$ with our specific version of $f(x)$ yields the following:

$$y' = \frac{(x+h)^3 + 3(x+h) + 10 - (x^3 + 3x + 10)}{h}$$

When we expand the terms on the numerator, we get this equation:

$$y' = \frac{((x^3 + 3hx^2 + 3h^2x + h^3) + (3x + 3h) + 10) - (x^3 + 3x + 10)}{h}$$

Simplifying the numerator gives us the equation below:

$$y' = \frac{3hx^2 + 3h^2x + h^3 + 3h}{h}$$

We then divide through by h to remove it from the denominator, and we get the following:

$$y' = 3x^2 + 3hx + h^2 + 3$$

Now, since h is arbitrarily close to 0, we can substitute 0 in for h and get

$$y' = 3x^2 + 3$$

This means that, on the graph of $y = x^3 + 3x + 10$, for any x value we can know the slope of the graph using the formula $y' = 3x^2 + 3$.

For instance, at $x = 2$, the value of the original graph is $y = 2^3 + 3 \cdot 2 + 10 = 24$, and the slope at that point will be $y' = 3 \cdot 2^2 + 3 = 15$. So, if you were to put your ruler on a graph of the original equation at the point $(2, 24)$ as a tangent line, the slope of that tangent line would be $\frac{15}{1}$.

—   Example 7.3

Find the derivative of the equation $y = x^3 + 1$. Then, find the exact slope of $y = x^3 + 1$ at $x = 2$.

Using the general form of the derivative (Equation 7.4), we can determine the derivative of this equation:

$$f(x) = x^3 + 1 \qquad \text{rewriting as a function of } x$$

$$y' = \frac{f(x+h) - f(x)}{h} \qquad \text{Equation 7.4}$$

$$= \frac{((x+h)^3 + 1) - (x^3 + 1)}{h} \qquad \text{substituting in } f(x)$$

$$= \frac{(x^3 + 3hx^2 + 3h^2x + h^3 + 1) - (x^3 + 1)}{h} \qquad \text{expanding } (x+h)^2$$

$$= \frac{3hx^2 + 3h^2x + h^3}{h} \qquad \text{simplifying the numerator}$$

$$= 3x^2 + 3hx + h^2 \qquad \text{dividing out } h$$

This equation will give us the slope between any two points whose x values are h units away from each other. As a sub-exercise, take this equation and apply it to Example 7.1 (to do this, you would set h to 0.01). Did you get the same value? You should!

Now, to find the *true* value of the slope at this point, we need to find two points that are so close that they are basically on top of each other. In other words, we need to set $h = 0$.

Doing so gives us this:

$$y' = 3x^2 + 3hx + h^2 \qquad \text{starting equation}$$
$$= 3x^2 + 3 \cdot 0 \cdot x + 0^2 \qquad \text{substituting for } h$$
$$= 3x^2 \qquad \text{simplified}$$

Therefore, the true value of the slope at any point in our original equation $y = x^3 + 1$ will be given by the equation $y' = 3x^2$. So, at $x = 2$, the slope will be:

$$y' = 3x^2$$
$$= 3 \cdot 2^2 \qquad\qquad\qquad = 12$$

The slope of the equation $y = x^3 + 1$ at $x = 2$ is 12.

7.6 Discovering New Truths

The development of the derivative is an important intellectual achievement, and I want to take some time to think about the thought processes involved in making developments like that. We won't all go on to develop something as foundational as the derivative, but we can use the ideas behind it to generate the constructive skills necessary to develop new mathematics when necessary. While there is not a single path to discovery, it is useful to examine the paths that are potentially fruitful to make sure that we know how to travel on them when necessary.

We started off with a foundational idea that we knew to be true. In our case, it was the slope formula. We have used the slope formula many times, and its operation is very straightforward and logical.

Then, we applied the slope formula with specific examples. We took an equation, and looked at several points along the graph to understand the mechanics of building a slope formula for points on an equation. Doing this repeatedly with specific examples helped to hone our intuitions about slopes and equations for later expansion.

When you work with concrete examples enough, eventually you see the places where you can generalize. In our case, we generalized in two places. The first place was to generalize y into a function of x. This allowed us to write out each point in the form of $(x, f(x))$. With this slight notation change, we were able to write our second point like this: $(x + 0.01, f(x + 0.01))$.

However, after doing several of these, we noticed that 0.01 was not intrinsic to the problem. It was changeable just like the other parts. Therefore, we generalized it away into the variable h. This left our points as being $(x, f(x))$ and $(x + h, f(x + h))$. With these two generalizations, we could then apply the slope formula directly to get the general formula for the derivative:

$$y' = \frac{f(x + h) - f(x)}{h}$$

Once we generalize, then we see if there are any simplifications we can do. We do this in two ways. First, we do a basic logical simplification where we take the results of the general equation with our specific $f(x)$ and simplify algebraically. This is a fairly mechanical process.

However, the more important simplification happens when we realize that, what we really want, is for h to be practically nothing. This allows for further simplification of the problem, because we realize that all of the terms in which h remain go to zero.

What we did is we asked ourselves the question, "what would happen to this equation if..." Sometimes, the answers don't give us any special insights. But, sometimes, like it does with the derivative, the answer gives us the key to unlocking powerful tools.

So, to summarize, the steps that we went through to construct our generalized derivative formula are:

1. Start with solid, foundational truths.

2. Work with these truths with specific, concrete examples.

3. Use your practical experience with these truths to help you form generalizations. You may need to generalize more than once, or even occasionally develop new notations for your generalizations.

4. Perform logical simplifications of the problem using the rules of mathematics.

5. Perform practical simplifications of the problem using reasoning about the problem domain (in our case, that we wanted h to be really close to zero).

Being able to think abstractly about problems will enable you to develop new solutions to problems you face throughout your life, even in non-mathematical areas. Using these tools, we can develop better systems for any set of tasks we have in life.

Review

In this chapter, we learned:

1. A derivative is an equation that tells us the slope of another equation at any given point identified by the x-coordinate.

2. A slope is merely the ratio of change in y to the change in x, which can be stated as the fraction $\frac{y \text{ change}}{x \text{ change}}$ or $\frac{rise}{run}$.

3. Because the slope is just a number, the derivative produces a function just like any other function, and can be graphed just like any other function.

4. Individual slopes can be calculated using the point-slope formula by selecting two points near to each other.

5. We can solve symbolically for any slope at an x value by using the point slope formula and substituting in x for x_0, $f(x)$ for y_0, $x + somesmallnumber$ for x_1, and $f(x + somesmallnumber)$ for y_1.

6. If we substitute a variable (normally h) in for the small distance between x-values, we can solve for the slope down to arbitrarily small distances.

7. The general formula for finding the derivative is $y' = \frac{f(x+h)-f(x)}{h}$ (and this should be memorized).

8. Subsituting 0 in for h allows us to find the *instantaneous* slope at any point—the slope precisely at the point we are looking for. This equation is the derivative.

9. We can use the procedure given in Section 7.5 to find the answer to many derivative problems, but we will later learn special rules that will simplify this process.

Exercises

1. Try to derive Equation 7.4 starting with the point-slope formula for yourself. Show the steps.

2. Write Equation 7.4 five times.

3. Use Equation 7.4 to find the derivative of $y = x^2$.

4. Use Equation 7.4 to find the derivative of $y = 3x^2$.

5. Find the derivative of $y = 3x^2 + 3$. Compare this to the result you got for the previous answer.

6. Find the derivative of $y = 6x^2$.

7. Find the derivative of $y = x^4$.

8. Find the derivative of $y = x^2 + 2x + 3$.

9. Find the derivative of $y = x^2 + 2x + 5$.

Chapter 8

Basic Derivative Rules for Polynomials

Equation 7.4 gives the general formula for the derivative. However, the problem with that equation is that it is a lot of work for all but the simplest problems. It is fairly straightforward to execute for simple, low-degree polynomials, but for more advanced derivatives, it would take all day.

Thankfully, however, over the centuries several rules for derivatives have been developed which makes finding the derivatives of complicated formulas much easier. However, as we will see, we have to be very careful when trying to use these rules in combination and can only do so using the specific rules for combining them.

When you first read the chapter, it may seem like there are a lot of rules. But, when you get to the end, you'll notice in the chapter summary that these rules are actually very simple and easy-to-use. You should be able to take the derivative of any polynomial more-or-less in your head by the end of the chapter.

8.1   The Derivative of a Constant Function

The easiest derivative is the derivative of a constant. Let's look at the line $y = 3$:

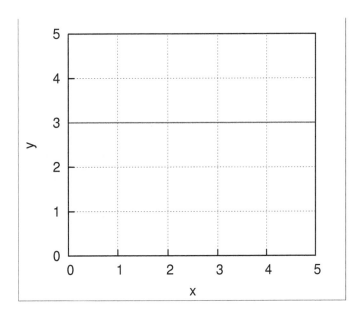

Remember that the derivative is simply the equation to tell you the slope at any point, and a slope, by definition, is $\frac{\text{rise}}{\text{run}}$. With this equation, how much rising is the line doing? It is doing none at all. Therefore, its slope at any point will be zero.

What is the slope at $x = 1$? Zero. What is the slope at $x = 2$? Still zero. What will the slope be at $x = 1,250$? Zero, yet again.

Therefore, the **constant rule** says that the derivative of $y = 3$ is $y' = 0$.

Every constant function yields a horizontal line. Here are the graphs of several constant functions: $y = 2$, $y = 5$, and $y = 10$:

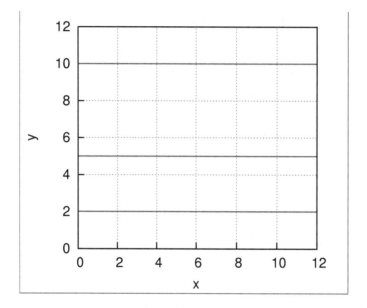

Each of them give a horizontal line. This will be true for *any* constant value function. No matter where you draw a horizontal line, by definition, a horizontal line will not move up and down. Therefore, the derivative of any constant function will be zero.

We can also use the general form of the derivative to prove this to be true. If we use C to represent our constant, so that $f(x) = C$, then we can solve for the derivative like this:

$y = C$ the original equation

$y' = \dfrac{f(x+h) - f(x)}{h}$ the general form of the derivative

$f(x) = C$ the right hand side as a function of f

$f(x+h) = C$ since the function is a constant, it is still the same constant even if we add on to x

$y' = \dfrac{C - C}{h}$ substituting into the general form

$y' = \dfrac{0}{h}$ simplifying the numerator

$y' = 0$ zero divided by anything is zero

8.2   The Derivative of a Constant Multiplier

The next type of derivative we will look at is the derivative of a function that is a constant multiplier of x, such as $y = 3x$ or $y = 12x$ or $y = \frac{2}{3}x$. Let's take a look at the graph of $y = \frac{3}{2}x$:

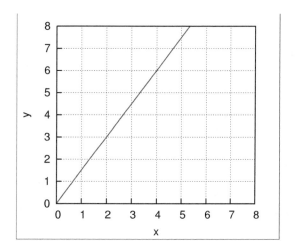

This is a simple line. In fact, every function that is a constant multiplier of x will form a line. What is interesting about a line is that its slope is the same everywhere. Therefore, since the slope never changes, we know the derivative will be some constant. But how do we figure out what that constant is?

If you think back to the general form for the equation of a line, you will see the answer:

$$y = mx + b$$

In this equation, m is the slope. So, therefore, if we have a constant multiplier of x, that constant multiplier will be the slope! Therefore, the derivative of our equation $y = \frac{3}{2}x$ will be $y' = \frac{3}{2}$. In other words, no matter what x value you use, the **constant rule** tells you that the slope of $y = \frac{3}{2}x$ will always be $\frac{3}{2}$.

We can also determine this analytically with the general form of the derivative, using n to represent our constant multiplier.

$$y = nx \qquad \text{the original equation}$$

$$f(x) = nx \qquad \text{the right-hand side as a function of } x$$

$$y' = \frac{f(x + h) - f(x)}{h} \qquad \text{the general formula of the derivative}$$

$$y' = \frac{n(x + h) - nx}{h} \qquad \text{substituting into the general formula}$$

$$y' = \frac{nx + nh - nx}{h} \qquad \text{simplifying}$$

$$y' = \frac{nh}{h}$$

$$y' = n$$

Therefore, for an constant multiplier of x, the derivative is simply the multiplier.

As a special case of this, we will note that the derivative of $y = x$ is simply $y' = 1$, since 1 is implicitly always a multiplier. We will call this the **identity rule**.

8.3   The Power Rule

The **power rule** tells us how to find the derivative of x raised to some constant power. We can already do this easily enough for any particular power using the general formula for the derivative. However, for higher-degree polynomials, this can take quite a bit of time and effort. The power rule makes this supremely simple.

First, let's look at two derivatives, the derivative of $y = x^2$ and $y = x^3$. Let's solve for the derivative of $y = x^2$ using the general formula for the derivative:

$$y = x^2 \qquad \text{the original equation}$$

$$y' = \frac{f(x + h) - f(x)}{h} \qquad \text{the general formula for the derivative}$$

$$f(x) = x^2 \qquad \text{the right-hand side as a function of } x$$

$$f(x + h) = (x + h)^2 = x^2 + 2hx + h^2 \qquad \text{the value of the function at } x + h$$

$$y' = \frac{x^2 + 2hx + h^2 - x^2}{h} \qquad \text{substituting into the general formula}$$

$$y' = \frac{2hx + h^2}{h} \qquad \text{simplifying the numerator}$$

$$y' = 2x + h \qquad \text{dividing through by } h$$

Since h represents an infinitely small distance, it is effectively zero. Therefore, this simplifies to

$$y' = 2x$$

Now let's look at $y = x^3$:

$$y = x^3 \qquad \text{the original equation}$$

$$y' = \frac{f(x + h) - f(x)}{h} \qquad \text{the general formula for the derivative}$$

$$f(x) = x^3 \qquad \text{the right-hand side as a function of } x$$

$$f(x + h) = (x + h)^3 = x^3 + 3hx^2 + 3h^2x + h^3 \qquad f(x) \text{ using } x + h \text{ as the parameter}$$

$$y' = \frac{x^3 + 3hx^2 + 3h^2x + h^3 - x^3}{h} \qquad \text{substituting into the general formula}$$

$$y' = \frac{3hx^2 + 3h^2x + h^3}{h} \qquad \text{simplifying the numerator}$$

$$y' = 3x^2 + 3hx + h^2 \qquad \text{dividing through by the denominator}$$

Again, since h represents a number that is infinitely close to zero, this causes every term that has it as a multiple to drop to zero, giving us:

$$y' = 3x^2$$

So now we have two derivatives:

$$y = x^2 \longrightarrow y' = 2x$$
$$y = x^3 \longrightarrow y' = 3x^2$$

Notice how in each of the derivatives, the exponent from the original equation dropped down in front to be a multiplier, and then the exponent of the derivative is reduced by 1. This is known as the *power rule*, and it works for x raised to *any* constant power. The general form is:

$$y = x^n \longrightarrow y' = nx^{n-1} \tag{8.1}$$

So, if we have $y = x^{234}$, then the derivative will be $y' = 234x^{233}$. If the equation is $y = x^{524}$, then the derivative will be $y' = 524x^{523}$. For a proof of this, see appendix F.1.

8.4 Combining Derivatives: The Addition Rule

In addition to having lots of rules for performing derivatives, there are also several rules for *combining* derivatives. This is what gives students the most troubles in doing derivatives. The derivative rules are fairly simple and can be easily memorized. Remembering to combine them correctly is not difficult but is easy to forget to do it properly if you are not careful. In this chapter we will cover the two easiest rules. Later, in chapter 11, we will look at a more general way of combining functions, but that takes a little more work.

Before we begin, let's work on a little notation. There are many ways to do the notation of the derivative, each being important in their own way. We will learn other notations in Chapter 10. Here we will introduce a new piece of notation for denoting the derivative of a *function*.

So far, we have used the notation y' to denote the derivative. This works when you are dealing with an entire equation. However, to combine derivative rules, we are going to need to break our equation up into pieces (i.e., separate functions), and deal with the derivatives of the pieces (functions) individually. Therefore, we are going to need a way to denote the derivative of a function.

If we denote a function of x as $f(x)$, we can denote the derivative of that function as $f'(x)$. Just like we used the $'$ character on y, we can also use it on the function itself to denote the derivative of the function. Therefore, we can say that if $f(x) = x^2$ then $f'(x) = 2x$. If $g(x) = 3x$, then $g'(x) = 3$. This notation will help us look at rules for combining different functions of x.

The first rule we will look at is the **addition rule**. The addition rule states that if you have a function of x that is made by adding together other functions of x, then the derivative of that function will be the derivatives of each function added together.

$$\text{If } f(x) = g(x) + h(x) + \ldots$$

$$\text{then } f'(x) = g'(x) + h'(x) + \ldots$$

So, let's say that we have the equation

$$y = x^3 + x^5$$

In order to find the derivative, we can separate this out into two different functions of x, find their derivative separately, and then add those derivatives together.

Therefore:

$y = x^3 + x^5$	the original equation
$f(x) = x^3 + x^5$	the whole right-hand side as a function of x
$g(x) = x^3$	the first term as a function of x
$h(x) = x^5$	the second term as a function of x
$f(x) = g(x) + h(x)$	the function rewritten in terms of the functions g and h
$f'(x) = g'(x) + h'(x)$	the addition rule
$g'(x) = 3x^2$	the derivative of the first term
$h'(x) = 5x^4$	the derivative of the second term
$f'(x) = 3x^2 + 5x^4$	the final derivative

— **Example 8.1**

Find the derivative of $y = x^9 + x^5 + x^4 + x^3 + x$.

This can be rewritten as a combination of functions:

$$f(x) = a(x) + b(x) + c(x) + d(x) + e(x)$$

Since these are all added together, we can use the addition rule to state the derivative as follows:

$$f'(x) = a'(x) + b'(x) + c'(x) + d'(x) + e'(x)$$

Each of the individual functions and their derivatives are below:

$a(x) = x^9$	
$a'(x) = 9x^8$	power rule
$b(x) = x^5$	
$b'(x) = 5x^4$	power rule

$$c(x) = x^4$$

$$c'(x) = 4x^3 \qquad \text{power rule}$$

$$d(x) = x^3$$

$$d'(x) = 3x^2 \qquad \text{power rule}$$

$$e(x) = x$$

$$e'(x) = 1 \qquad \text{constant multiplier rule}$$

Now that we have the derivatives of each function, we can roll this back up into the original equation using the addition rule:

$$f'(x) = a'(x) + b'(x) + c'(x) + d'(x) + e'(x)$$

$$f'(x) = 9x^8 + 5x^4 + 4x^3 + 3x^2 + 1$$

$$y' = 9x^8 + 5x^4 + 4x^3 + 3x^2 + 1$$

While we have spelled all of these examples out explicitly, it is easy enough to do these types of derivatives in a single step. Look at the following equation:

$$y = x^5 + x^2 + x^7$$

We can just *notice* that the addition rule applies, and then we can just apply the derivatives of each term directly:

$$y' = 5x^4 + 2x + 7x^6$$

There is an interesting consequence of the addition rule and the rule for derivatives of a constant function. Since the derivative of any constant function is zero, that means that *adding* a constant to a function *will not alter* its derivative (i.e., you will just be adding zero).

The derivative of $y = x^2$ is $y' = 2x$ and the derivative of $y = x^2 + 5$ is $y' = 2x + 0 = 2x$. Likewise, the derivative of $x^2 + 20$ is $2x + 0 = 2x$.

This should make sense if you think about it graphically. Adding or subtracting a constant to a function is the same as shifting the graph up or down on the y axis. The *shape* (and therefore the *slope*) of a graph does not change by shifting the graph up and down the y axis. Therefore, adding a constant to a derivative does not change its value.

8.5 Combining Derivatives: The Function Constant Multiplier Rule

The next rule for combining derivatives is simply an extension of the constant multiplier rule learned earlier, known as the **function constant multiplier rule**.

The original rule learned in Section 8.2 applies to functions of x just like it applies to x itself. If you have a function which consists of a constant multiplier n of another function of x, then the derivative of the whole function will be the constant multiplied by the derivative of the inner function.

In mathematical symbols, this means that for $f(x) = n \cdot g(x)$ the derivative of the function is $f'(x) = n \cdot g'(x)$.

So, let's say that I had the equation $y = 5x^3$. Below is the method to find the derivative:

$$y = 5x^3 \qquad \text{original equation}$$

$$f(x) = 5x^3 \qquad \text{the right-hand side as a function of } x$$

$$g(x) = x^3 \qquad \text{a sub-function of } x \text{ within } f(x)$$

$$f(x) = 5 \cdot g(x) \qquad f(x) \text{ rewritten using } g(x)$$

$$f'(x) = 5 \cdot g'(x) \qquad \text{applying the constant multiplier rule}$$

$$g'(x) = 3x^2 \qquad \text{the derivative of } g(x) \text{ using the power rule}$$

$$f'(x) = 5 \cdot 3x^2 \qquad \text{substituting } g'(x) \text{ back into the equation}$$

$$f'(x) = 15x^2 \qquad \text{simplifying}$$

$$y' = 15x^2 \qquad \text{giving the new, full equation}$$

I have broken this out into a large number of steps just to make sure you get the point, but in reality you can do this all very simply in one step. Say you are given $y = 23x^6$. You should be able to see that this is a constant multiplier of x raised to a power. Therefore, you can apply the constant multiplier rule and the power rule in one step very easily, and see that $y' = 23 \cdot 6x^5$ which simplifies to $y' = 138x^5$.

Note that because subtraction is simply addition where the second term is multiplied by -1, the constant multiplier rule means that the addition rule can work for any combination of addition and subtraction.

If you have $y = x^3 - x^2$ we can reinterpret this as $y = x^3 + -1 \cdot x^2$. Therefore, the derivative is $y' = 3x^2 + -1 \cdot 2x$ or $3x^2 - 2x$.

8.6   Combining the Rules to Find Derivatives of Polynomials

Combining the addition rule, the power rule, and the constant multiplier rule, we can now find out the derivative of *any* polynomial of x very quickly. Let's look at the derivative of $y = 5x^4 + 3x^2 + 23$:

$$y = 5x^4 + 3x^2 + 23 \qquad \text{original equation}$$

$$y = f(x) + g(x) + h(x) \qquad \text{original equation with terms broken into functions}$$

$$y' = f'(x) + g'(x) + h'(x) \qquad \text{applying the addition rule}$$

$$f(x) = 5x^4 \qquad \text{determining the derivatives of each function}$$

$$f'(x) = 4 \cdot 5x^3 = 20x^3$$

$$g(x) = 3x^2$$

$$g'(x) = 2 \cdot 3x^1 = 6x$$

$$h(x) = 23$$

$$h'(x) = 0$$

$$y' = 20x^3 + 6x + 0 \qquad \text{putting the derivative back together}$$

$$y' = 20x^3 + 6x \qquad \text{simplifying}$$

Again, once you are familiar with the rules, it is pretty easy to break this apart in your head and do the derivative in one line. Let's look at a few:

$$y = 23x + 5$$
$$y' = 23 + 0 = 23$$

$$y = 6x^3 + 5x^2 + 4x + 10$$
$$y' = 6 \cdot 3x^2 + 5 \cdot 2x^1 + 4 + 0$$
$$= 18x^2 + 10x + 4$$

$$y = 9x^8 - 4x^3 + 24x^2 - 20$$
$$y' = 9 \cdot 8x^7 - 4 \cdot 3x^2 + 24 \cdot 2x - 0$$
$$= 72x^7 - 12x^2 + 48x$$

That is a *lot* less work than individually identifying and naming each function of x, and even less work than trying to plug these into the general formula for the derivative. The general formula for the derivative helps us prove rules for the derivative, but by the end of the book we will never use it in practice. The general formula for the derivative should remain memorized, however, because it helps you always keep in mind *what* a derivative is and where it came from—that derivatives are merely slopes derived from a special version of the slope formula for points that are infinitely close together.

You should keep in mind that the constant multiplier rule *only* works for *constant* multipliers. For instance, let's say that you had an equation written like this: $y = 5x^3 \cdot 6x^2$. In order to solve this derivative with the tools you have now, you *must* combine these into a single term *before* doing the derivative. Therefore, we would solve it like this:

$$y = 5x^3 \cdot 6x^2$$
$$y = 5 \cdot 6x^3 \cdot x^2$$
$$y = 30x^{3+2}$$
$$y = 30x^5$$
$$y' = 5 \cdot 30x^4 = 150x^4$$

Later chapters will cover the product rule and the chain rule which will allow you to find derivatives of multiplication in general, but *you do not have these tools yet.*

8.7 Division, Square Roots, and Strange Powers of x

You might not realize it yet, but you currently have the tools to solve for the derivative of equations like $y = \frac{5}{x}$, $y = \sqrt{x}$, or even $y = \frac{23\sqrt{x}}{\sqrt[3]{x}}$. In order to solve equations like these, you just need to keep in mind that roots and divisors can all be expressed as exponents. Then, once it is expressed as an exponent, you can use the power rule to find the derivative.

So, let's start with divisors. If I have the expression $\frac{a}{b}$ this can be rewritten as a multiplication with a negative exponent. Therefore,

$$\frac{a}{b} = ab^{-1}$$

Similarly, if I have $y = \frac{5}{x}$, then that can be rewritten as $y = 5x^{-1}$. Negative exponents work in the power rule just as well as positive ones. Therefore, to solve for the derivative of this equation, we bring the exponent (along with the negative sign!) down as a multiplier, and reduce the exponent by one, in this case making it -2. This makes the derivative:

$$y' = 5 \cdot -1x^{-2} = -5x^{-2}$$

If the bottom half is a larger power of x, then it works the same, just with a larger negative power.

— Example 8.2

Find the derivative of $y = \frac{23}{5x^2}$.

Because we have the power of x in the bottom of the fraction, we must rewrite the problem in terms of negative exponents in order to solve this with the power rule.

$$y = \frac{23}{5x^2} \qquad \qquad \text{the starting equation}$$

$$y = \frac{23}{5}x^{-2} \qquad \qquad \text{rewriting so we can use the power rule}$$

$$y' = \frac{23}{5} \cdot -2x^{-3} \qquad \qquad \text{taking the derivative with the power rule}$$

$$y' = \frac{-46}{5}x^{-3} \qquad \qquad \text{combining constant terms}$$

$$y' = \frac{-46}{5x^3} \qquad \qquad \text{rewriting as a fraction}$$

Roots of x can similarly be expressed as a fractional exponent. Therefore, $\sqrt{x}$ can be rewritten as $x^{\frac{1}{2}}$ and $\sqrt[3]{x}$ can be rewritten as $x^{\frac{1}{3}}$. Then, the same rules apply.

— Example 8.3

Find the derivative of $y = \sqrt{x}$.

To find this derivative, we have to convert the square root into a power of x. A square root is equivalent to raising x to a half power, like this:

$$y = x^{\frac{1}{2}}$$

Now, we can use the power rule just like before. We will bring the exponent down in front, and reduce the exponent by 1 ($\frac{1}{2} - 1$ will give us an exponent of $\frac{-1}{2}$).

Here is the whole problem worked out:

$$y = \sqrt{x} \qquad\qquad \text{original problem}$$

$$y = x^{\frac{1}{2}} \qquad\qquad \text{convert to an exponent}$$

$$y' = \frac{1}{2}x^{\frac{1}{2}-1} \qquad\qquad \text{apply the power rule}$$

$$y' = \frac{1}{2}x^{\frac{-1}{2}} \qquad\qquad \text{simplify the exponent}$$

We can also go another step further, and convert the fractional exponent back into a more natural representation:

$$y' = \frac{1}{2}x^{\frac{-1}{2}} \qquad\qquad \text{our derivative}$$

$$y' = \frac{1}{2}\frac{1}{\sqrt{x}} \qquad\qquad \text{removing the fractional exponent}$$

$$y' = \frac{1}{2\sqrt{2}} \qquad\qquad \text{simplifying}$$

— Example 8.4

Find the derivative of $y = \sqrt[3]{x}$.

$$y = \sqrt[3]{x} \qquad\qquad \text{the original equation}$$

$$y = x^{\frac{1}{3}} \qquad\qquad \text{rewriting as a power of } x$$

$$y' = \frac{1}{3}x^{\frac{1}{3}-1} \qquad\qquad \text{applying the power rule}$$

$$y' = \frac{1}{3}x^{\frac{-2}{3}} \qquad\qquad \text{simplifying the exponent}$$

$$y' = \frac{1}{3}\frac{1}{\sqrt[3]{x^2}} \qquad\qquad \text{rewriting without a fractional exponent (optional)}$$

--- **Example 8.5**

Find the derivative of $y = \frac{23\sqrt{x}}{\sqrt[3]{x}}$.

$$y = \frac{23\sqrt{x}}{\sqrt[3]{x}}$$ the original equation

$$y = 23\frac{\sqrt{x}}{\sqrt[3]{x}}$$ separating out the constant

$$y = 23x^{\frac{1}{2}}x^{-\frac{1}{3}}$$ converting divisors and roots to exponents

$$y = 23x^{\frac{1}{2}+-\frac{1}{3}}$$ rule for combining exponents

$$y = 23x^{\frac{1}{6}}$$ added exponents

$$y' = 23 \cdot \frac{1}{6}x^{-\frac{5}{6}}$$ derivative using the power rule

$$y' = \frac{23}{6}x^{-\frac{5}{6}}$$ combining constants

$$y' = \frac{23}{6\sqrt[6]{x^5}}$$ rewriting without a fractional exponent (optional)

Note that this rule works with *any* power of x, including irrational powers. As long as the power of x is a constant value, the power rule can be applied.

The power rule *cannot* be applied if a variable is in the exponent. For instance, we cannot solve for the derivative of $y = 2^x$ (though that is the subject of the next section) or the derivative of $y = x^x$ using the tools we have presented so far.

8.8 The Derivative of n^x

The last derivative we will cover in this chapter is the derivative of $y = n^x$, where n is a constant value. The rule for this sort of form is known as the **exponent rule**.

The exponent rules says that, for equations of the form:

$$y = n^x$$

If n is a constant, the derivative of such an equation is:

$$y' = \ln(n)n^x$$

Therefore, let's find the derivative of $y = 2^x$:

$$y = 2^x$$ the original equation

$$y' = \ln(2)2^x$$ applying the exponent rule

Not too hard.

However, there is a surprising result buried in the exponent rule. Let's look at the derivative of $y = e^x$, where e is Euler's number (approximately $2.71828\ldots$). In this case, we have:

$$y = e^x \qquad \text{the original equation}$$
$$y' = \ln(e)e^x \qquad \text{applying the exponent rule}$$
$$y' = 1 \cdot e^x \qquad \ln(e) = 1 \text{ by definition}$$
$$y' = e^x$$

So here we have the very interesting equation $y = e^x$, whose derivative is the same, $y' = e^x$. In other words, e^x is very special because each *value* of e^x is also the *slope* at that point!

Again, I need to note that the exponent rule only works for derivatives that look like n^x. It does not apply directly to more complicated expressions like n^{2x} or n^{x^2} or x^x or $x \cdot 2^x$. We will learn to do those in chapter 11, but we have a long way to go until then.

— Example 8.6

Find the derivative of $y = 8^x$.

$$y = 8^x \qquad \text{original equation}$$
$$y' = \ln(8)8^x \qquad \text{the exponent rule}$$

Just like for our other rules, we can use the addition rule to include n^x as part of a series of terms. Let's look at how we could solve for the derivative of $y = x^2 + 3^x$:

$$y = x^2 + 3^x \qquad \text{the original equation}$$
$$f(x) = g(x) + h(x) \qquad \text{splitting the right-hand side up into functions}$$
$$g(x) = x^2$$
$$h(x) = 3^x$$
$$f'(x) = g'(x) + h'(x) \qquad \text{the addition rule}$$
$$g'(x) = 2x \qquad \text{the power rule}$$
$$h'(x) = \ln(3)3^x \qquad \text{the exponent rule}$$
$$f'(x) = 2x + \ln(3)3^x \qquad \text{substituting}$$
$$y' = 2x + \ln(3)3^x$$

— Example 8.7

Find the derivative of $y = 3e^x + 4x^2$.

$$y = 3e^x + 4x^2 \qquad \text{original equation}$$
$$y' = 3\ln(e)e^x + 8x \qquad \text{exponent, power, and constant multiplier rules}$$
$$y' = 3e^x + 8x \qquad \text{simplifying } (\ln(e) = 1)$$

8.9   Derivatives You Cannot Do (yet)

One thing I want to emphasize is that the rules for the derivative *must* be followed *exactly*. You can only combine derivative rules using the rules for combining derivatives. You cannot combine derivative rules in any other way.

Therefore, I want to take some time to show you some derivatives that you cannot yet perform because you don't have the rules to do so.

Let's look at the equation:

$$y = (e^x + 3)^2$$

Note that even though this contains addition, exponentiation, and powers, they are not present in a way that can be combined by our rules. The addition rule doesn't help us because, even though we can express $e^x + 3$ as an addition, we don't have any rules for how to take the derivative of a *function* raised to a power.

It would look like this:

$$y = (e^x + 3)^2$$
$$f(x) = e^x + 3$$
$$y = (f(x))^2$$
$$y' = ?$$

Since we have no rule for raising a *function* of x to a power (only for raising x itself to a power), this does not work. The fact that we can use the addition rule on the *inside* of the function doesn't help us take the derivative of the whole thing at this point.

On the other hand, rules like the addition rule and the constant multiplier rule *do* work for functions. So we can indeed solve for the derivative of the following equation $y = 2(x^3 + x^4)$. The constant multiplier rule says that if we know the derivative of $f(x)$ then we can just multiply by our constant multiplier. In this case, we can do:

$$y = 2(x^3 + x^4)$$

$$f(x) = x^3 + x^4$$

$$f'(x) = 3x^2 + 4x^3 \qquad \text{power and addition rules}$$

$$y = 2 \cdot f(x)$$

$$y' = 2 \cdot f'(x) \qquad \text{constant multiplier rule}$$

$$y' = 2(3x^2 + 4x^3)$$

$$y' = 6x^2 + 8x^3$$

Chapter 11 will introduce a technique that will allow us to combine derivatives in a very generalized way, but for now just realize that if derivative rules *aren't* combined in exactly the right way that the rules allow for, the results will be wrong.

Review

In this chapter, we learned:

1. There are many rules to simplify taking a derivative, but they can only be combined together in specific ways.

2. The derivative of a constant function is zero (constant rule).

3. The derivative of a constant multiplied by x is just the constant (constant multiplier rule).

4. The derivative of x by itself is 1 (identity rule)

5. The derivative of x^n is nx^{n-1} (power rule).

6. The power rule also works for strange powers of x, such as negative, fractional, or even real exponents.

7. Oftentimes a strange-looking problem can be simplified by converting a fraction into a negative exponent or other exponent simplifications.

8. The derivative of two functions added together is the sum of the separate derivatives of each function (addition rule).

9. The derivative of a function multiplied by a constant is the derivative of the function itself multiplied by the same constant (constant multiplier rule).

10. The addition rule can be extended to any combination of addition and subtraction.

11. The derivative of n^x is $\ln(n)n^x$ (exponent rule).

12. The derivative of e^x is itself, e^x. This means that each value for e^x is also its slope.

13. Derivative rules can only be applied if the derivative *exactly* matches the formula being used for it, or if a rule for combining the derivatives allows for their combination.

14. Two equations that only differ by the addition of a constant will have the same derivative.

Exercises

1. Find the derivative of $y = x^{27}$.

2. Find the derivative of $y = x^9$.

3. Find the derivative of $y = 7x^5$.

4. Find the derivative of $y = 8x^2$.

5. Find the derivative of $y = x^{13}$.

6. Find the derivative of $y = 2x$.

7. Find the derivative of $y = 373$.

8. Find the derivative of $y = 6^x$.

9. Find the derivative of $y = 25x^{27}$.

10. Find the derivative of $y = 2\sqrt{x}$

11. Find the derivative of $y = 4^x - 23x$.

12. Find the derivative of $y = x^2 + x$.

13. Find the derivative of $y = \frac{5}{\sqrt{x}}$

14. Find the derivative of $y = 3x^2 + 2x + 5$.

15. Find the derivative of $y = 25e^x + 23 \cdot 4^x - x^3$.

16. Find the derivative of $y = x^{\frac{2}{5}} + \frac{6}{x^2} - \frac{2}{\sqrt{x}}$

17. Find the derivative of $y = (x^2 + 3x)(x - 1)$.

18. For the equation $y = x^3 - x^2 + 5x$, what is the slope of that equation at $x = 10$?

19. For the equation $y = e^x + x^3 - 5x$, find the slope at $x = 0$.

20. For the equation $y = x^2 + x - 6$ find the x value where the slope is $\frac{3}{2}$.

21. For the equation $y = x^2 - 3x + 5$, find the equation of the line that is tangent to this graph (i.e., has the same slope as the graph and touches it at a single point) at $x = 4$.

22. For the equation $y = e^x + x$ find the equation of the line tangent to this graph at $x = 0$.

Chapter 9

Basic Uses of the Derivative

The concept of a derivative is fairly simple—it is an equation that represents the slopes at every point of another equation. The next question, then, is how is it used? This chapter will focus on some basic uses of the derivative as we have learned it so far.

9.1 An Introduction to Maximum Values

The derivative is interesting because it gives you additional information about another equation. Prior to learning calculus, most equations we used might inform us about the value of x, but calculus is the first place where we have built a new equation to tell us something important about our original equation.

To see how this can be used, take a look at the following graph of $y = -x^2 + 6.5x - 1$:

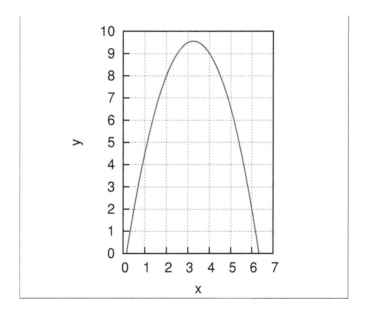

Notice that the graph forms a hump. At the top of that hump is the *maximum value* of this equation. The graph goes down infinitely on both sides, but it never rises above this maximum point. So where does this maximum point occur? It is hard to tell from the given equation.

In order to determine where the maximum value is, we need to think about what it *means* for something to be a maximum point on a smooth graph. Notice how on the left side of the hump all of the slopes slope upwards, and on the right side of the hump all of the slopes slope downwards. Get out your ruler, and try to make a tangent line with several parts of the graph. If you are on the left side of the hump, the slope will always be positive, but on the right side of the hump, the slope is negative.

So what is the slope at the top of the graph? Since the curve is continuous and smooth, that means that the slopes have to be changing smoothly as well. Therefore, since all of the slopes on the left side are positive, and all of the slopes on the right side are negative, then the slope at the top of the hump must be zero!

If you have ever climbed a hill (or driven up one), you should recognize this. When you are on the pinnacle of the hill, the road is essentially flat. This means that the slope is zero—no change in height during your change in x. Of course, this only lasts for an instantaneous moment. But the question is, *where* does this happen?

Derivatives are here to answer this question! Again, a derivative is an equation that tells us the slope at any given point. What does it mean to be at the top of a hump on a smooth graph? It means that the *slope* at that point *is zero*. If you put those two ideas together, then what we need to do is find out where the derivative is zero, and that will tell us where (i.e., at what x value) the maximum value occurs on the graph.

So, therefore, we need to take the derivative of the original equation:

$$y = -x^2 + 6.5x - 1 \qquad \text{the original equation}$$

$$y' = -2x^1 + 6.5 - 0 \qquad \text{taking the derivative using the power rule}$$

$$y' = -2x + 6.5 \qquad \text{simplifying the result}$$

Now we have the derivative. Remember that when the original equation hits the top then the derivative will be zero. Therefore we will set the derivative to zero and solve for x:

$$y' = -2x + 6.5 \qquad \text{the derivative}$$

$$y' = 0 \qquad \text{we are looking for where the derivative is zero}$$

$$0 = -2x + 6.5 \qquad \text{combining the previous two equations}$$

$$2x = 6.5 \qquad \text{adding } 2x \text{ to both sides}$$

$$x = 3.25 \qquad \text{dividing both sides by 2}$$

Therefore, the derivative is zero when x is 3.25, which means that the original equation will be at its maximum value when x is 3.25. But what value is that? To find that out, we have to plug 3.25 back into the original equation.

$$y = -x^2 + 6.5x - 1 \qquad \text{the original equation}$$

$$y = -3.25^2 + 6.5 \cdot 3.25 - 1 \qquad \text{substituting 3.25 in for } x$$

$$y = 9.5625 \qquad \text{simplifying}$$

Therefore, the maximum value for this equation is 9.5625, which occurs at $x = 3.25$.

What about the minimum value for the graph? Since the graph slopes downward on both sides forever, the minimum value for the graph has no lower bound, which can also be referred to as $-\infty$. Therefore, this graph has a global maximum at $(3.25, 9.5625)$ and no lower bound for the minimum value.

What about a graph that points the other way? Let's look at the equation $y = x^2 + 2x + -1$. The graph of this equation looks like this:

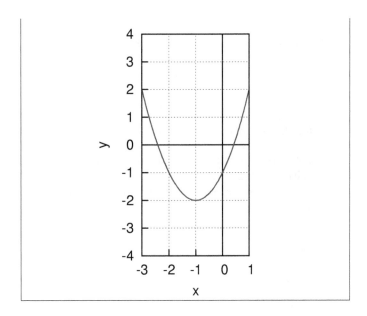

Now, instead of having a single hump on the top, this graph has a single hump on the bottom. Again, at the very bottom of the hump, the graph is momentarily flat—it has a derivative of zero. However, unlike the previous graph, on this graph the slopes on the left side of the hump are all negative, and the slopes on the right side of the hump are all positive.

Notice that maximum and minimum values *both* have a derivative of zero. Therefore, if we didn't know what the graph looked like, and we found a location where the derivative was zero, we wouldn't know whether it was a maximum or a minimum value.

There are a few ways to solve for this. A simple but inexact way is to calculate the derivative for an x value slightly to the left of your target and another one slightly to the right of it. As we have seen, for a minimum, it will be a negative slope on the left and a positive slope on the right. For a maximum, it will be the reverse—a positive slope on the left and a negative slope on the right. However, we will come to a more exact method later in the chapter.

So, on this graph, to find the minimum value, we again take the derivative, and find where the derivative is zero:

$$y = x^2 + 2x + -1 \qquad \text{the original equation}$$
$$y' = 2x + 2 \qquad \text{derivative via the power rule}$$
$$y' = 0 \qquad \text{this is what we want to find}$$
$$2x + 2 = 0 \qquad \text{putting the previous two equations together}$$
$$2x = -2 \qquad \text{solve for } x$$
$$x = -1$$

Therefore, the derivative is zero where $x = -1$. That must mean that this is where the bottom of the graph occurs. Now we can insert -1 for x in the original equation, and find the value for y, which will be the minimum value for the graph:

$y = x^2 + 2x + -1$	the original equation
$x = -1$	the location of the minimum value
$y = (-1)^2 + 2(-1) + -1$	substituting for x
$y = 1 - 2 - 1$	simplifying
$y = -2$	

Therefore, the minimum value for this graph occurs at $(-1, -2)$.

So far, we have seen a derivative of zero for a maximum and a derivative of zero for a minimum. Occasionally you will find derivatives that is neither a maximum nor a minimum value. An example of that is the equation $y = x^3 - 6x^2 + 12x - 6$. In the graph below you will see what this looks like—the graph levels off, but then keeps going in the same direction:

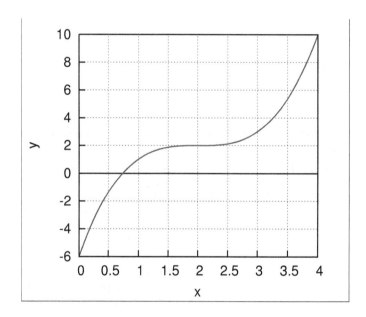

For a maximum value, the derivative went from positive to negative; for a minimum value, the derivative went from negative to positive. For a value that is neither a maximum nor a minimum value, the derivative will be the same sign on both sides of the zero derivative.

In the next section, we will look at graphs with more than one maxima or minima.

9.2   Local and Global Maximas and Minimas

We have been looking at minimas and maximas, which are collectively knows as **extremas**.

In mathematics, only a few types of equations are so simple that it only has one hump on the graph. Many have several. For instance, take a look at the equation $y = x^3 - 12x^2 + 47x - 60$:

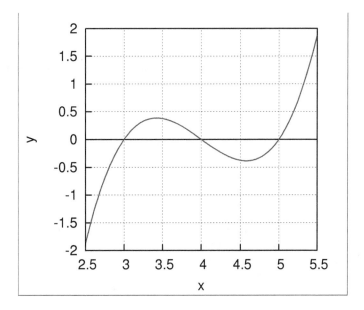

Note that this equation has more than one hump. When this happens, the humps are not necessarily the maximum or minimum for the *whole equation* (though they may be). They are, however, **local maxima** and **local minima** (maxima being the plural of maximum, and minima being the plural of minimum). This means that, at least in the immediate vicinity of the point, it is a maximum or a minimum.

But what about globally? Are either of the humps the *global* maximum or minimum? Looking at the graph, you can see that on the left side it points downwards indefinitely towards $-\infty$. Therefore, there is no global minimum—the function just gets more and more negative as far as you go to the left. Likewise, on the right, it points up indefinitely towards $+\infty$. Therefore, there is no global maximum—the function just gets more and more positive as far as you go to the right.

So, when looking for an absolute maximum or minimum, you have to find not only the largest of the local maxima or the smallest of the local minima, but you have to see if the graph itself continues on indefinitely in one direction or the other.

Many times, however, even if the graph itself slopes towards positive or negative infinity, the problem will have boundaries that prevent some of these values from being useful. For instance, in the graph above, if x represented the length of something, since I can't have a negative length, all of the areas below the x axis would be invalid. That means that there would be no sloping towards negative infinity on the left—it would end where $x = 0$.

However, we don't know whether that is going to be a minimum value or not—since it was sloping downwards at that point, it may or may not be the minimum for the whole graph. Therefore, we have add any points where the graph starts and stops to the list of points that we check for maximas and minimas.

Additionally, we have to check positive and negative infinity, if x can validly go towarsd infinity (i.e., there is not a physical or mathematical reason preventing x from going this way). For right now, we can just look at the graph to see where the graph is going. In Chapter 29 we will learn more explicit tools to find these values precisely.

Finally, we need to check all of the locations where the derivative doesn't exist for one reason or another. Usually the reason is that either the graph isn't smooth or continuous (non-smooth and non-continuous areas of graphs don't have a derivative) or the graph goes straight vertical (this would yield a divide-by-zero for calculating the derivative). In any case, if it doesn't have a derivative at a given point, we have to check the point manually.

All of these points that we need to check are known as **critical points**. These are points at which a global maximum or minimum might occur.

So, in short, if we want to know the absolute maxima and minima of a function, we need to compile a list of *all* of the critical points. Then, we will evaluate the function at each of these points (including, if applicable, $+\infty$ and $-\infty$). The global maximum will be the greatest of all of these values and the global minimum will be the least of all these values.

So, in any graph, if you want to find the absolute minimum or maximum point, you can follow these steps:

1. Begin by making a list of critical points. Start by listing out every place (i.e., x-value) where the derivative is zero.

2. Add to the list every place where the function starts and stops, either due to mathematical reasons (i.e., the calculation does not operate on that x value) or for practical reasons (that x value would yield a result that doesn't match reality, such as negative lengths).

3. Add to the list every place where the derivative does not exist (i.e., divides by zero).

4. Add to the list the beginning and ending values of the graph in question. For many graphs this will be $-\infty$ and $+\infty$, but if the graph is constrained, wherever the edges occur, those points should be taken into account.

5. Take this list of x values and find out what the value of the original function is at each x value. If $-\infty$ or $+\infty$ is on your list this may be difficult, but you can look at the graph to see if it shoots off towards infinity in one direction or another.

6. Check the y value for each of these critical points. The absolute maximum and absolute minimum of this function will be the maximum and minimum y values in the list you just made.

— Example 9.1

Find the global maximum and minimum for the equation $y = x^3 - 12x^2 + 47x - 60$.

To find the global maximum and minimum, we need to get a list of critical points. The first set of points to start with are the local maxima and minima for the equation. To find these, we need to find the locations where the derivative is zero:

$$y = x^3 - 12x^2 + 47x - 60 \qquad \text{the original equation}$$

$$y' = 3x^2 - 24x + 47 \qquad \text{derivative with the power rule}$$

$$y' = 0 \qquad \text{we are looking for where the derivative is zero}$$

$$0 = 3x^2 - 24x + 47 \qquad \text{substituting}$$

$$x = \frac{24 \pm \sqrt{(-24)^2 - 4 \cdot 3 \cdot 47}}{2 \cdot 3} \qquad \text{quadratic formula}$$

$$x = \frac{24 \pm \sqrt{576 - 564}}{6} \qquad \text{simplifying}$$

$$x = \frac{24 \pm \sqrt{12}}{6}$$

$$x = \frac{24}{6} \pm \frac{2\sqrt{3}}{6}$$

$$x = 4 \pm \frac{\sqrt{3}}{3}$$

$$x = 4 + \frac{\sqrt{3}}{3}, x = 4 - \frac{\sqrt{3}}{3}$$

The value of this graph at $x = 4 + \frac{\sqrt{3}}{3}$ is $\frac{-2}{3\sqrt{3}}$ If we look at the derivative of the equation a little to the left at $x = 4$, we will see that the slope is -1, and if we look at the derivative a little to the right at $x = 5$, we will see that the slope is 2. Therefore, since the slope goes from negative to positive, it is a minimum.

The value at $x = 4 - \frac{\sqrt{3}}{3}$ is $\frac{2}{3\sqrt{3}}$. If we look at the derivative of the equation a little to the left at $x = 3$, we will see that the slope is 2, and, to the right, at $x = 4$, the slope is -1. Therefore, since the slope goes from positive to negative, it is a maximum.

This graph is defined everywhere, and is smooth and continuous everywhere, so it won't have critical points related to these.

Now, we also need to add the beginning and end of this graph, $-\infty$ and $+\infty$. Notice that the graph is pointing down to the left. The graph goes toward negative infinity on the left, so the global minimum is $-\infty$. This means that our other minimum is only a local minimum. The graph is pointing up to the right, so the global maximum is $+\infty$. This means that our other maximum is only a local maximum.

Therefore, the global minimum of this graph is $-\infty$ and the global maximum of this graph is $+\infty$.

9.3 Solving Problems with Maximas and Minimas

Finding the maximum and minimum value is interesting, but what is it used for? Think of the words themselves—maximum and minimum. If you wanted to get the most out of something, you are looking for a *maximum* result. If you wanted to get something done with the least amount of effort, you are looking for a *minimum* of effort.

Therefore, whenever you are asked for the maximum, the most, the greatest of something, or if you are asked for the least, the minimum, the smallest of something, you can use the derivative to find the answer.

In any area of life, the best way to get good answers is to have a well-phrased question. In math, the "question" is the equation. In fact, the practice of converting word problems into equations is great practice for learning to convert vague, difficult-to-answer questions into precise and solvable questions.

For maxima and minima problems, what you want to do is create an equation so that the dependent variable (the one on the y-axis) contains the value to be maximized or minimized. Additionally, we want to be able to reduce everything else to a function of some single other quantity (which will be put on the x-axis).

Once that is done, you can then use our general procedure to find maximas and minimas.

Let's say that you are going to make an open rectangular box with a square base. You have a limited amount of material (let's say 48 square feet), but you want to make a box with the largest volume that you can with that material. What are the dimensions of the box that will give us the largest volume?

Is there a word in there that indicates what we are trying to do? The question asked for the *largest* volume, which suggests a maximum. A maximum what? A maximum *volume*. Therefore, the volume will be our dependent variable (our y value) since it is the thing we are trying to maximize.

Is there an equation that you know for the volume of a box? In geometry, you should have learned that the volume of a box is the product of the length times the width times the height. In mathematical terms, this means that $v = l \cdot w \cdot h$.

This equation, however, has *three* independent variables, and we need it to have one. Is there some other information in the question that can help us *reduce* the number of variables? The question said that the box will have a square base. What is a square? A square is a rectangle where the length and width are equal. What does that mean mathematically? It means $l = w$. Therefore, anywhere in our equation that we have l we can replace it with w. That transforms our equation into $v = w \cdot w \cdot h$

Now we are down to *two* independent variables. Is there any more information in the description of the problem that we can use? It also says that the total amount of material that we have is 48 square feet. Mathematically, what does that correspond to? The amount of material used to make a box is the same as its *surface area*. Therefore, the surface area is 48 square feet.

The method to determine the surface area of a box is to simply add up the area of each side. In this case, it is an *open* box, so the top of the box will not be included, meaning that our box will only have five sides. This let's us generate the following formulas, using a for the surface area:

$$a = lw + wh + wh + lh + lh$$ the surface area is the sum of each area

$$a = lw + 2wh + 2lh$$ simplified

$$l = w$$ since the base is a square, these are equal

$$a = ww + 2wh + 2wh$$ substituting

$$a = w^2 + 4wh$$ simplifying

$$a = 48$$ given in the original problem

$$48 = w^2 + 4wh$$ substituting

$$4wh = 48 - w^2$$ solving for h

$$h = \frac{48}{4w} - \frac{w^2}{4w}$$

$$h = \frac{12}{w} - \frac{w}{4}$$

So now we can substitute in h in the volume equation. The new volume equation is:

$$v = lwh \qquad \text{the original volume equation}$$

$$l = w \qquad \text{because the base is square}$$

$$h = \frac{12}{w} - \frac{w}{4} \qquad \text{based on the surface area}$$

$$v = ww(\frac{12}{w} - \frac{w}{4}) \qquad \text{substituting}$$

$$v = w^2(\frac{12}{w} - \frac{w}{4}) \qquad \text{simplifying}$$

$$v = \frac{12w^2}{w} - \frac{w^3}{4}$$

$$v = 12w - \frac{w^3}{4}$$

Now we have the volume of the box (which we are trying to maximize) as the dependent (y-axis) variable, and, by tracing through the dependencies listed in the problem we have reduced the rest of the independent variables to a single variable, w. Since the goal is to *maximize* the volume (i.e., find the global maximum), we now need to find the critical points.

To aid our search for critical points, let's take a moment to look at the graph of this equation (note that you can use a calculator or computer to graph equations in this course if you need to):

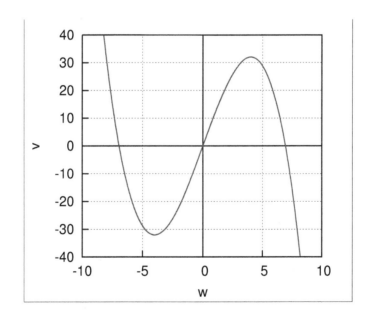

This has a local maximum on the right side of the graph. However, notice that the graph goes to positive infinity on the left-hand side. That means that the global maximum for this graph is at $x = -\infty$.

But what does that mean for our question? Remember that the x-axis is the *width* of the box. Can a width be negative? No, it cannot. In fact, neither the length, the width, nor the height can be negative.

Therefore, for only positive measurements, the graph actaully looks like this:

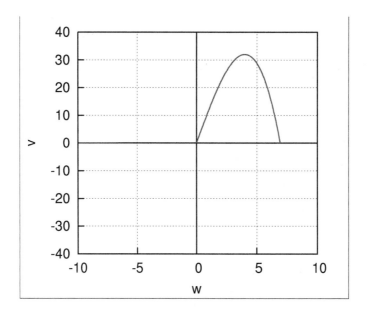

When the equation is restricted to this range, the local maxima *becomes* a global maximum. If you look at the critical points (where the equation starts and stops), you will notice that they are all at zero, below our local maxima.

Local maximas occur when the slope is zero. Therefore, we will take the derivative of this to find where the slope becomes zero.

$$v = 12w - \frac{w^3}{4}$$ the equation for volume

$$v' = 12 - 3\frac{w^2}{4}$$ power rule

$$v' = 12 - \frac{3}{4}w^2$$ simplify

$$v' = 0$$ find where the slope is zero

$$0 = 12 - \frac{3}{4}w^2$$ substituting

$$12 = \frac{3}{4}w^2$$ solve for w

$$12 \cdot \frac{4}{3} = w^2$$

$$\frac{48}{3} = w^2$$

$$16 = w^2$$

$$w = \pm 4$$

The derivative is zero at both $w = 4$ and $w = -4$. As we noted earlier, the width cannot be negative, so that leaves 4 as the width that gives us the local maximum.

At that width, the volume of the box will be:

$$12w - \frac{w^3}{4} = 48 - \frac{64}{4} \qquad\qquad = 48 - 16 = 32$$

So what are the other dimensions? If you remember, the length and the width are the same, so the length is 4. The height was $\frac{12}{w} - \frac{w}{4}$, which gives $3 - 1 = 2$.

Since our units are in feet, that means that the dimensions are 4 feet by 4 feet by 2 feet and the volume is 32ft^3.

9.4 Generalizing the Solution

In the introduction to this book, I promised to teach you how to come up with equations for yourself. Therefore, what we are going to do in this section is take the results of the previous section and *generalize* it for similar situations. But what counts as a similar situation?

Usually, when applying calculus in real life, you can take a problem for which you have certain, given numbers, and find a general equation that will fit every set of initial numbers. This way, you only have to do the calculus steps once—the result will be a reusable equation that you can simply plug numbers into. The reason that this works is because, if you look at the derivative rules, you will see that constants don't really modify the results. They more or less stay put. The derivative of *any* constant is zero, and the derivative of any constant multiplied by a function of x is merely that function multiplied by the unchanged constant.

Therefore, to derive new equations with calculus, we simply need to replace our initial constants with what I will call **constant variables**. These are constant throughout the life of the problem, but a person can substitute them out for different values when doing new problems. Therefore, for the purposes of calculus we can treat them as a constant, but in the final result we can treat them like a variable.

Let's look at our previous problem:

> Let's say that you are going to make an open rectangular box with a square base. You have a limited amount of material (let's say 48 square feet), but you want to make a box with the largest volume that you can with that material. What are the dimensions of the box that will give us the largest volume?

Did you notice the constant lurking in that problem? The amount of material we had to work with, 48 square feet, was our constant. Let's revisit the work we did for this equation, but, instead of using the number 48, we will substitute it with the constant variable C. However, when we take the derivative, we will treat C as a constant.

So, the first thing we did was to rewrite the equation for the volume in terms of the width of the box.

We will quickly recap the steps for that using our new constant variable:

$$v = lwh \qquad\qquad \text{volume equation}$$

$$a = lw + 2lh + 2wh \qquad\qquad \text{surface area for open box}$$

$$l = w \qquad\qquad \text{because it has a square base}$$

$$a = ww + 2wh + 2wh \qquad\qquad \text{substituting}$$

$$a = w^2 + 4wh \qquad\qquad \text{simplifying}$$

$$a = C \qquad\qquad \text{using our constant variable}$$

$$C = w^2 + 4wh \qquad\qquad \text{substituting}$$

$$4wh = C - w^2 \qquad\qquad \text{solving for } h$$

$$h = \frac{C}{4w} - \frac{w^2}{4w}$$

$$h = \frac{C}{4w} - \frac{w}{4}$$

$$v = ww\left(\frac{C}{4w} - \frac{w}{4}\right) \qquad\qquad \text{volume equation}$$

$$v = \frac{Cw^2}{4w} - \frac{w^3}{4} \qquad\qquad \text{simplifying}$$

$$v = \frac{C}{4}w - \frac{w^3}{4}$$

Notice that there is a constant 4 that got added to the mix. When doing equations, I always like to ask where different numbers came in from because it helps me to understand what is going on. In this case, the 4 arose because there are 4 equal sides to the box. Since $l = w$, the four middle areas are all equal.

Now that we have the equation for the volume, we can now find the derivative:

$$v = \frac{C}{4}w - \frac{w^3}{4} \qquad\qquad \text{the volume equation}$$

$$v' = \frac{C}{4} - \frac{3}{4}w^2 \qquad\qquad \text{derivative with the power rule}$$

Remember that C is a constant, and, therefore, so is $\frac{C}{4}$.

Now we solve the equation for w where v' is zero:

$$v' = \frac{C}{4} - \frac{3}{4}w^2 \qquad\qquad \text{the derivative of volume}$$

$$v' = 0 \qquad\qquad \text{this will be our maxima and minima}$$

$$0 = \frac{C}{4} - \frac{3}{4}w^2 \qquad\qquad \text{substituting}$$

$$\frac{3}{4}w^2 = \frac{C}{4} \qquad\qquad \text{solve for } w$$

$$w^2 = \frac{4}{3} \cdot \frac{C}{4}$$

$$w^2 = \frac{C}{3}$$

$$w = \pm\sqrt{\frac{C}{3}}$$

$$w = \sqrt{\frac{C}{3}} \qquad \text{since we are only considering positive widths}$$

If you remember from the graph, this will in fact be the maximum value. Therefore, for any similar problem as before, we can say that for a given total surface area C, the width of the box will be $\sqrt{\frac{C}{3}}$.

Likewise, since the length and width are equal, then the length will be the same. The height was determined to be $\frac{C}{4w} - \frac{w}{4}$, so the final height will be $\frac{C}{4\sqrt{\frac{C}{3}}} - \frac{\sqrt{\frac{C}{3}}}{4}$.

Now, to check our results, we just need to substitute 48 back in for C and see if we get the same answer: $w = \sqrt{\frac{48}{3}} = \sqrt{16} = 4$. That's our original answer! Then, substituing C in to determine h, we get $\frac{48}{4*4} - \frac{4}{4} = 3 - 1 = 2$.

Therefore, by taking our original problem and substituting in constant variables for the constants, we were able to derive a brand new equation for solving a certain type of problem. Once you have the new equation, you don't need calculus anymore—you can just plug in the numbers. Calculus was used to *generate* the equation, but now anyone can *use* the equation even without a calculus background.

So, for our new equation, we could say the following:

The dimensions of the box with the maximum volume for a given surface area C where the box has a square base and an open top, the length, width, and height of the box with the maximized volume will be:

$$w = \sqrt{\frac{C}{3}}$$

$$l = \sqrt{\frac{C}{3}}$$

$$h = \frac{C}{4\sqrt{\frac{C}{3}}} - \frac{\sqrt{\frac{C}{3}}}{4}$$

And now anyone can calculate it!

9.5   The Second Derivative Test

Earlier, I noted that there was a more explicit way of telling whether or not a given point with a derivative of zero is a local minima or maxima. If you think about it, relying on looking at the graph means that you actually have to plot the graph, which is time-consuming. Relying on looking at points or derivatives before and after the value is also time-consuming *and error-prone*. In theory, at least, a graph could have both an up and a down swing in the space between the points you are looking at. Therefore, we are going to establish a more precise way of finding whether a point is a minima or maxima using the second derivative.

In Chapter 6, we noted that, since the result of a derivative is itself an equation, therefore we can also take the derivative of that new equation. This is known as the *second derivative*, which, using our current notation, is marked as y''.

The derivative is an equation which tells the slope of another equation at any point. The slope tells the relative changes of the dependent(y) variable to the independent (x) variable. For the graph of a derivative, the dependent variable is y', which is the slope of the main equation. Therefore, on a second derivative, the new equation will tell us the relative changes of the *slope* of the original graph to the x variable.

In other words, while the first derivative tells us the relative changes in value (i.e., the slope), the second derivative tells us the relative change of the slope (i.e., the slope of the slope). In physics, if you start with an equation for the position of an object, the first derivative is usually considered the velocity (the change in an object's position over time), and the second derivative is considered the acceleration (the change in an object's velocity over time).

To understand this better, let's take a look at the graph of $y = x^2 + 1$ with the slope of the graph's slopes marked at a few places:

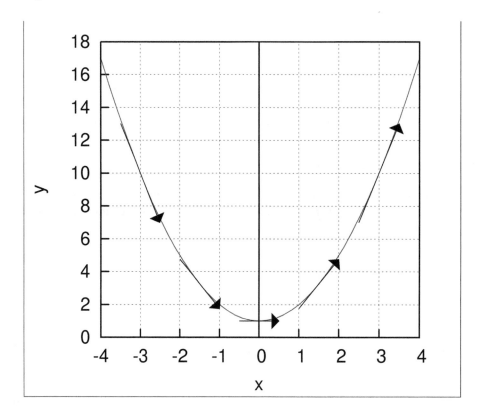

Let's take note as to what each of the slopes are. At the top left, you have a very negative slope. Next, you have a slightly negative slope. Then, you have a zero slope. Then, you have a slightly positive slope. Finally, you have a very positive slope.

The thing to notice about this is that all of your slopes in this graph are are *increasing*. It goes from very negative, to a little negative, to zero, to a little positive, to very positive.

If we have a slope that starts off negative and then continues to increase, then what does it form? It forms a bottom, or a *local minimum*. Likewise, for a *local maximum*, the slopes will start off positive, and then get more and more negative until the slope itself is negative.

This change in slopes that we are looking at is the second derivative. Now, we noted earlier that if we have a bottom or a top, then the slope at that point must be zero. We can use the second derivative to tell us if that point is a bottom or a top. If the second derivative is negative, then our slopes are decreasing, which means that the very next point will be going down (i.e., a negative slope, since the current slope is zero), which means our present point must be at a top. If the second derivative is positive, then our slopes are increasing, which means that the very next point will be going up, which means that our present point must be at a bottom. If the second derivative is zero, then we can draw no certain conclusions, but this usually happens when the graph temporarily flattens out to neither a top nor a bottom (this happens, for instance, at $x = 0$ for the graph $y = x^3$).

This set of criteria is known as the *second derivative test*. If you have a local maximum or minimum (i.e., you found that the slope at a given point is zero), then you can check the second derivative at that point to find out if it is a maximum or minimum. If the second derivative is negative, then the point is a maximum. If the second derivative is positive, then the point is a minimum. If the second derivative is zero, then you should graph the equation and check the graph.

— Example 9.2

Find any local maxima or minima for the graph $y = x^2 + 2x + 3$ and determine if each point is a local maximum or minimum.

As you should know by now, a local maximum or minimum occurs when the *slope* of the equation is zero, which also means that the derivative is zero. The derivative of our equation is:

$$y = x^2 + 2x + 3$$
$$y' = 2x + 2$$

Now we solve for where $y' = 0$:

$$y' = 2x + 2$$
$$0 = 2x + 2$$
$$2x = -2$$
$$x = -1$$

Therefore, the equation has a slope of zero where $x = -1$. If we plug that x value back into the original equation, we find that the corresponding y value is $(-1)^2 + 2(-1) + 3 = 1 - 2 + 3 = 2$.

However, is this a local maximum or a minimum value? To find this out, we will use the second derivative test. To use the second derivative test, we first need to know the second derivative:

$$y' = 2x + 2$$
$$y'' = 2$$

Since $y'' = 2$, that means that y'' is 2 for *any* value of x. So the second derivative is positive for

$x = -1$. Therefore, since the second derivative is positive at this point, then the point represents a local minimum.

— Example 9.3

Find any local maxima or minima for the graph $y = x^3 - 8x^2 + 19x - 12$ and determine if each point is a local maximum or minimum.

Again, our first step is to take the derivative of the equation:

$$y = x^3 - 8x^2 + 19x - 12$$
$$y' = 3x^2 - 16x + 19$$

To find where the local maxima and minima are, we need to find where the slope, y', is zero. Since y' is a quadratic equation, we can use the quadratic formula to find the zeros:

$$y' = 3x^2 - 16x + 19$$
$$0 = 3x^2 - 16x + 19$$
$$x = \frac{-(-16) \pm \sqrt{(-16)^2 - 4(3)(19)}}{2(3)}$$
$$= \frac{16 \pm \sqrt{256 - 225}}{6}$$
$$= \frac{16 \pm \sqrt{28}}{6}$$
$$\approx \frac{16 \pm 5.2915}{6}$$
$$\approx 3.55, 1.78$$

Therefore, our two x values where the slope is zero are approximately 3.55 and 1.78.

Now, which of these are maxima and minima?

To find this out, we find the second derivative:

$$y' = 3x^2 - 16x + 19$$
$$y'' = 6x - 16$$

If we plug in our two x values, we can find whether they are local maxima or local minima:

$$y'' = 6x - 16$$
$$y'' = 6(3.55) - 16$$
$$= 6.3$$

$$y'' = 6x - 16$$
$$y'' = 6(1.78) - 16$$
$$y'' = -4.32$$

As you can see, when $x = 3.55$, the first derivative is zero and the second derivative is positive, which means that the graph is at a local minimum. When $x = 1.78$, the first derivative is zero and the second derivative is negative, which means that the graph is at a local maximum.

9.6 Deriving the Vertex Formula for Quadratics

In Algebra, you may have learned the **vertex formula** for quadratics. The vertex formula states that for any equation of the form $y = Ax^2 + Bx + C$ the vertex occurs at the x value $x = \frac{-B}{2A}$. You probably had to memorize this at some point. But how might we figure out the formula for ourselves?

The vertex of a quadratic is at the local minima or maxima of the quadratic. Therefore, if we find the derivative, then the location where the derivative is zero will tell us where the vertex is.

Therefore, to find this minima or maxima, we need only to take the derivative of the quadratic and set it to zero (remembering that constant-variables are treated as constants!):

$$y = Ax^2 + Bx + C \qquad \text{original equation}$$
$$y' = 2Ax + B \qquad \text{take the derivative}$$
$$0 = 2Ax + B \qquad \text{find where derivative is zero}$$
$$2Ax = -B \qquad \text{solve for } x$$
$$x = \frac{-B}{2A}$$

Therefore, we can see how calculus can be used to derive general formulas that you may have already memorized. Note that there are other ways to derive this formula as well which do not use calculus. Nonetheless, the basics of calculus provide and easy and effective way to develop this formula and many others.

9.7 Creating Models for Applying Extrema Analysis

In many business operations, every thing that you might plan to do has both a potential benefit and a potential detriment. Oftentimes, only one side of the coin is focused on. However, if you really want to think about the impact of decisions on the results of your business, you have to think about both the upside and the downside.

If we model both the upside and the downside with numbers, we can often take the results and use the extrema analysis (i.e., finding the minima and maxima as appropriate) to find the sweet spot where the actual output is optimized (i.e., profits maximized, costs minimized, etc.).

This usually works by analyzing upsides and downsides separately and then combining them into a total function. For instance, *profit* is a combination of upside (revenue) and downside (all of the costs associated with the product). Because revenue and cost are in the same units (dollars), you can write this into an equation:

$$\text{profit} = \text{revenue} - \text{cost}$$

We also often mistakenly think of these things as fixed or linear functions. That is, we think that producing 2,000 units costs ten times as much as producing 200. But that isn't always so. You might have to use a different manufacturing process to get more units out. You might have to pay some people overtime wages. You might have to open a new factory. You might have to operate during a time when utility costs are higher.

Likewise, we also might think that the revenue is the same no matter how many units we sell. That is also not true. We might have to lower the price to sell more units. We might have a standard volume discount, and the only way to sell more units, is for bigger distributors to use those discounts.

Since this is a beginning calculus course, some of the functions we use might be overly simplistic and not extremely close to the real world equations. The point is to think about the process of taking equations, combining them, and using calculus to determine the optimal values to use.

Given a particular problem, to find a solution you need to think about the following:

1. Which variable are we trying to optimize for (either minima or maxima)? This should be the dependent variable in your equation. This will produce the correct derivative for the process.

2. Can the different features of the problem be combined together into a single equation? Sometimes, it is best to write down each piece of the equation individually, and then think about how they might be put together.

3. Can the equation be written so that there is a single independent variable? For this level of calculus, we are doing optimizations where there is a single independent variable which we are adjusting to find an optimum value. Therefore, we need to think about how to combine all of the knowledge of the situation into a single variable. Review Section 4.5 for additional review on this topic.

4. Preferably, the independent variable is one that is *under your control*. For instance, you can't directly control the number of units that people buy of something. However, if you know how the price affects consumer behavior (i.e., you have an equation relating price and sales), you *can* control the price. In short, the independent variable should be the piece of the puzzle that you can control directly and the dependent variable should be the outcome that you are trying to optimize for.

—   Example 9.4

A baseball field, at its current ticket price of $25, sells 3,000 tickets to its ball game. They have determined that, for every 1 they increase the price, they will sell 40 fewer tickets. Likewise, for every 1 that they decrease the price, they will sell 40 more tickets. Additionally, every person attending will spend an average of $8 on concessions. What is the optimal ticket price that they should charge to maximize revenue? How much revenue should they expect at this ticket price?

In this example, what is happening is that revenue is being generated, but increasing the ticket prices will decrease the number of people buying tickets at that price. This will also affect the concession revenue.

To build our equation, we need to realize that the revenue (r) has two components: ticket sales and concessions. Ticket sales are simply the number of people buying tickets (n) multiplied by the ticket price (p), or $n \cdot p$. Concessions average \$8 per customer no matter how many people buy tickets. Therefore, concession revenue will allways be $8n$. Therefore, total revenue can be given by the equation:

$$r = np + 8n$$

However, that's not all. The number of people attending is dependent upon the ticket price as well. At \$25, we sell $3,000$ tickets. So that's the starting point. At $p = 25$, $n = 3,000$. As we increase p, we decrease n. In fact, every increase of p by 1 decreases n by 40. Therefore, the number of people attending can be given by the equation:

$n = $ base number of people $\qquad$ +the distance from the base price $\cdot -40$

$n = 3,000 \qquad\qquad\qquad\qquad\qquad\qquad +(p - 25) \cdot -40$

$n = 3,000 + -40p + 1000$

$n = 4,000 - 40p$

Therefore, we can substitute that into our revenue equation like this:

$$r = np + 8n$$
$$r = (4,000 - 40p)p + 8(4,000 - 40p)$$
$$r = 4,000p - 40p^2 + 32,000 - 320p$$
$$r = 3,680p - 40p^2 + 32,000$$

Now that we have an equation for the revenue, we can take a derivative to find the maximum value:

$r = 3,680p - 40p^2 + 32,000 \qquad$ our original equation

$r' = 3,680 - 80p \qquad\qquad\qquad$ the derivative

To find an extrema, we set the derivative to zero:

$$0 = 3,680 - 80p$$
$$80p = 3,680$$
$$p = 46$$

To determine if this is a maxima or minima, we use the second derivative test:

$r' = 3,680 - 80p \qquad\qquad$ the derivative

$r'' = -80$

Because the second derivative is negative, this is indeed a maxima. If you graph the equation, you will find that the curve is simply an inverted parabola, so this is also a global maxima.

Therefore, our optimal price per ticket is \$46.

To determine the revenue, we just stick it back into our equation:

$$r = 3,680p - 40p^2 + 32,000 \qquad \text{our original equation}$$

$$= 3,680 \cdot 46 - 40 \cdot 46^2 + 32,000$$

$$= 116,640$$

Therefore, our revenue will be \$116,640 at this price point.

Review

In this chapter, we learned:

1. The derivative is an equation that gives you the slope of another equation at any point.

2. Local maxima and minima points on a smooth graph occur where the slope is zero.

3. To determine whether a point is a local maximum or local minimum (or possibly neither), look at the second derivative. If the second derivative is negative it is a local maximum, if it is positive, it is a local minimum, and if it is zero it is inconclusive, and may be neither.

4. Therefore, when looking for local maximum and minimum points on a graph, solve for when the derivative is zero and then check the second derivative.

5. To find a global maximum, we need to check an equations critical points. Critical points include:

    (a) All of the locations where the derivative is zero (local minima and maxima)

    (b) All of the locations where the derivative is undefiend

    (c) All of the locations where the original equation is discontinuous, either because of the equation or because of the limitations of reality.

    (d) The beginning and end of the graph, possibly where $x = \pm\infty$.

    One of these locations will contain the global maximum and minimum.

6. Oftentimes you can use calculus to develop equations for solving certain types of problems.

7. To convert specific problems into general equations, substitute the starting constants for "constant variables". These will be treated as constants when we do calculus operations, but will be treated as variables in the resulting equations.

8. To think about practical uses of minima and maxima processes, remember that nearly every decision has upsides and downsides. Modeling the upsides and downsides explicitly in an equation allows you to use calculus to determine the optimal value for your unknown parameter.

Exercises

To solve some of these problems you may need to refer to some of the standard geometry formulas in Appendix H.3.

1. Find the point on the graph of $y = 3x^2 + 10x$ where the slope is 40.

2. What is the slope of the equation $y = 5x^4 + 3x - 5$ at $x = 2$?

3. Find the second derivative of $y = e^x + 3x^2$ at $x = 0$.

4. Find the third derivative of $y = x^5 - x^3$.

For the equations below, find both the x and y values for all local maxima and minima *using the derivative* (don't just use the vertex formula even if it applies). For each point found, use the second derivative test to find out if the point is a local maximum or minimum.

5. $y = x^2 + 3x + 10$

6. $y = x^3 + 7x^2 - 34x - 40$

7. $y = -6x^2 + 7x + 5$

8. $y = 2x^2 + 8x + 6$

9. $y = 18x^3 + 102x^2 - 40x - 24$

Solve the following problems *using derivatives*:

10. Find the global minimum and maximum of the equation $y = x^2$.

11. Take the equation $y = x^3 + 4x^2 + x - 6$ on the interval from $x = -4$ to $x = 2$. What is the maximum value on this interval?

12. I am building a rectangular fence bordering a straight river (so I don't need fence on one side) and I have 200ft of fencing. First, establish an equation that finds the total area enclosed based on one variable (probably one of the sides of the fence). Second, solve that equation to find out what the lengths of the sides need to be in order to maximize the amount of area enclosed by that fence.

13. Imagine a cardboard box with a **square** base that has no top. Find the dimensions of the box with the largest volume that can be made out of 35 square feet of cardboard.

14. Create an equation for the previous question so that it can be solved for any given amount of cardboard using just a calculator.

15. A drink company is wanting to minimize the amount of material needed to make a can for their product. A standard drink serving is 355 mL (1 mL is a cubic centimeter). What dimensions should they make the can (which is a cylinder) in order to minimize the material needed (i.e., the surface area)?

16. Find the closed cylinder (i.e., height and radius) with the largest volume that can be made out of 200 square feet of paper.

17. Create an equation for the previous question so that it can be solved for any given amount of paper using just a calculator.

18. Just like there is a vertex formula for quadratics, develop a vertex formula for cubic equations (i.e., equations where the highest power of x is 3).

19. Use the formula derived in the previous question to find the x values of the vertices of the following equation: $y = x^3 + 5x^2 + 3x + 2$. Also find the corresponding y values of the vertices.

20. A smart phone manufacturer decides that in order to sell n units of their new cell phone, the wholesale price (w) per unit must be $(300-w) \cdot 1,000,000$. The cost to produce the unit is \$150 per unit. Profit (p) is the difference between revenue and cost. What price should they set their cell phone for maximum profit, and what profit will they get?

Chapter 10

The Differential

This chapter introduces a shift in thinking about the derivative, accompanied by a shift in notation. When we introduced the derivative, y' was seen as a new variable that gave the slope at any desired point. The slope is the change in y value divided by the change in x value at a given point. In other words, the slope is $\frac{\text{change in } y}{\text{change in } x}$.

In the old notation, y' was viewed as a single entity. In this chapter, we are going to break y' down into its parts, called *differentials*. We are going to replace y' with $\frac{dy}{dx}$, where dy and dx are the relative sizes of change in y and x. y' and $\frac{dy}{dx}$ both represent the same quantity, but, by splitting it out into its constituent parts, we can work with more complicated problems a lot easier.

10.1   Differential Notation

Previously, when we worked with derivatives, we solved for a new variable, y', that represented the slope of the original equation. So, if we had the equation $y = x^2$, then the derivative would be written as $y' = 2x$.

To begin our study of differentials, we are going to replace y' with the fraction $\frac{dy}{dx}$. In other words, for the equation $y = x^2$, we are going to write the derivative as $\frac{dy}{dx} = 2x$.

Simple enough, right?

Now, dy does *not* mean that it is some variable d multiplied by y. This is a *brand new* quantity. Think of the dy as being a single term, with the letters just being smashed together.

Another way of thinking of it is to think of d as an operator. We are applying d to y to get its relative change, as if we had written $d(y)$.

So, if we have the following equation:
$$y = 3x^2 + 4x + 5$$

Then we can write the derivative as follows:
$$\frac{dy}{dx} = 6x + 4$$

It's just a change in the notation, but notations have a habit of teaching you to think about things in different ways.

So why do we use the notation $\frac{dy}{dx}$?

With $\frac{dy}{dx}$, we see that the derivative represents the ratio of the change of two values. These two values are the *relative amounts of change* between dy and dx at a given point on the graph.

If you remember back to our first discussion of derivatives, the equation for the derivative was:

$$y' = \frac{f(x+h) - f(x)}{h}$$

In this equation, h is basically dx because it represents the amount of change of our x value. Similarly, $f(x+h) - f(x)$ is dy because it represents the amount of change in our y value for the given (ultra-tiny) amount of change in our x value. The derivative looks at this equation as h (i.e, dx) becomes incredibly small. In fact, both the numerator and the denominator become incredibly small *individually*, but the *slope* (the ratio of the numerator to the denominator) generally stabilizes to a more recognizable value (i.e., one that is not necessarily infinitely small).

So, we can think of dy and dx as really small numbers representing really small changes in the variables, which, by themselves, are too small to write out as a number. However, when they are put in ratio with each other, they represent the slope of the line at a given point. dy and dx are called **differentials**, and they represent the corresponding small changes (differences) in the y and x values in an equation.

So, again, the only change we've made so far is that, where we used to have y', we now have $\frac{dy}{dx}$. Writing out derivatives using this notation is often called the **Liebniz notation** for the derivative.

— Example 10.1

Find the derivative of $y = 6x^{10} - 5x^3 + 4x^2$ and write it in Liebniz notation.

This is just like any other derivative we have done, using our basic rules for polynomials. Normally, we would write the derivative as:

$$y' = 60x^9 - 15x^2 + 8x$$

Using Liebniz notation, however, we write the answer as:

$$\frac{dy}{dx} = 60x^9 - 15x^2 + 8x$$

— Example 10.2

Find the derivative of $y = 6^x - x^5$ and write it using Liebniz notation.

To solve this, we need both our polynomial rules and our exponent rules. Normally, we would write the derivative like this:

$$y' = \ln(6) \cdot 6^x - 5x^4$$

However, for Liebniz notation, we instead write it as:

$$\frac{dy}{dx} = \ln(6) \cdot 6^x - 5x^4$$

10.2   Separating Out the Differentials

Now that we have dy and dx as two distinct quantities in our equations, we can manipulate them individually using normal algebraic means. So, if we have the equation:

$$y = x^3$$

The derivative of this equation is:

$$\frac{dy}{dx} = 3x^2$$

Because dy and dx are separate algebraic entities, we can actually multiply both sides of this equation by dx, and get the following result:

$$dy = 3x^2\, dx$$

Now, since dy and dx are both incredibly close to zero, you wouldn't actually solve for a value for dy. What this equation communicates is the relationship between changes in x (represented by dx) and changes in y (represented by dy) at any point in the equation.

Separating out dy and dx to their own sides of the equation will help us do a lot of things going forward in calculus. Most importantly, it allows us to treat the differentials *independently*. This independence will not only help you with this calculus course, but also upper-level calculus-based courses, such as Differential Equations. More importantly it will help your mathematical imagination, because in the long term it will help you to analyze problems by looking at the little tiny bits and putting them together into reasonable formulas, and recognize other formulas which were built in the same way.

REMINDER—dy and dx are each complete units. dy is not d multiplied by y, but rather a combined unit, kind of a shorthand for $d(y)$, which represents an infinitely small amount of change in y. Likewise for dx or any other differential you encounter.

10.3   Rewriting Our Rules as Differential Rules

In Chapter 8, we laid out the basic rules for taking the derivative of polynomials. We can rewrite these rules where we separate out dy and dx to opposite sides of the equation.

Take the power rule, for instance. The power rule says that, if $y = x^n$, then $y' = nx^{n-1}$.

We can rewrite this rule using Liebniz notation like this:

$$\frac{dy}{dx} = nx^{n-1}$$

We can then multiply both sides by dx. This gives us the following equation:

$$dy = nx^{n-1}\, dx$$

We will call this the **differential form**. We can actually take any of our rules and write them in differential form.

Figure 10.1 shows a table of all of our rules in differential form.

So, for any derivative we have, since we could write it out in Liebniz notation, we can also write it out in differential notation, simply by multiplying both sides by dx.

If we started out with the equation:

$$y = x^2 + 2x + 3$$

Figure 10.1: Derivative Rules in Differential Form

Rule	Original Equation	Derivative Form	Differential Form
Constant Rule	$y = n$	$\frac{dy}{dx} = 0$	$dy = 0$
Identity Rule	$y = x$	$\frac{dy}{dx} = 1$	$dy = dx$
Constant Multiplier Rule	$y = nx$	$\frac{dy}{dx} = n$	$dy = n\,dx$
Power Rule	$y = x^n$	$\frac{dy}{dx} = nx^{n-1}$	$dy = nx^{n-1}\,dx$
Exponent Rule	$y = n^x$	$\frac{dy}{dx} = \ln(n) \cdot n^x$	$dy = \ln(n) \cdot n^x\,dx$
Addition Rule	$y = f + g$	$\frac{dy}{dx} = \frac{df}{dx} + \frac{dg}{dx}$	$dy = df + dg$

We could write the Liebniz notation of the derivative as follows:

$$\frac{dy}{dx} = 2x + 2$$

The differential notation is then given by multiplying both sides by dx:

$$dy = 2x\,dx + 2\,dx$$

— Example 10.3

Write out the derivative of $y = e^x + 5x^2 - 2x$ in differential notation.

To solve, we start by taking the derivative using Liebniz notation:

$$\frac{dy}{dx} = e^x + 10x - 2$$

Next, to get it into differential notation, we multiply both sides by dx:

$$dy = e^x\,dx + 10x\,dx - 2\,dx$$

— Example 10.4

Write out the derivative of $y = \sqrt{x}$ in differential notation.

To solve, first we need to convert the right-hand side into an exponent so we can use the power rule:

$$y = x^{\frac{1}{2}}$$

Next, we need to find the derivative using Liebniz notation:

$$\frac{dy}{dx} = \frac{1}{2}x^{\frac{-1}{2}}$$

Finally, we need to multiply both sides by dx to get it in differential notation:

$$dy = \frac{1}{2}x^{\frac{-1}{2}}\,dx$$

10.4   The Differential as an Operator

What our new notation allows us to do is to treat the differential not just as a notation, but as an *operation*. That is, while we have previously thought about the derivative in terms of an entire equation, the differential allows us to apply the differential operation to each side independently.

For instance, let's say you had the following equation:

$$y^2 = e^x$$

How do you take the derivative of that? Using differential notation will help us.

Remember earlier when we said that the differential was like an operator. You can apply the differential to get back the relative change of something. In other words, if I said $d(x)$, I am asking for the relative change in x. Now, the relative change of any particular variable is, by definition, its differential (dx in this case).

But, what is the differential of $5x^2$? That is, can I apply an operation to $5x^2$ which will give me the relative amount that this quantity changes?

Yes, I can.

Imagine that this was part of an equation, $y = 5x^2$. This would allow me to take the differential of both sides. I could write this as:

$$d(y) = d(5x^2)$$

We said earlier that the differential of a variable by itself is just the differential itself. So, we can change $d(y)$ into dy and rewrite this equation as:

$$dy = d(5x^2)$$

If we do this, we see that we know what $d(5x^2)$ is—it is the result of writing the derivative in differential notation. The differential of $5x^2$ is $10x\,dx$. Therefore:

$$dy = 10x\,dx$$

This may not seem very amazing to you yet, but what it means is that we can now utilize the differential *as a function* and take the differential of various pieces of our equations independently.

We can actually write down all of our differential rules as differentials of functions (i.e., without reference to y), using the rules listed in Figure 10.2.

So, let's go back to the equation we couldn't do:

$$y^2 = e^x$$

If we focus on differentials instead of derivatives, we can take the differential of both sides. Doing so will give us:

$$d(y^2) = d(e^x)$$

Now, because we can take each of these separately, let's look at them.

What will the differential of e^x be? It will be $e^x\,dx$.

Figure 10.2: Differentials of Functions

Name	Rule
Constant Rule	$\mathrm{d}(n) = 0$
Identity Rule	$\mathrm{d}(x) = \mathrm{d}x$
Constant Multiplier Rule	$\mathrm{d}(nx) = n\,\mathrm{d}x$
Power Rule	$\mathrm{d}(x^n) = nx^{n-1}\,\mathrm{d}x$
Exponent Rule	$\mathrm{d}(n^x) = \ln(n) \cdot n^x\,\mathrm{d}x$
Addition Rule	$\mathrm{d}(f + g) = \mathrm{d}f + \mathrm{d}g$

What will be the differential of y^2? To answer this question, you just have to remember that, in mathematics, variable names are arbitrary. If I have a rule that tells me how to do an operation, and that rule is written with one variable in mind, I can do the same operation with other variables as well. Therefore, I can use the power rule on y^2 as well! Therefore, $\mathrm{d}(y^2)$ just becomes $2y\,\mathrm{d}y$. Note that, since we are using y in the rule, we use $\mathrm{d}y$ in the result, not $\mathrm{d}x$.

Therefore, the steps we have done so far are as follows:

$$y^2 = e^x \qquad\qquad \text{the original equation}$$

$$\mathrm{d}(y^2) = \mathrm{d}(e^x) \qquad\qquad \text{take the differential of both sides}$$

$$2y\,\mathrm{d}y = e^x\,\mathrm{d}x \qquad\qquad \text{differential rules}$$

So, that's an interesting equation, but what can I do with it? Well, if I want to find the derivative, I can solve for it. In other words, I can manipulate the equation so that I wind up with $\frac{\mathrm{d}y}{\mathrm{d}x}$ all alone on one side of the equation, like this:

$$2y\,\mathrm{d}y = e^x\,\mathrm{d}x \qquad\qquad \text{the differential}$$

$$\frac{2y\,\mathrm{d}y}{\mathrm{d}x} = e^x \qquad\qquad \text{divide both sides by } \mathrm{d}x$$

$$\frac{\mathrm{d}y}{\mathrm{d}x} = \frac{e^x}{2y} \qquad\qquad \text{divide both sides by } 2y$$

Now I have an equation for the derivative! Note that this equation includes *both* x and y terms. This is known as an **implicit derivative**.

Example 10.5

Find the derivative of $e^y = 3x^5 - 2x^2$.

$$e^y = 3x^5 - 2x^2 \qquad \text{original equation}$$

$$d(e^y) = d(3x^5 - 2x^2) \qquad \text{take the differential of both sides}$$

$$d(e^y) = d(3x^5) - d(2x^2) \qquad \text{addition rule}$$

$$e^y\, dy = 15x^4\, dx - 4x\, dx \qquad \text{exponent rule and power rule}$$

$$\frac{e^y\, dy}{dx} = 15x^4 - 4x \qquad \text{solve for } \frac{dy}{dx}$$

$$\frac{dy}{dx} = \frac{15x^4 - 4x}{e^y}$$

— Example 10.6

Find the derivative of $3y^2 + x^3 - 2y^5 = 5x$.

$$3y^2 + x^3 - 2y^5 = 5x \qquad \text{original equation}$$

$$d(3y^2 + x^3 - 2y^5) = d(5x) \qquad \text{take differential of both sides}$$

$$d(3y^2) + d(x^3) - d(2y^5) = d(5x) \qquad \text{addition rule}$$

$$6y\, dy + 3x^2\, dx - 10y^4\, dy = 5\, dx \qquad \text{power rule}$$

$$6y\, dy - 10y^4\, dy = 5\, dx - 3x^2\, dx \qquad \text{solve for } \frac{dy}{dx}$$

$$\frac{6y\, dy - 10y^4\, dy}{dx} = 5 - 3x^2$$

$$\frac{(6y - 10y^4)dy}{dx} = 5 - 3x^2$$

$$\frac{dy}{dx} = \frac{5 - 3x^2}{6y - 10y^4}$$

From here on out, this will usually be the technique we will use for solving for derivatives. First we will take the differential of both sides of the equation, and then we will solve for $\frac{dy}{dx}$.

Let's look at the equation of the unit circle, $x^2 + y^2 = 1$. Using differentials, we can take the derivative of this equation.

$$x^2 + y^2 = 1 \qquad \text{the original equation}$$

$$\mathrm{d}(x^2 + y^2) = \mathrm{d}(1) \qquad \text{taking the differential of both sides of the equation}$$

$$\mathrm{d}(x^2 + y^2) = 0 \qquad \text{applying the constant rule}$$

$$\mathrm{d}(x^2) + \mathrm{d}(y^2) = 0 \qquad \text{applying the addition rule}$$

$$2x\,\mathrm{d}x + 2y\,\mathrm{d}y = 0 \qquad \text{applying the power rule to each term}$$

$$2y\,\mathrm{d}y = -2x\,\mathrm{d}x \qquad \text{solve for } \frac{\mathrm{d}y}{\mathrm{d}x}$$

$$\mathrm{d}y = \frac{-2x\,\mathrm{d}x}{2y}$$

$$\mathrm{d}y = \mathrm{d}x\frac{-2x}{2y}$$

$$\mathrm{d}y = \mathrm{d}x\frac{-x}{y}$$

$$\frac{\mathrm{d}y}{\mathrm{d}x} = \frac{-x}{y}$$

So, the derivative of the unit circle is $\frac{-x}{y}$. What does this mean? It means that, for every point on the circle, if you divide the x value by the y value and multiply by -1, you will have the slope of the line. Take a moment to draw a unit circle on some graph paper to prove this to yourself.

10.5   The Infinitesimals

So what are these strange creatures, $\mathrm{d}y$ and $\mathrm{d}x$. Well, actually, there is quite a bit of controversy of what they really indicate. There are two main schools of thought. I imagine that there are probably other ways to conceive of them as well.

In the first school, $\mathrm{d}y$ and $\mathrm{d}x$ represent what are known as *limits*. A limit is where values are headed *towards*. We will deal with limits explicitly in Chapter 28. In any case, using limits, we can think of $\mathrm{d}y$ and $\mathrm{d}x$ as being arbitrarily small real numbers. Because they are small and non-zero, they can be manipulated like any other algebraic quantity. However, because of how small they are, you can't actually read their numeric values except as a ratio with other, similarly small numbers.

The other school of thought treats these values as new types of numbers altogether, known as **infinitesimals**. An infinitesimal is a value that is *infinitely* close to zero, without actually being zero. An infinitesimal is smaller than every real number.[1] It isn't a real number itself, as it is smaller than any real, non-zero number. Numbers that include these infinitesimal portions are known as hyperreal numbers. We will look at these more in-depth in Chapter 27.

Having a new type of number may sound scary or crazy, but in fact, most of the mathematics you deal with every day is based on some new type of number that someone once found scary or crazy. The natural numbers (positive integers) were, at first, the only numbers. Then someone introduced zero and the negative numbers which gave us our current set of integers. Then someone noticed that you could put these integers

---

[1]Note that in this section, as in most of mathematics, "real number" refers to the set of numbers known as the "reals." Infinitesimals are in fact actual numbers, just as imaginary numbers are actual numbers. They are just a different type of number than those given the designation "reals." Sorry for the confusion—I didn't invent the names of the numbers.

into ratio with each other and get fractions. This gave us the rational numbers. Someone then pointed out that there were numbers (like $\sqrt{2}$ and π) that could not be expressed as a ratio of integers (the so-called irrational numbers). Adding these to our number line gave us the real numbers that we know and love today. This development took hundreds of years, but now we use these numbers without even thinking about it. Likewise, the hyperreals, though seemingly strange, may some day wind up being thought of as just as normal as the square root of two.

10.6 Clarifying Terminology

I wanted to take a moment to just make sure that you understand the various terminologies we have discussed in this chapter, because they can get confusing.

First of all, the **derivative** is the relationship between the changes in two variables. Typically, we have been talking about y', which can also be termed $\frac{dy}{dx}$, which you would say as "the derivative of y with respect to x."

If we want to apply the derivative to both sides of an equation (this is what we have been doing in the chapters before this one), you normally use $D_x()$ to signify this. This means "take the derivative with respect to x."

So, let's start with $y = x^2$. The derivative of both sides with respect to x is $D_x(y) = D_x(x^2)$. The result of this is $y' = 2x$ or, in Liebniz notation, $\frac{dy}{dx} = 2x$.

The **differential** is not as picky, as you don't have to specify what the differential is with respect to. The differential simply converts a function into its dynamic equivalent.

So, with $y = x^2$, if we take the *differential* of both sides, we get $d(y) = d(x^2)$, which then becomes $dy = 2x\,dx$.

To convert the differential to the derivative, we simply divide both sides of the equation by the differential of x (or whatever variable the derivative is with respect to). To convert a derivative into a differential, we simply multiply both sides of the equation by that same differential.

Because the derivative is merely the differential of a function divided by dx (or whatever variable), another way of notating the derivative is $\frac{d}{dx}()$. So, we can also notate the derivative of $y = x^2$ by saying $\frac{d}{dx}y = \frac{d}{dx}x^2$. This essentially tells us to take the differential of both sides and divide by dx, which gives $\frac{dy}{dx} = \frac{2x\,dx}{dx}$ and simplifies to $\frac{dy}{dx} = 2x$.

Different people prefer different notations depending on what they are trying to do and also what they are comfortable with. For simple relationships, the derivative is a little more straightforward. For anything more complex, the differential is usually easier to work with, and therefore we will focus on it for the remainder of the book.

In the next chapter, we are going to look at the final pieces of the puzzle that let us connect all of the rules of the derivative together for nearly every equation.

Review

In this chapter, we learned:

1. Because y' represents a slope, it can be seen as a ratio of two values, dy (the change in y) and dx (the change in x), represented as $\frac{dy}{dx}$.

2. Writing a derivative using $\frac{dy}{dx}$ is known as Liebniz notation.

3. dy and dx are called differentials because they represent the relative changes in values for these variables.

4. A derivative formula written in Liebniz notation can be converted into a differential formula by simply using the $\frac{dy}{dx}$ notation and then multiplying both sides by dx.

5. Likewise, a differential formula can be converted into a derivative by manipulating the equation so that $\frac{dy}{dx}$ is on a side by itself.

6. The differential of a function can be represented by saying $d(f(x))$.

7. Complicated equations are much easier to solve using differentials first and then converting to derivatives than by trying to solve using derivatives directly.

8. Figure 10.2 shows a list of differentials for the types of functions we have explored so far.

Exercises

1. Write down the differential rules listed in Figure 10.2 three times.

2. Take the differential of $y = x^6$.

3. Take the differential of $y = e^x$.

4. Take the differential of $y = 4x^3$.

5. Take the differential of $y = 2x^2 + 5x + 4$.

6. Take the differential of $y = \frac{5}{\sqrt{x}}$.

7. Take the differential of $y^3 = 2x^2$.

8. Take the differential of $y^2 - x^2 + e^x = 3$.

9. Find the derivative of $2y + 5 = 5x - 3$.

10. Find the derivative of $e^y - x^3 = 2x$.

11. Find the derivative of $3y^3 - 2x^2 + 5y + 20 = e^x$.

12. The equation $e^y - 3x^2 = 5$ has one non-infinite minimum value for y that occurs at a local minima (you may use this as an assumption—if you find a local extremum, you can assume it is the value you are looking for). At what value of x does this occur? What is the y value at this point?

13. Find the slope of the equation $y^2 = 4x^3$ at the point $(4, 16)$

14. At what x value does the equation $y = 7\sqrt{x}$ have a slope of 10?

15. Find the equation of the line tangent to the graph of $x^2 + y^2 = 8$ at $(2, 2)$.

Chapter 11

Differentials of Composite Functions

In this chapter we are going to cover the derivatives of *composite* functions. So far, we have been able to take the derivatives of a wide range of equations. We can take the derivative of $y = 2^x$ and $y = x^3$, but we have not yet learned to take the derivative of *combinations* of functions, such as $y = 2^{x^3}$ or even $y = 2^x \cdot x^3$.

In this chapter we will learn to use the *chain rule* to do derivatives of much greater complexity.

11.1 The Differentials of Sine and Cosine

In order to make more interesting examples, we will start off by looking at the differentials of $\sin(x)$ and $\cos(x)$ in this section. They are actually very simple.

First, the differential of $\sin(x)$:
$$d(\sin(x)) = \cos(x)\,dx \tag{11.1}$$

Then, the differential of $\cos(x)$:
$$d(\cos(x)) = -\sin(x)\,dx \tag{11.2}$$

That's all there is to it!

— Example 11.1

Find the derivative of $y = \sin(x) + x^3$.

$y = \sin(x) + x^3$	original equation
$d(y) = d(\sin(x) + x^3)$	take the differential of both sides
$dy = d(\sin(x)) + d(x^3)$	addition rule
$dy = \cos(x)\,dx + 3x^2\,dx$	Sine and Power Rules
$\dfrac{dy}{dx} = \cos(x) + 3x^2$	Solve for $\dfrac{dy}{dx}$

—   Example 11.2

Find the derivative of $\cos(y) = 2^x - \sin(x)$.

$$\cos(y) = 2^x - \sin(x) \qquad \text{original equation}$$

$$d(\cos(y)) = d(2^x - \sin(x)) \qquad \text{differentiate both sides}$$

$$d(\cos(y)) = d(2^x) - d(\sin(x)) \qquad \text{addition rule}$$

$$-\sin(y)\,dy = \ln(2)2^x\,dx - \cos(x)\,dx \qquad \text{Sine, cosine, and exponent rules}$$

$$\frac{dy}{dx} = \frac{\ln(2)2^x - \cos(x)}{-\sin(y)} \qquad \text{Solve for } \frac{dy}{dx}$$

When dealing with trigonometric functions in calculus, the arguments are always assumed to be in *radians*, not degrees. Without this, their derivatives would be much more complicated.

Also keep in mind that, with radians, dimensions are usually not specified but merely assumed or implied (that is, the actual word "radian" is usually not used in the equation like you would with other units like ft or sec).[1] In fact, if you tried to keep track of radians as a unit in the normal fashion, your results would probably be confusing at best. Leaving it as an implied unit prevents this confusion.

In short, always use radians for angle measurements in calculus, but never try to write or manipulate the unit name itself when working problems.

—   Example 11.3

If $y = \sin(2x)$, what is $\frac{dy}{dx}$ when $x = \pi$?

First, find the derivative:

$$y = \sin(2x)$$

$$u = 2x$$

$$du = 2\,dxy \qquad\qquad = \sin(u)$$

$$dy = \cos(u)\,du$$

$$dy = 2\cos(2x)\,dx$$

$$\frac{dy}{dx} = 2\cos(2x)$$

---

[1] There is currently some controversy in the physics community over this. Historically, radians have been assumed to be "dimensionless" and thus not require a unit marker. However, that leads to some absurd results, and there has been a move to try to find an underpinning combination of logic and practice that will deal with angle units intuitively and consistently. For right now, just leave off the term "radian" and assume it is there whenever it makes sense for it to be there.

Now, we evaluate it at $x = \pi$.

$$\frac{dy}{dx} = 2\cos(2x)$$

$$\frac{dy}{dx} = 2\cos(2\pi)$$

$$\frac{dy}{dx} = 2 \cdot 1$$

$$\frac{dy}{dx} = 2$$

Therefore, at $x = \pi$, $\frac{dy}{dx} = 2$. Notice how we never listed "radians" in any of the problems. That is because the radian is an implied unit, and does not need to be stated explicitly.

11.2 Making Substitutions

In this chapter, we are going to learn how to take the differentials of **composite functions**—functions that are embedded in other functions. But before we work with differentials, this section will focus just on the general technique of making substitutions. We covered this topic briefly in Section 4.7.

Once we have an equation, it is ours to manipulate, as long as you follow all the rules. You can even introduce new variables of your choosing, defined to mean anything you want them to mean, provided you keep their definitions consistent. Because we can introduce new variables with our own definitions, we can identify terms in an expression that we want to replace with a variable, define a variable for it, and do the replacement.

For instance, let's say that we have the equation $(2^x)^2 - 4(2^x) + 4 = 0$. This is *almost* a quadratic equation. In fact, it would be a quadratic equation, if, instead of having 2^x, we instead had a variable in its place.

Therefore, what we should do is to actually *put* a new variable in its place. Usually, people use the variable u for this kind of substitution (not for any particular reason, but because u is usually not being used for anything else). Therefore, if we set $u = 2^x$, then we can make the equation become $u^2 - 4u + 4 = 0$, which can be easily solved with the quadratic formula:

$$0 = u^2 - 4u + 4 \qquad \text{the equation with a } u \text{ substitution}$$

$$u = \frac{4 \pm \sqrt{(-4)^2 - 4 \cdot 1 \cdot 4}}{2 \cdot 1} \qquad \text{the quadratic formula}$$

$$u = \frac{4 \pm \sqrt{16 - 16}}{2} \qquad \text{simplifying}$$

$$u = \frac{4}{2}$$

$$u = 2$$

So now we have solved for u. However, we are not done yet!

u was substituted in for a function of x, and what we *really* want is the value of x. Therefore, we now need to go back and use u to solve for x.

The substitution we used was $u = 2^x$. Therefore, u is *still equal* to 2^x, so we can plug our value of u into the equation and solve for it. Therefore:

$u = 2^x$	the original substitution
$u = 2$	the result from the equation above
$2^x = 2$	substituting
$\log_2(2^x) = \log_2(2)$	get the log base 2 of both sides to get rid of the exponent
$x = 1$	

The important points are the following:

1. If a problem is difficult, you can sometimes substitute a new variable in for some part of that equation to make it easier to solve.

2. Once you solve for the equation, *don't forget to go back and solve for the original variable!*

In the next section, we will see how doing such substitutions allow us to take differentials of more complicated expressions.

11.3   The Chain Rule

Now for the chain rule.

The chain rule is a technique used to find the derivative of composite functions using substitutions. For example, let's take the derivative of $y = 2^{x^3}$

How could we go about solving this? Remember that we *cannot* combine derivative rules *except* when we have a specific rule allow it. We have a rule for 2^x, but *not* a rule for 2^{x^n}. We have a rule for x^n, but we can't combine it with the other rule—our current combining rules are for addition and multiplication by a constant.

So, let's try a different route. Let's take the technique we talked about in the previous section—let's do a u-substitution. We don't know how to take the derivative of 2^{x^3}. However, if we were to create a new variable u and set $u = x^3$, then that makes things easier. We can now rewrite the original expression as 2^u, which is one that we can do with our basic rules! The differential of 2^u can be found using the exponent rule, yielding $\ln(2)2^u \, du$.

Now, here is the part that all new students mess up. Over half of my students at this point want to say that the differential of 2^u is $\ln(2)2^u \, dx$. That is *not* the right answer. In the expression 2^u, is there *any* instance of x in that expression? Anywhere?

No, there isn't.

Now that we have substituted in a u, the expression only deals in u, and therefore, the differential must only deal in u. Therefore, the actual differential of 2^u will be $\ln(2)2^u \, du$. That's du not dx.

Wrong Way	Right Way
$\mathrm{d}(2^u) = \ln(2)2^u \, \mathrm{d}x$	$\mathrm{d}(2^u) = \ln(2)2^u \, \mathrm{d}u$

We took one step forward, but now we are one step backward. We did a u-substitution which allowed us to take a differential, but now we have a new item in the picture—du! How do we find and/or get rid of this new piece of the puzzle?

Well, what was our u-substitution? It was the equation $u = x^3$. What happens if we take the differential of both sides of this equation?

$$u = x^3 \qquad \text{the substitution equation}$$

$$d(u) = d(x^3) \qquad \text{take the differential of both sides}$$

$$du = 3x^2 dx \qquad \text{power rule}$$

Now we have an equation that gives us the value of du! So, since we know that $u = x^3$ (because that was our substitution) and that $du = 3x^2 dx$ (because of the differential of our substitution), we can now plug these back in and get the whole differential:

$$dy = \ln(2)2^u du \qquad \text{the original differential}$$

$$dy = \ln(2)2^{x^3} \cdot 3x^2 dx \qquad \text{substituting } u \text{ and } du \text{ back in}$$

$$\frac{dy}{dx} = \ln(2)2^{x^3} \cdot 3x^2 \qquad \text{solving for } \frac{dy}{dx}$$

$$\frac{dy}{dx} = 3\ln(2)2^{x^3} x^2 \qquad \text{simplified}$$

So, as you can see, by using a u-substitution, and then finding the derivative of that u, we are then able to take the derivative of composite functions in a straightforward (though sometimes tedious) way.

Because that explanation covered a lot of ground, here is the complete list of steps to take that derivative all in one place:

$$y = 2^{x^3} \qquad \text{the original equation}$$

$$u = x^3 \qquad \text{choose a } u \text{ that makes the equation easy to take a differential}$$

$$y = 2^u \qquad \text{substituted}$$

$$d(y) = d(2^u) \qquad \text{take the differential of both sides}$$

$$dy = \ln(2)2^u du \qquad \text{the exponent rule}$$

$$u = x^3 \qquad \text{this was our substitution}$$

$$d(u) = d(x^3) \qquad \text{take the differential of both sides}$$

$$du = 3x^2 dx \qquad \text{use the power rule}$$

$$dy = \ln(2)2^u du \qquad \text{our differential from above}$$

$$dy = \ln(2)2^{x^3} du \qquad \text{substituting back in for } u$$

$$\mathrm{d}y = \ln(2)2^{x^3}3x^2\mathrm{d}x \qquad\qquad \text{substituting back in for } \mathrm{d}u$$

$$\frac{\mathrm{d}y}{\mathrm{d}x} = \ln(2)2^{x^3}3x^2 \qquad\qquad \text{dividing both sides by } \mathrm{d}x$$

$$\frac{\mathrm{d}y}{\mathrm{d}x} = 3\ln(2)2^{x^3}x^2 \qquad\qquad \text{moving the constants to the front to make it look nicer}$$

The chain rule just says that when you need the differential of a composite function, you can easily do a u-substitution to make it work with a standard differential rule. It is called the chain rule because it allows you to take derivatives of functions within functions by chaining together u-substitutions.

This works no matter how many composite functions you have. However, if you have more than one substitution then, for sanity's sake, I would use different variable names for each composite function you want to substitute for (use v for the second one, w for the third, etc.). Otherwise, you won't know which u you are working with. Complicated functions like this are covered in more depth in Section 11.5.

— Example 11.4

Find the derivative of the equation $y = 5^{x+x^3}$.

Since we don't know how to take the differential of this equation *directly*, we will use u-substitution.

So, we will set $u = x + x^3$. Now, our equation becomes:

$$y = 5^u$$

This is incredibly easy:

$$\mathrm{d}y = \ln(5)5^u\,\mathrm{d}u$$

However, this is in terms of u and $\mathrm{d}u$, not x and $\mathrm{d}x$. We know what u is (because we defined it ourselves!) but we need to find $\mathrm{d}u$. Since we have an equation for u (because we made it ourselves!) we can simply take the differential of that equation:

$$u = x + x^3$$

$$\mathrm{d}(u) = \mathrm{d}(x + x^3)$$

$$\mathrm{d}u = \mathrm{d}(x) + \mathrm{d}(x^3)$$

$$\mathrm{d}u = \mathrm{d}x + 3x^2\,\mathrm{d}x$$

So, now we will take our differential, and substitute in the equivalents for u and $\mathrm{d}u$:

$$\mathrm{d}y = \ln(5)5^u\,\mathrm{d}u \qquad\qquad \text{the original differential}$$

$$\mathrm{d}y = \ln(5)5^{x+x^3}(\mathrm{d}x + 3x^2\,\mathrm{d}x) \qquad\qquad \text{substituting in our values}$$

$$\mathrm{d}y = \ln(5)5^{x+x^3}\mathrm{d}x + 3x^2\ln(5)5^{x+x^3}\,\mathrm{d}x \qquad\qquad \text{simplifying}$$

Now that we have the differential, we can divide both sides by $\mathrm{d}x$ to get the derivative:

$$\frac{\mathrm{d}y}{\mathrm{d}x} = \ln(5)5^{x+x^3} + 3x^2\ln(5)5^{x+x^3}$$

— Example 11.5

Find the derivative of $y = \sin(x^2)$.

We know the differential rule for $\sin(x)$, but not for $\sin(x^2)$. Therefore, we can use a substitution to make it solvable:

$$u = x^2$$

Now the equation becomes:

$$y = \sin(u)$$

The differential is:

$$\mathrm{d}y = \cos(u)\,\mathrm{d}u$$

We already know what u is, but we will need to take its differential to find $\mathrm{d}u$:

$$u = x^2$$

$$\mathrm{d}u = 2x\,\mathrm{d}x$$

Now we can substitute these back in to our differential, and then solve for $\frac{\mathrm{d}y}{\mathrm{d}x}$:

$$\mathrm{d}y = \cos(u)\,\mathrm{d}u$$

$$\mathrm{d}y = \cos(x^2)2x\,\mathrm{d}x$$

$$\mathrm{d}y = 2x\,\cos(x^2)\,\mathrm{d}x$$

$$\frac{\mathrm{d}y}{\mathrm{d}x} = 2x\,\cos(x^2)$$

11.4   The Standard Chain Rule

The way that I have defined the chain rule is a little different than in other books. This book focuses on u-substitution, because it is the easiest and most general way to apply the chain rule, and it works with differentials of both single and multiple variables.

In this section, I want you to at lease see how the chain rule is defined elsewhere, as other books you may encounter in the future may refer to it. If you find it confusing, you can skip this section, and just keep doing the chain rule the way we have defined it so far.

Let's start by looking at a simple example of the chain rule:

$$y = \sin(x^3)$$

To find the differential, we set $u = x^3$, giving us $y = \sin(u)$. The differential of this is:

$$\mathrm{d}y = \cos(u)\,\mathrm{d}u$$

To find $\mathrm{d}u$, we just take the differential of u:

$$\mathrm{d}u = 3x^2\,\mathrm{d}x$$

This gives us:

$$\mathrm{d}y = \cos(x^3)\,3x^2\,\mathrm{d}x$$

And the derivative is therefore:

$$\frac{dy}{dx} = \cos(x^3)\, 3x^2$$

Now, if we rewrite this in Newtonian notation, we get:

$$y' = \cos(x^3)\, 3x^2$$

Now, I want you to notice something. The original equation was $\sin(x^3)$. Notice that part of our answer is $\cos(x^3)$. This is the basic derivative rule for $\sin()$ alone, ignoring the fact that the inside is a *function* of x instead of x alone. This is then multiplied by $3x^2$. What is this? This is the derivative of the inside function!

So, in other words, to take a derivative of a composite function, you take the derivative of the outside function and multiply it by the derivative of the inside function.

This is often written like this:

$$\text{If} \quad y = f(g(x))$$

$$\text{Then} \quad y' = f'(g(x))g'(x)$$

So, for $y = \sin(x^3)$, we would say that $f(x) = \sin(x)$ and $g(x) = x^3$. Therefore, $f'(x) = \cos(x)$ and $g'(x) = 3x^2$. Using the chain rule, we can say:

$y = f(g(x))$	prerequisite for the chain rule
$y' = f'(g(x))g'(x)$	the chain rule itself
$y' = \sin(x^3)\, 3x^2$	substituting our own f, f', g, and g'

There is one other way of describing the chain rule that is also important. If you think about $y = \sin(x^3)$ we could set $u = x^3$ and therefor we would have $y = \sin(u)$. The *derivative* of this is $\frac{dy}{du} = \cos(u)$. However, if we take the derivative of $u = x^3$ we will have $\frac{du}{dx} = 3x^2$. The full derivative of the original equation is $\frac{dy}{dx}$. We currently have found $\frac{dy}{du}$ and $\frac{du}{dx}$. Therefore, to get the derivative we just multiple them together and the du terms will cancel each other out:

$$\frac{dy}{du} \cdot \frac{du}{dx} = \frac{dy}{dx} \tag{11.3}$$

Applying this equation, we can see that the final derivative will be our two derivatives multiplied together: $\frac{dy}{dx} = \cos(u)\, 3x^2$. Back-substituting $u = x^3$ will give us $\frac{dy}{dx} = \cos(x^3)\, 3x^2$.

I would suggest that you just use the chain rule in the way specified in the previous sections, but I thought it was important for you to know how other books do it as well, because you will see it referred to in advanced calculus and differential equations texts.

11.5   Composite Functions of Composite Functions

We have established that we can do u-substitution to solve for the derivative of composite functions. However, several students don't realize that if you have functions within functions within functions, you can keep doing u-substitution as many times as you need to in order to get the derivative.

The most important thing to remember is always perform the differential of the *outer function* first. That is what allows the chain rule to work.

Let's say we want to take the differential of $2^{\sin(x^2)}$. Here we have three functions: the exponent on the outside, the sine function within that, and a power within that. Remember, always look at the outer function first. The outer function is the exponent. So first, we say that $u = \sin(x^2)$. This will convert our outer function from a composite function into a simple function of u, 2^u.

We know that the differential of 2^u is $\ln(2)2^u\,du$. Now we need to find du.

So, if $u = \sin(x^2)$, then here, again, we have a composite function, and need to do a substitution to find the differential. Therefore, we will create another variable, v, and set $v = x^2$.

Now we can write u as a simple function of v: $u = \sin(v)$. Using our rule for the sine function, we can see that $du = d(\sin(v)) = \cos(v)dv$.

Now we have to find dv. Thankfully, v is already a simple function, so we don't need to do any more substituting to find the answer: $dv = d(x^2) = 2x\,dx$.

Now that we have everything solved, we can just substitute back in until we have everything we need. The outermost differential was $\ln(2)2^u\,du$. Since $u = \sin(x^2)$ and $du = \cos(v)dv$, if we substitute these back in, the differential becomes $\ln(2)2^{\sin(x^2)}\cos(v)dv$.

Now we need to substitute v and dv back in. Since $v = x^2$ and $dv = 2x\,dx$, then we get:

$$\ln(2)2^{\sin(x^2)}\cos(x^2)2x\,dx$$

—   Example 11.6

Find the differential of $\sin(x + y) = \cos(x + \sin(y^2))$

To start with, we will need substitutions for both the right and the left:

$$u = x + y$$
$$v = x + \sin(y^2)$$

This makes the equation look like this:

$$\sin(u) = \cos(v)$$

Now we will take the differential of both sides, giving:

$$\cos(u)\,du = -\sin(v)\,dv$$

Now we need to find du and dv:

$$u = x + y$$
$$du = dx + dy$$

To find dv we will need another substitution:

$$w = y^2$$

Now, we can find the differential of v:

$$v = x + \sin(w)$$
$$\mathrm{d}v = \mathrm{d}(x + \sin(w))$$
$$\mathrm{d}v = \mathrm{d}(x) + \mathrm{d}(\sin(w))$$
$$\mathrm{d}v = \mathrm{d}x + \cos(w)\,\mathrm{d}w$$

Finally, we can see that $\mathrm{d}w = 2y\,\mathrm{d}y$.

Below is the list of all of the equations we've done:

$$\cos(u)\,\mathrm{d}u = -\sin(v)\,\mathrm{d}v \qquad\qquad \text{the top-level differential}$$
$$u = x + y$$
$$\mathrm{d}u = \mathrm{d}x + \mathrm{d}y$$
$$v = x + \sin(w)$$
$$\mathrm{d}v = \mathrm{d}x + \cos(w)\,\mathrm{d}w$$
$$w = y^2$$
$$\mathrm{d}w = 2y\,\mathrm{d}y$$

If you substitute them all back in, you get:

$$\cos(u)\,\mathrm{d}u = -\sin(v)\,\mathrm{d}v \qquad\qquad \text{the top-level differential}$$
$$\cos(x + y)\,\mathrm{d}u = -\sin(x + \sin(w))\,\mathrm{d}v \qquad\qquad \text{replacing } u \text{ and } v$$
$$\cos(x + y)(\mathrm{d}x + \mathrm{d}y) = -\sin(x + \sin(w))(\mathrm{d}x + \cos(w)\,\mathrm{d}w) \qquad\qquad \text{replacing } \mathrm{d}u \text{ and } \mathrm{d}v$$
$$\cos(x + y)(\mathrm{d}x + \mathrm{d}y) = -\sin(x + \sin(y^2))(\mathrm{d}x + \cos(y^2)2y\,\mathrm{d}y) \qquad\qquad \text{replacing } w \text{ and } \mathrm{d}w$$

You could solve for the full derivative, but it might take you quite a bit of paper to isolate $\frac{\mathrm{d}y}{\mathrm{d}x}$ on one side.

The biggest place where students fall down on this is trying to do more than one step at a time. Just remember to do one function at a time, *outer function first*.

Also remember that in notations such as $sin^2(x)$ that really means $(sin(x))^2$, so the squaring is the outer function.

—   **Example 11.7**

Find the differential of $3^{\sin(x^2)}$.

First off, note that in this case we don't have a full equation. That's just fine! When working with differentials, you can find the differential of an expression without it being a part of an equation.

In this case, we have multiple composite functions. Therefore, we have to unwrap this a step at a time. When taking the differential of a function, you always work with the *outer functions first*! Otherwise, we would not be able to express it in terms of simple variables.

The outer function is the exponential function. Therefore, we will assing u to the exponent. So, our function becomes 3^u where $u = \sin(x^2)$.

Therefore, we now take the differential of 3^u:

$$d(3^u) = \ln(3)3^u \, du$$

So what is du?

We have $u = \sin(x^2)$. Therefore, to find du we need to take the differential. However, u is itself a composite function. Therefore, we need to find the next outer function, which is $\sin()$. This means that we need to create a substitution for the inner function. So we will introduce a new variable, v, such that $v = x^2$. Now we can write $u = \sin(v)$, which is a function for which we can find the differential, using the rule given at the start of this example:

$$u = \sin(v)$$
$$d(u) = d(\sin(v))$$
$$du = \cos(v) \, dv$$

Now we have du, but it introduced a new term, dv. So, again, we will need to find dv. Since $v = x^2$ we can use the power rule to find that:

$$dv = 2x \, dx$$

Finally, we have all of the parts of our differential in terms of x and dx. Therefore, we can go back through and substitute everything.

$d(3^u) = \ln(3)3^u \, du$	the top-level differential
$= \ln(3)3^{sin(x^2)} \, du$	substituting u back in
$= \ln(3)3^{sin(x^2)} \cos(v) \, dv$	substituing du back in
$= \ln(3)3^{sin(x^2)} \cos(x^2) \, dv$	substituting v back in
$= \ln(3)3^{sin(x^2)} \cos(x^2)2x \, dx$	substituting dv back in

Now we have the differential entirely in terms of x and dx.

As you can see, as the number of composite functions grows, there are more and more steps, but each step is basically the same—create a substitution so that the outermost function is a simple function, take the differential of the simple function, and substitute back in. Repeat this process until you have everything in terms of the original variables and the differentials of the original variables.

Review

In this chapter, we learned:

1. In equations, we can always substitute a variable for a complicated term in order to simplify the equation, as long as we do so consistently.

2. If we make a substitution, we must remember to substitute the original expression back in for the final solution.

3. The rules that we use for making differentials can only be combined using specific rules.

4. A differential for a composite function can be found by converting it into a simple function by substitution.

5. A composite function can be converted into a simple one by merely creating a new variable (often u) to stand in for the inner expression. This is known as u-substitution.

6. Remember when taking the differential of an expression with u that the result will have a du term, *not* a dx term.

7. After finding the result in terms of du, the equation setting the value for u can then be differentiated to find the replacement for du, and both u and du can be substituted back into the equation.

8. For composite functions of composite functions, this process may have to go several levels deep before you finally arrive at a simple function of x and dx (or whatever your original variable(s) were).

9. Because this rules chains together differentials of different functions, it is often called the chain rule.

10. When taking the differential of a complicated expression, always remember to take the differential of the outer function first.

11. Using these rules can also allow you to take differentials of implicit functions (equations where x and y intermingle) as well as functions of several variables.

Exercises

Find the differential:

1. $y = 3x^2 + 6x + 5$

2. $y = 2^{3x} - 20x$

3. $y = \sin(x) + 6x^2$

4. $y = \sin(3x^5)$

5. $\sin(x + y) = x^2$

6. $y = \sin(3^{x^5})$

7. $\sin(x - \cos(x^2)) = e^{x-y}$

Find the derivative:

8. $y = x^3 + 2x^2 + 5x + 10$

9. $y^3 - x^2 = 3x$

10. $\sin(x^2) = y$

11. $\sin(y - 2) = \cos(x^2)$

12. $\cos(3^x) = 5y^2$

13. $y = 3^{x^2 + 5x}$

14. $\sin(x - 3y) = 2^x$

15. $\sin(x^3) = x^2 + 5x + \cos(y - 6)$

Chapter 12

Additional Differential Rules

This chapter is the last chapter to explicitly introduce new differential rules. After this chapter, for any additional rule you need, you can consult the rules in Appendix H.6.

12.1 The Product Rule

The product rule is a rule for taking the differential of two or more functions multiplied together. Let's say, for instance, that we want to take the differential of $3x \cdot 2^x$. We know how to take the differential of both $3x$ and 2^x, but what about when you multiply them together?

The product rule tells us how to multiply together two functions. The form of the product rule is:

$$d(uv) = u\,dv + v\,du \tag{12.1}$$

Here, we are doing *two* substitutions, because we have two functions. Therefore, we use u for one function, and v for the other function. Therefore, for $d(3x \cdot 2^x)$ we would say:

$$u = 3x$$
$$v = 2^x$$

Now our differential is just $d(uv)$. According to the rule in Equation 12.1, we can write this as:

$$d(uv) = u\,dv + v\,du$$

We know what u and v are (since we just defined them), but what are du and dv? We will have to take the differentials of u and v to find out. First we will find the differential of u:

$$u = 3x$$
$$d(u) = d(3x)$$
$$du = 3\,dx$$

145

Then the differential of v:

$$v = 2^x$$

$$\mathrm{d}(v) = \mathrm{d}(2^x)$$

$$\mathrm{d}v = \ln(2)\, 2^x\, \mathrm{d}x$$

Now, we can combine these back into the original equation and find out that:

$$\mathrm{d}(uv) = u\, \mathrm{d}v + v\, \mathrm{d}u$$

$$= (3x)(\ln(2)\, 2^x\, \mathrm{d}x) + (2^x)(3\, \mathrm{d}x)$$

$$= 3\ln(2)\, x\, 2^x\, \mathrm{d}x + 3 \cdot 2^x\, \mathrm{d}x$$

Interestingly, we can actually prove the constant multiplier rule from the product rule. The constant multiplier rule is just like the product rule, except that one of the functions is a constant function.

The constant multiplier rule say sthat $\mathrm{d}(nx) = n\, \mathrm{d}x$. Let's use the product rule to prove it to be true:

$\mathrm{d}(nx) = n\, \mathrm{d}(x) + \mathrm{d}(n)\, x$	the product rule
$\mathrm{d}(x) = \mathrm{d}x$	the definition of a differential
$\mathrm{d}(n) = 0$	the constant rule for differentials
$\mathrm{d}(nx) = n\, \mathrm{d}x + 0 \cdot x$	replacing
$= n\, \mathrm{d}x + 0$	simplifying
$= n\, \mathrm{d}x$	

So, as you can see, the constant multiplier rule is just a special case of the product rule.

—   Example 12.1

Find the derivative of $y = x\,\sin(x)$.

Here, x is being multipled by $\sin(x)$. Therefore, we can use the product rule:

$$y = x\,\sin(x)$$

$$u = x$$

$$v = \sin(x)$$

$$y = uv$$

$$\mathrm{d}(y) = \mathrm{d}(uv)$$

$$\mathrm{d}y = u\, \mathrm{d}v + v\, \mathrm{d}u$$

$$u = x$$

$$\mathrm{d}u = \mathrm{d}x$$

$$v = \sin(x)$$

$$\mathrm{d}v = \cos(x)\, \mathrm{d}x$$

$$\mathrm{d}y = u\, \mathrm{d}v + v\, \mathrm{d}u$$

$$dy = x \cos(x) \, dx + \sin(x) \, dx$$

$$\frac{dy}{dx} = x \cos(x) + \sin(x)$$

Additionally, if you have three terms multiplied by each other, you can simple use the associative rules of multiplication to break it out into multiple applications of the product rule. See the below example.

— **Example 12.2**

Find the derivative of $y = 2^x \, 3^x x^2$.

To find this derivative, we will have to choose which terms we group together for our first application of the product rule. We could group and of them together, but we will choose to put $3^x x^2$ together to solve this:

$$y = 2^x \, 3^x x^2$$

$$d(y) = d(2^x \, 3^x x^2)$$

$$d(y) = d((2^x)(3^x x^2))$$

$$u = 2^x$$

$$v = (3^x x^2)$$

$$d(y) = d(uv)$$

$$dy = u \, dv + v \, du$$

$$du = \ln(2)2^x \, dx$$

$$dv = ?$$

Now, at this point, we have to find dv. To do that, we will have to apply the product rule again:

$$v = (3^x x^2)$$

$$w = 3^x$$

$$dw = \ln(3)3^x \, dx$$

$$z = x^2$$

$$dz = 2x \, dx$$

$$v = (wz)$$

$$dv = w \, dz + z \, dw$$

$$dv = (3^x)(2x \, dx) + (x^2)(\ln(3)3^x \, dx)$$

Now, we can take that dv back into our original differential:

$$dy = u\,dv + v\,du$$

$$dy = (2^x)((3^x)(2x\,dx) + (x^2)(\ln(3)3^x\,dx)) + (3^x x^2)(\ln(2)2^x\,dx)$$

$$dy = (2^x)(3^x)(2x\,dx) + (2^x)(x^2)(\ln(3)3^x\,dx) + (3^x x^2)(\ln(2)2^x\,dx)$$

$$\frac{dy}{dx} = 2^x 3^x 2x + 2^x x^2 \ln(3)3^x + 3^x x^2 \ln(2)2^x$$

And that is the derivative.

12.2   The Quotient Rule

Another similar rule is the quotient rule, which is used for any function divided by another function.

The quotient rule is:

$$d\left(\frac{u}{v}\right) = \frac{v\,du - u\,dv}{v^2} \tag{12.2}$$

Similar to the product rule, the quotient rule uses both u and v for substituting.

To see how this works, let's look at a simple problem:

$$y = \frac{x^2}{\sin(x)}$$

First, we will use u-substitution to reduce this to the quotient rule. We will set $u = x^2$ and $v = \sin(x)$. That means that $du = 2x\,dx$ and $dv = \cos(x)\,dx$.

Now, our equation becomes simply:

$$y = \frac{u}{v}$$

If we take the differential of both sides, this becomes:

$$y = \frac{u}{v}$$

$$d(y) = d\left(\frac{u}{v}\right)$$

$$dy = \frac{v\,du - u\,dv}{v^2}$$

Now we can substitute our *u*s and *v*s back in to arrive at the solution:

$$dy = \frac{v\,du - u\,dv}{v^2}$$

$$dy = \frac{\sin(x)\,2x\,dx - x^2\cos(x)\,dx}{\sin^2(x)}$$

$$dy = \frac{2x\sin(x)\,dx - x^2\cos(x)\,dx}{\sin^2(x)}$$

$$\frac{dy}{dx} = \frac{2x\sin(x) - x^2\cos(x)}{\sin^2(x)}$$

As you can see, the quotient rule is straightforward, but takes a lot of work.

— Example 12.3

Find the derivative of the equation $y = \frac{x^2 - 3x}{5^x}$.

To solve this, we will need to use the quotient rule:

$$y = \frac{x^2 - 3x}{5^x} \qquad\qquad \text{the original equation}$$

$$d(y) = d\left(\frac{x^2 - 3x}{5^x}\right) \qquad\qquad \text{take the differential of both sides}$$

$$u = x^2 - 3x \qquad\qquad \text{make substitutions}$$

$$du = 2x\,dx - 3\,dx \qquad\qquad \text{find the differential of } u$$

$$v = 5^x$$

$$dv = \ln(5)5^x\,dx \qquad\qquad \text{find the differential of } v$$

$$d(y) = d\left(\frac{u}{v}\right) \qquad\qquad \text{substitute back into the equation}$$

$$dy = \frac{v\,du - u\,dv}{v^2} \qquad\qquad \text{apply the quotient rule}$$

$$dy = \frac{5^x(2x\,dx - 3\,dx) - (x^2 - 3x)\ln(5)5^x\,dx}{(5^x)^2} \qquad\qquad \text{substitute everything back in}$$

$$dy = \frac{5^x(2x - 3)\,dx - (x^2 - 3x)\ln(5)5^x\,dx}{5^{2x}} \qquad\qquad \text{simplify the denominator and factor out } dx$$

$$dy = \frac{(5^x(2x - 3) - (x^2 - 3x)\ln(5)5^x)\,dx}{5^{2x}}$$

$$\frac{dy}{dx} = \frac{(5^x(2x - 3) - (x^2 - 3x)\ln(5)5^x)}{5^{2x}} \qquad\qquad \text{divide both sides by } dx$$

12.3   The Generalized Power Rule

The generalized power rule is used for any exponential function where both the base and the exponent are functions of *x*. Note that the power rule and the exponent rule are both special cases of this rule when the base or the exponent are constants instead of being in terms of a variable.

The generalized power rule states:

$$d(u^v) = vu^{v-1}du + \ln(u)u^v dv \qquad (12.3)$$

The following equation has a function of variable raised to another function of a variable:

$$y = (2x)^{x-2}$$

Therefore, we can use the generalized power rule to find the derivative:

$$y = (2x)^{x-2}$$ the original equation

$$d(y) = d((2x)^{x-2})$$ take the differential of both sides

$$u = 2x$$ find u and v for substitutions

$$du = 2dx$$

$$v = x - 2$$

$$dv = dx - 0 = dx$$

$$d(y) = d(u^v)$$ substituting in u and v

$$dy = vu^{v-1}du + u^v \ln(u)dv$$ the generalized power rule

$$dy = (x-2)(2x)^{x-2-1}2\,dx + \ln(2x)(2x)^{x-2}dx$$ substituting back in

$$\frac{dy}{dx} = 2(x-2)(2x)^{x-3} + ln(2x)(2x)^{x-2}$$ divide by dx and simplify

12.4   Using the Differential Rules in the Appendix

In Chapter 11 and this chapter, you have worked with u, v, and other variables as substitutes for functions of a variable. Now that you are proficient at doing substitutions with u and v, you are now ready to use the appendix to look up the differential rules for functions you do not know. All of the differential rules needed for this course (plus a few extra) are given in Appendix H.6.

To use the table, all you need to do is to figure out what function you are needing the differential of, and look it up in the table. The table of differentials always gives the differential in terms of u, v, du, and dv to make it more obvious that you can use u-substitution to find the differential.

Let's find the derivative of the equation $y = \tan(x^2)$.

If we start by taking the differential, we will get dy on the left, but what is the differential of $\tan(x^2)$?

At this point you need to recognize that you have a function that you need the differential of—tan. This is complicated by the fact that not only do we need to find the differential of tan, it has an inner function that we have to worry about as well, x^2. Therefore, we need to make a substitution with $u = x^2$, which gives us $dy = d(\tan(u))$.

Now, we look it up in the table of differentials, and we can see a rule that says $d(\tan(u)) = -\sec^2(u)\,du$.

Now our equation is:

$$dy = -\sec^2(u)\,du$$

To finish the problem, we need to substitute back in both u and its differential, du. Using the power rule, we can quite easily see that $du = 2x\,dx$. Substituting back in, we get the following:

$$dy = -\sec^2(x^2)2x\,dx$$

Dividing both sides by dx will give us the derivative:

$$\frac{dy}{dx} = -\sec^2(x^2)2x\,dx$$

— Example 12.4

Find the derivative of $y = \tan(x^2) + \sin(3x) + 4x$.

$y = \tan(x^2) + \sin(3x) + 4x$ the original equation

$d(y) = d(\tan(x^2) + \sin(3x) + 4x)$ take the differential of both sides

$dy = d(\tan(x^2)) + d(\sin(3x)) + d(4x)$ the addition rule

$dy = d(\tan(x^2)) + d(\sin(3x)) + 4dx$ constant multiplier rule

At this point, we have taken it as far as we can go with the rules we have memorized. Now we need to figure out how to do each part using the rules in the appendix.

First we will look at $d(\tan(x^2))$. We will make the subsitution $u = x^2$ to simplify that expression to $d(\tan(u))$. The table of differentials says that $d(\tan(u)) = \sec^2(u)\,du$. The power rule tells us that $du = 2x\,dx$. Therefore, substituting back in for u and du, we get:

$$d(\tan(x^2)) = \sec^2(x^2)2x\,dx$$

Next we need to look at $d(\sin(3x))$.

We can say that $v = 3x$, which gives us $d(\sin(v))$. The table of differentials says that $d(\sin(v)) = \cos(v)\,dv$. To find dv we can take the differential of our equation for v, giving us $dv = 3\,dx$. Therefore, we can say:

$$d(\sin(3x)) = \cos(3x)3, dx$$

Substituting everything back in, we get:

$$dy = \sec^2(x^2)2xdx + \cos(3x)3\,dx + 4\,dx$$

$$dy = 2x\sec^2(x^2)\,dx + 3\cos(3x)\,dx + 4\,dx$$

$$\frac{dy}{dx} = \sec^2(x^2)2x + 3\cos(3x) + 4$$

So, now that you know the chain rule and you know how to use the table of derivatives in the back, you can now take the derivative of *any* equation that is composed of these functions.

Even though there is a nice table of differentials in the Appendix H.6, you should memorize all of the differentials listed in the section titled "Differentials of Basic Functions." From the section titled "Differentials of Trigonometric Functions," you should memorize the differentials of sin, cos, and tan.

When using the table, note that u and v both can refer to entire functions, while n and C refer to *constants only*. Therefore, if you have the expression x^y you *cannot* use the formula for u^n or n^u, because n refers to a constant, not a function. Therefore, for x^y you would have to refer to the formula for u^v, since both u and v represent actual functions.

Also note that, when looking at the formulas, that there may be an implicit constant in your expression.

For instance, if you were needing the differential of arcsin(x), then you would use the formula for arcsin $\left(\frac{u}{n}\right)$ and just set $u = x$ and set $n = 1$.

—   Example 12.5

Find the derivative of $\ln(2y) = \csc(x^2)$.

To find the derivative, first we take the differential of both sides:

$$\ln(2y) = \csc(x^2)$$

$$d(\ln(2y)) = d(\csc(x^2))$$

On the left, we are looking for the differential of the natural log function. If we do u-substitution, that gives us $u = 2y$, and we need to find the differential of $\ln(u)$. In the back of the book it says that the differential is $\frac{du}{u}$. Therefore we need to also find du, which will be $2\,dy$. Therefore, the left side becomes $\frac{2\,dy}{2y}$ or just $\frac{dy}{y}$.

On the right we are looking for the differential of the cosecant of x^2, or d($\csc(x^2)$). We can make a substitution $v = x^2$ (and therefore d$v = 2x\,dx$), which will convert that to d($\csc(v)$).

In the table of differentials, there is an entry for $\csc(u)$. As you should realize, even though the table lists it for u, it works just the same if it is $\csc(v)$. The table says that d($\csc(v)$) will give us $-\csc(v)\cot(v)\,dv$. If we substitute v and dv back in, that gives us:

$$-\csc(x^2)2x\,dx$$

Putting these two parts together, we can solve for the derivative:

$$\frac{dy}{y} = -\csc(x^2)2x\,dx$$

$$\frac{dy}{dx} = -2xy\,\csc(x^2)$$

—   Example 12.6

Find the derivative of $y = \cos(x^2 + \sin^2(x + \ln(3x))) + x^{\sin(x)}$

This is a really long and hard example. The point of this is not that most derivatives are this hard—most of them are much easier. However, I want to show that using just these rules, it doesn't matter how complex the equation is, we have the tools to take the derivative.

If you get lost in this example, that's okay. But if you can work through it, it will help you to see that it is just the same process over and over and over again.

$$y = \cos(x^2 + \sin^2(x + \ln(3x))) + x^{\sin(x)} \qquad \text{the original equation}$$

$$d(y) = d(\cos(x^2 + \sin^2(x + \ln(3x))) + x^{\sin(x)}) \qquad \text{take the differential of both sides}$$

$$dy = d(\cos(x^2 + \sin^2(x + \ln(3x)))) + d(x^{\sin(x)}) \qquad \text{break it apart using the addition rule}$$

Note that the amount of work that the addition rule can do is pretty limited. We can only apply rules to the outermost functions. We can't apply the addition rule to the inside of the cosine yet.

Next, we will use variable substitutions to simplify the problem:

$$u = x^2 + \sin^2(x + \ln(3x))$$

$$v = \sin(x)$$

$$dy = d(\cos(u)) + d(x^v) \qquad \text{use variable substitutions so we can take the differential of simple functions}$$

$$dy = -\sin(u)du + vx^{v-1}dx + x^v \ln(x)dv \qquad \text{solved using basic differential rules}$$

$$d(v) = d(\sin(x)) \qquad \text{solve for } dv$$

$$dv = \cos(x)\,dx$$

$$d(u) = d(x^2 + \sin^2(x + \ln(3x))) \qquad \text{solve for } du$$

$$du = d(x^2) + d(\sin^2(x + \ln(3x))) \qquad \text{use the addition rule to break up terms}$$

$$w = \sin(x + \ln(3x)) \qquad \text{create a new variable for doing deeper substitutions}$$

$$du = d(x^2) + d(w^2) \qquad \text{substitute using a new variable}$$

$$du = 2x\,dx + 2wdw \qquad \text{power rule}$$

$$d(w) = d(\sin(x + \ln(3x))) \qquad \text{solve for } dw$$

$$z = x + \ln(3x)$$

$$dw = d(\sin(z)) \qquad \text{substitute with a new variable}$$

$$dw = \cos(z)dz \qquad \text{differential of } \sin(z)$$

$$d(z) = d(x + \ln(3x) \qquad \text{find the differential of } z$$

$$dz = d(x) + d(\ln(3x)) \qquad \text{addition rule}$$

$$q = 3x \qquad \text{substitute with a new variable}$$

$$dz = d(x) + d(\ln(q))$$

$$dz = dx + \frac{dq}{q} \qquad \text{use the natural log rule from the appendix}$$

$$dq = 3\,dx$$

Now that we have everything differentiated out all of the way, we can now substitute back in. Unfortunately, this will get pretty long. Remember, this isn't meant to scare you, it's just mean to show you that the method works no matter how complicated the equation is.

Each of these will substitute back in for more and more variables until we have the final answer in terms of x and dx:

$$dy = -\sin(u)du + vx^{v-1}dx + x^v \ln(x)dv$$

$$dy = -\sin(x^2 + \sin^2(x + \ln(3x)))(2xdx + 2wdw)+$$

$$\sin(x)x^{\sin(x)-1}dx + x^{\sin(x)} \ln(x)\cos(x)dx$$

$$dy = -\sin(x^2 + \sin^2(x + \ln(3x)))(2xdx + 2\sin(x + \ln(3x))\cos(z)dz)+$$

$$\sin(x)x^{\sin(x)-1}dx + x^{\sin(x)} \ln(x)\cos(x)dx$$

$$dy = -\sin(x^2 + \sin^2(x + \ln(3x)))(2xdx + 2\sin(x + \ln(3x))\cos(x + \ln(3x))(dx + \frac{dq}{q}))+$$

$$\sin(x)x^{\sin(x)-1}dx + x^{\sin(x)} \ln(x)\cos(x)dx$$

$$dy = -\sin(x^2 + \sin^2(x + \ln(3x)))(2xdx + 2\sin(x + \ln(3x))\cos(x + \ln(3x))(dx + \frac{3dx}{3x}))+$$

$$\sin(x)x^{\sin(x)-1}dx + x^{\sin(x)} \ln(x)\cos(x)dx$$

$$\frac{dy}{dx} = -\sin(x^2 + \sin^2(x + \ln(3x)))(2x + 2\sin(x + \ln(3x))\cos(x + \ln(3x))(1 + \frac{1}{x}))+$$

$$\sin(x)x^{\sin(x)-1} + x^{\sin(x)} \ln(x)\cos(x)$$

As you can see, you can solve for the derivative of equations combining *any* combination of the functions in Appendix H.6, as long as you are patient enough to do it a step at a time.

12.5   A Note on Implicit Derivatives

An implicit derivative is the derivative of an equation where the variables are intermixed on both sides of the equation. The rules we have shown work just fine for implicit derivatives, but, occasionally, if you rewrite the equation you can get different derivatives. Such derivatives are not technically wrong, even though they are different equations. For the points that are valid on the original equation, the different derivatives will be the same. They may not be the same for points outside of the original equation.

For example, the equation of a unit circle is $x^2 + y^2 = 1$. A direct application of our rules would give the following:

$$x^2 + y^2 = 1$$

$$2x\,dx + 2y\,dy = 0$$

$$2y\,dy = -2x\,dx$$

$$\frac{dy}{dx} = \frac{-x}{y}$$

That is a correct derivative for the equation. However, I could also solve the original equation for y and then do the derivative. That would give me:

$$x^2 + y^2 = 1$$
$$y^2 = 1 - x^2$$
$$y = \sqrt{1 - x^2}$$
$$y = (1 - x^2)^{\frac{1}{2}}$$
$$u = 1 - x^2$$
$$du = -2x\,dx$$
$$y = u^{\frac{1}{2}}$$
$$dy = \frac{1}{2}u^{\frac{-1}{2}}\,du$$
$$dy = \frac{1}{2}(1 - x^2)^{\frac{-1}{2}}(-2x\,dx)$$
$$dy = (1 - x^2)^{\frac{-1}{2}}(-x\,dx)$$
$$dy = \frac{-x}{\sqrt{1 - x^2}}\,dx$$
$$\frac{dy}{dx} = \frac{-x}{\sqrt{1 - x^2}}$$

Now, this looks a lot different than our original equation, but, for the points that are valid on our original equation, they are the same.

For instance, take the point $(0, 1)$. This is a valid point on our original graph. Likewise, both derivative formulas will give me the same result—zero. However, take the point $(2, 2)$. The first derivative formula will give me a slope of -1, while the second derivative formula (if I just use the x value since there is no y in the formula) won't give me a slope at all. But that's not a problem because $(2, 2)$ isn't a valid point on our original equation!

So, on complicated implicit derivatives, it is possible to get results that vary from the "official" solution, yet still be correct where the function is defined. To get your answers to match the solution guide, you should generally just differentiate the given formula or equation as-is, without manipulating it first. That should give you resulting equations and formulas which match the solution guide.

12.6 Proofs of Differential Rules

We haven't focused too much on proving any but the most basic derivative rules. However, I personally find the proofs of these quite fascinating. If this is an interest of yours, I have put the proofs of most of the basic functions in Appendix F.

Review

In this chapter, we learned:

1. The Product Rule allows us to take the differential of two functions multiplied together.

2. The Quotient Rule allows us to take the differential of a function divided by another function.

3. The Generalized Power Rule allows us to take the differential of a function raised to the power of another function.

4. Combining the chain rule with a table of differentials such as those found in Appendix H.6 will allow you to take the differential (and likewise the derivative) of any equation using any combination of those functions.

Exercises

Find the differential (you don't need to simplify):

1. $y = x \cdot 2^x$

2. $y^2 = x^3\, 4^x$

3. $y^x = 3x^2$

4. $y = \frac{x^2 - 3}{x^4 + 5}$

5. $\frac{y}{x} = x^2$

6. $y^2\, x^2 = e^x$

7. $x^{y-5x} = 2xy$

8. $3xy^2 = 5$

Find the derivative:

9. $x^{x^2} = xy$

10. $y^x = 3x^2 + 6x$

Use the derivative tables in Appendix H.6 to perform the following derivatives:

11. $y = \sec(x^2)$

12. $\ln(y) = \cos(x)$

13. $y = \cot(\ln(x))$

14. $\sin(y) = \log_4(x^2)$

15. $y^2 = \sec(x^2 + \ln(x))$

16. $xy = \arccos(x^2)$

17. $\sin(x) = \log_y(x^2)$

18. $\frac{\tan(y^2)}{x^3} = 5$

19. Find the minimum value (both x and y) of the equation $y = 3^{x^2 + x}$. You can assume that the minima occurs at the only local extremum.

Chapter 13

Multivariable Differentials

So far, the differentials and derivatives we have used rely on two variables—usually x and y. However, most problems in the real world have more variables, and more interesting names for their variables. The nice thing is that all of the rules that you have learned that govern x, y, dy, and dx apply exactly the same to equations with multiple variables.

Therefore, this chapter is largely review—just practicing the cases when we have more than two variables, and thinking about it more explicitly.

13.1   Differentials with Multiple Variables

Let's say that we have the equation $y = x^2 + z^3 + 2^m$.

Using the addition rule, we can separate this out as follows:

$$y = x^2 + z^3 + 2^m$$
$$d(y) = d(x^2 + z^3 + 2^m) \qquad \text{take the differential of both sides}$$
$$d(y) = d(x^2) + d(z^3) + d(2^m) \qquad \text{addition rule}$$

Note that at this point, each differential has a different variable contained within it. Therefore, solving this is now no different than solving any other differential:

$$d(y) = d(x^2) + d(z^3) + d(2^m)$$
$$dy = 2x\,dx + 3z^2\,dz + \ln(2)2^m\,dm \qquad \text{applying our differential rules to each term}$$

So, because we are taking the differentials of each piece, working with multiple variables becomes a piece of cake.

So what does this equation *mean*? It means that the amount of change in y is dependent on not only these other variables but also the amount that they are changing as well.

13.2   Solving for the Derivative

So, we were able to take the differential of the function, but what about the *derivative*? In equations we have looked at so far, the derivative is usually expressed as $\frac{dy}{dx}$. However, in this case, there are so many variables each with differentials. What is the derivative in this case?

The derivative is merely the ratio of the changes of two values. Usually it is dy and dx we are interested in, but it could be any two differentials. So, to be true to our form, let's solve this for $\frac{dy}{dx}$. All we need to do is divide both sides by dx:

$$dy = 2x\,dx + 3z^2\,dz + \ln(2)2^m\,dm$$

$$\frac{dy}{dx} = 2x + 3z^2\,\frac{dz}{dx} + \ln(2)2^m\,\frac{dm}{dx}$$

When you solve for $\frac{dy}{dx}$, you say it as "the derivative of y with respect to x."

Now, we isolated $\frac{dy}{dx}$, but it left over a lot of other differentials on the other side of the equation. What does that mean? It means that the amount of change between dy and dx is dependent upon the amount of change in all of the other variables with respect to x as well.

When you add a third variable into an equation, it is like adding in a third dimension to a graph. The curves along the surface that your equation defines can be complicated, and the slope between any two dimensions will largely depend on the slope between the other dimensions. When you have more than three variables, you are in the same situation (the slope between any two variables is dependent on the other slopes), but you are no longer in a situation where you can imagine what the graph looks like.

We can solve for other derivatives as well. Let's say we wanted to know the derivative of y with respect to m. We would just solve for $\frac{dy}{dm}$ like this:

$$dy = 2x\,dx + 3z^2\,dz + \ln(2)2^m\,dm$$

$$\frac{dy}{dm} = 2x\,\frac{dx}{dm} + 3z^2\,\frac{dz}{dm} + ln(2)2^m$$

There is also no necessary reason why we need to find the derivative of y. We can find the derivative of z with respect to m (i.e., $\frac{dz}{dm}$). That would look like this:

$$dy = 2x\,dx + 3z^2\,dz + \ln(2)2^m\,dm$$

$$dy - 2x\,dx - \ln(2)2^m\,dm = 3z^2\,dz$$

$$\frac{1}{3z^2}\,\frac{dy}{dm} - \frac{2x}{3z^2}\,\frac{dx}{dm} - \frac{\ln(2)2^m}{3z^2} = \frac{dz}{dm}$$

As you can see, for equations of multiple variables, the rules are just the same, there are just more options for things that we can solve for.

You may be wondering why we wrote our final answer the way we did. Normally, doing cross-division, we might leave our final answer like this:

$$\frac{dy - 2x\,dx - \ln(2)2^m\,dm}{3z^2\,dm} = \frac{dz}{dm}$$

The answer is that, by separating out the pieces of the top fraction, we can explicitly get our answer in terms of other derivatives. The equation above tells us about $\frac{dz}{dm}$ in terms of differentials, but it doesn't help a lot because we rarely use differentials by themselves. If this were a physical system we were monitoring, we probably are better able to measure changes with respect to other changes rather than absolute differentials.

That is, we are more likely to make use of quantities like $\frac{dy}{dm}$ than we are to make use of dy or dm separately. Therefore, when we solve for a derivative, we usually like to divide things out in such a way that the terms on the other side include derivatives themselves rather than bare differentials.

— Example 13.1

Find the differential of $y^2 - 3g^2 = x^3 + z^8 + 5q^2 4$, and then find the derivative of z with respect to q.

First, we will find the differential:

$$y^2 - 3g^2 = x^3 + z^8 + 5q^2 4$$

$$\mathrm{d}(y^2 - 3g^2) = \mathrm{d}(x^3 + z^8 + 5q^{24}) \qquad \text{differentiate both sides}$$

$$\mathrm{d}(y^2) - \mathrm{d}(3g^2) = \mathrm{d}(x^3) + \mathrm{d}(z^8) + \mathrm{d}(5q^{24}) \qquad \text{addition rule}$$

$$2y\,\mathrm{d}y - 6g\,\mathrm{d}g = 3x^2\,\mathrm{d}x + 8z^7\,\mathrm{d}z + 120q^{23}\,\mathrm{d}q \qquad \text{power rule}$$

That is the differential. The question was to find "the derivative of z with respect to q." This means we need to solve for $\frac{dz}{dq}$:

$$2y\,\mathrm{d}y - 6g\,\mathrm{d}g = 3x^2\,\mathrm{d}x + 8z^7\,\mathrm{d}z + 120q^{23}\,\mathrm{d}q \qquad \text{our starting differential}$$

$$8z^7\,\mathrm{d}z = 2y\,\mathrm{d}y - 6g\,\mathrm{d}g - 3x^2\,\mathrm{d}x - 120q^{23}\,\mathrm{d}q \qquad \text{get } \mathrm{d}z \text{ by itself}$$

$$\frac{\mathrm{d}z}{\mathrm{d}q} = \frac{2y}{8z^7}\frac{\mathrm{d}y}{\mathrm{d}q} - \frac{6g}{8z^7}\frac{\mathrm{d}g}{\mathrm{d}q} - \frac{120q^{23}}{8z^7} \qquad \text{cross-divide to find } \frac{\mathrm{d}z}{\mathrm{d}q}$$

13.3 Functions of Two or More Variables

Just like we can use the addition rule to split up differentials of multiple variables, and then tackle them separately, we can also use any rule that we have used for functions of x and use them on actual multivariable equations.

For instance, let's look at the differential of the following equation:

$$zx = xy + yz$$

In this case, we have variables multiplied by each other. This can be solved simply by applying the product rule, just as we have always applied it. The only difference is that we will indeed wind up with multiple variables and differentials at the end.

$$zx = xy + yz \qquad \text{the original equation}$$

$$\mathrm{d}(zx) = \mathrm{d}(xy + yz) \qquad \text{take the differential of both sides}$$

$$\mathrm{d}(zx) = \mathrm{d}(xy) + \mathrm{d}(yz) \qquad \text{the addition rule}$$

$$z\,\mathrm{d}x + x\,\mathrm{d}z = (x\,\mathrm{d}y + y\,\mathrm{d}x) + (y\,\mathrm{d}z + z\,\mathrm{d}y) \qquad \text{the product rule}$$

$$z\,\mathrm{d}x + x\,\mathrm{d}z = x\,\mathrm{d}y + y\,\mathrm{d}x + y\,\mathrm{d}z + z\,\mathrm{d}y \qquad \text{ungrouped}$$

Now that we have the differentials, we can solve for the derivative. However, as we saw in the last section, with three variables there are a number of derivatives we could solve for. If we wanted to know how fast y was changing with respect to x, we can solve for $\frac{dy}{dx}$. But we could also find out how fast z was changing with respect to y by solving for $\frac{dz}{dy}$.

Let's solve for $\frac{dz}{dy}$ and see what it looks like:

$$z\,dx + x\,dz = x\,dy + y\,dx + y\,dz + z\,dy \qquad\qquad \text{the differential}$$

$$z\frac{dx}{dy} + x\frac{dz}{dy} = y\frac{dx}{dy} + y\frac{dz}{dy} + z \qquad\qquad \text{divide both sides by } dy$$

$$x\frac{dz}{dy} = y\frac{dx}{dy} + y\frac{dz}{dy} + z - z\frac{dx}{dy} \qquad\qquad \text{subtract } z\frac{dx}{dy} \text{ from both sides}$$

$$x\frac{dz}{dy} - y\frac{dz}{dy} = y\frac{dx}{dy} + z - z\frac{dx}{dy} \qquad\qquad \text{subtract } y\frac{dz}{dy} \text{ from both sides}$$

$$(x - y)\frac{dz}{dy} = (y - z)\frac{dx}{dy} + z \qquad\qquad \text{factor both sides}$$

$$\frac{dz}{dy} = \frac{y - z}{x - y}\frac{dx}{dy} + \frac{z}{x - y} \qquad\qquad \text{divide both sides by } x - y$$

This solves for $\frac{dz}{dy}$ like we wanted. As we saw in the previous section, the right-hand side still has differentials in it. This is because the slope of $\frac{dz}{dy}$ depends not only on the specific x, y, and z positions of the point, but also on the slope $\frac{dx}{dy}$. This is common in equations with more than two variables. The answer will usually be not only in terms of the variables, but also in terms of the *other slopes between the variables.*

——   Example 13.2

Find the derivative of y with respect to x for the equation $\sin(y) = x^2 + x\,\cos(z) - xz^2$.

$$\sin(y) = x^2 + x\,\cos(z) - xz^2 \qquad\qquad \text{original equation}$$

$$d(\sin(y)) = d(x^2 + x\,\cos(z) - xz^2) \qquad\qquad \text{take the differential of both sides}$$

$$d(\sin(y)) = d(x^2) + d(x\,\cos(z)) - d(xz^2) \qquad\qquad \text{addition rule}$$

Now to find the differential of the term $x\,\cos(z)$ we need to use the product rule, which says that $d(uv) = u\,dv + v\,du$. The differential of x is just dx and the differential of $\cos(z)$ is $-\sin(z)\,dz$. Therefore, the differential of the term becomes $(x)(-\sin(z)\,dz) + (\cos(z)(dx)$. We can write it more naturally as $-x\,\sin(z)\,dz + \cos(z)\,dz$.

Likewise the term xz^2 can be differentiated using the product rule. The differential of x is dx and the differential of z^2 is $2z\,dz$. Therefore, the differential of the term becomes $(x)(2z\,dz) + (z^2)(dx)$. Written more naturally, this becomes $2xz\,dz + z^2\,dx$.

With this information, we can easily perform our differential:

$$d(\sin(y)) = d(x^2) + d(x\,\cos(z)) - d(xz^2)$$

$$\cos(y)\,dy = 2x\,dx + (-x\,\sin(z)\,dz + \cos(z)\,dz) - (2xz\,dz + z^2\,dx) \qquad \text{perform the differentials}$$

$$\cos(y)\,dy = 2x\,dx - x\,\sin(z)\,dz + \cos(z)\,dz - 2xz\,dz - z^2\,dx \qquad \text{ungroup the results}$$

$$\frac{dy}{dx} = \frac{2x}{\cos(y)} - \frac{x\,\sin(z)}{\cos(y)}\frac{dz}{dx} + \frac{\cos(z)}{\cos(y)}\frac{dz}{dx} - \frac{2xz}{\cos(y)}\frac{dz}{dx} - \frac{z^2}{\cos(y)} \qquad \text{solve for } \frac{dy}{dx}$$

As a side note, there is a small theoretical issue with multivariable differentials. All of our differential rules are defined and proved with equations of just two variables, so how do we know that they would work for even more?

The answer is that we are assuming that we, at least in theory, *could* conceive of a variable for which all of our other variables are a function. This is usually the case when we have continuous functions. In other words, let's say we have the equation $y = q + r + s$. Even though q, r, and s are separate variables, we can presume there is some other, hidden variable which these are all a function of.

In physical systems, the variable we are usually presupposing is underlying all of these is t—time. That is, each variable, though relatively independent of each other, is dependent upon time. So, instead of q (whatever that represents) being an independent variable, it is dependent in some way (even though it is unspecified) on t.

If that is confusing, that's okay. The important thing to note is that even when we have a variable by itself, it may actually represent a function of another variable that we don't see or don't have in our equation. If the graph looks smooth and continuous, then the differential rules will usually apply just fine. This isn't always possible to check, but you can usually assume that a graph is smooth and continuous unless you have specific reasons to think that it isn't.

13.4   Taking the Derivative With Respect to a Non-Present Variable

You should note that when we take the derivative with respect to a variable (let's say u), the only thing that "with respect to u" does in the operation is to divide by $\mathrm{d}u$. Remember that you can do anything to an equation *as long as you do the same thing to both sides*. Therefore, you can take the derivative with respect to a variable *that is not listed in the equation*, because all you are doing is dividing both sides by the differential of that variable.

So, let's look at the following equation:

$$y^2 = \ln(x)$$

Let's take the derivative of y with respect to v. Even though there is no variable v in the equation, we can still take the derivative with respect to this variable. Just do the steps.

First, take the differential:

$$y^2 = \ln(x)$$
$$2y \, \mathrm{d}y = \frac{\mathrm{d}x}{x}$$

Next, since we are taking the derivative with respect to v, we will divide both sides by $\mathrm{d}v$ and solve for $\frac{\mathrm{d}y}{\mathrm{d}v}$:

$$2y \, \mathrm{d}y = \frac{\mathrm{d}x}{x}$$
$$\frac{2y \, \mathrm{d}y}{\mathrm{d}v} = \frac{\frac{\mathrm{d}x}{x}}{\mathrm{d}v}$$
$$2y \frac{\mathrm{d}y}{\mathrm{d}v} = \frac{1}{x} \frac{\mathrm{d}x}{\mathrm{d}v}$$
$$\frac{\mathrm{d}y}{\mathrm{d}v} = \frac{1}{2xy} \frac{\mathrm{d}x}{\mathrm{d}v}$$

This is the derivative of y with respect to v. Doing this operation implicitly assumes that v is tied in some way to x and y, but we don't have to know or specify what this relationship is.

This may seem pointless, but we will make a lot of use of it in Chapter 14.

— Example 13.3

Take the derivate of y with respect to z for the equation $y = 5x^3 - 4m$.

To do this problem, first we take the differential of both sides:

$$y = 5x^3 - 4m \qquad\qquad \text{the original equation}$$

$$d(y) = d(5x^3 - 4m) \qquad\qquad \text{differentiate both sides}$$

$$dy = 15x^2\,dx - 4\,dm$$

$$\frac{dy}{dz} = 15x^2\,\frac{dx}{dz} - 4\,\frac{dm}{dz} \qquad\qquad \text{divide both sides by } dz$$

13.5   Higher Order Derivatives in Leibniz Notation

In Chapter 9 we covered the concept of a second derivative—that is, the derivative of a derivative. At the time, we hadn't started using Leibniz notation to talk about derivatives. Therefore, using our first notation, we said that, since the first derivative is labeled as y', then the second derivative is labeled y''. So how do we notate the second derivative using Leibniz notation?

There are actually a number of different ways to notate the second derivative, some of which are more confusing than others, and some of which actually lead to problematic results if taken too seriously. If you are interested in some of the details, please see Appendix B.

However, here I wanted to present a very simple method for notating second, third, and other higher-order derivatives.

The basic steps we will use are as follows:

1. Find the first derivative. For the remainder of these steps we will presume we are taking the derivative of y with respect to x (i.e., finding $\frac{dy}{dx}$).

2. Next, create a new variable to represent the derivative (we will use q here). Say that $q = \frac{dy}{dx}$. Replace $\frac{dy}{dx}$ in the equation with q.

3. Now, take the derivative of q with respect to x. This will yield $\frac{dq}{dx}$. $\frac{dq}{dx}$ represents the second derivative of y with respect to x, because it is the derivative of $\frac{dy}{dx}$.

So, let's say that $y = 5x^4$. We can find the derivative as follows:

$$y = 5x^4$$

$$d(y) = d(5x^4)$$

$$dy = 20x^3 \, dx$$

$$\frac{dy}{dx} = 20x^3$$

That's the first derivative. Next, we will set q equal to the first derivative. We will say $q = \frac{dy}{dx}$. That means that $q = 20x^3$.

To find the second derivative, we will take the derivative of q (the first derivative) with respect to x:

$$q = 20x^3$$

$$d(q) = d(20x^3)$$

$$dq = 60x^2 \, dx$$

$$\frac{dq}{dx} = 60x^2$$

Therefore, the second derivative of y with respect to x is $60x^2$.

If we wanted the third derivative, we would do something similar. We will set r to be the second derivative. In other words, $r = \frac{dq}{dx}$. Now we can solve for the derivative of r with respect to x:

$$r = 60x^2$$

$$d(r) = d(60x^2)$$

$$dr = 120x \, dx$$

$$\frac{dr}{dx} = 120x$$

As you can see, the third derivative of y with respect to x is $120x$.

Derivatives of derivatives are known collectively as higher order derivatives.

13.6   Multiple Variables with Higher Order Derivatives

This section is kind of complicated. I am including it only so that the methodology presented here is fully fleshed out. There are no homework assignments based on it. So, if you have had enough, feel free to skip this section. But, if this sort of thing interests you, let's keep going.

Let's say we have an equation like $x^2 + 4y^3 + 2z = 9$. Now, let's say we want to find the second derivative of z with respect to y. How would we do that?

Well, the first derivative is simple enough, so let's start there. As usual, we will take the differential and solve for $\frac{dz}{dy}$:

$$x^2 + 4y^3 + z^2 = 9 \qquad \text{original problem}$$

$$d(x^2 + 4y^3 + 5z) = d(9) \qquad \text{differentiate both sides}$$

$$2x\,dx + 12y^2\,dy + 2\,dz = 0$$

$$2\,dz = -2x\,dx - 12y^2\,dy \qquad \text{solve for } \frac{dz}{dy}$$

$$dz = -x\,dx - 6y^2\,dy$$

$$\frac{dz}{dy} = -x\frac{dx}{dy} - 6y^2$$

So that's the first derivative of z with respect to y. For the second derivative, we will set $q = \frac{dz}{dy}$ and then find the derivative of q with respect to y.

To do this we will take the differential of both sides, and then solve for $\frac{dq}{dy}$. That looks like this:

$$q = -x\frac{dx}{dy} - 6y^2 \qquad \text{first derivative}$$

$$d(q) = d\left(-x\frac{dx}{dy} - 6y^2\right) \qquad \text{differentiate both sides}$$

$$dq = d\left(-x\frac{dx}{dy}\right) - d(6y^2)$$

$$dq = d\left(-x\frac{dx}{dy}\right) - 12y\,dy$$

So how do we differentiate $-x\frac{dx}{dy}$? It's actually pretty straightforward. It is just $-x$ multiplied by $\frac{dx}{dy}$, so you use the product rule plus the quotient rule. Therefore, we can continue our calculation like this:

$$dq = d\left(-x\frac{dx}{dy}\right) - 12y\,dy \qquad \text{where we left off}$$

$$dq = -x\,d\left(\frac{dx}{dy}\right) + \frac{dx}{dy}\,d(-x) - 12y\,dy \qquad \text{product rule}$$

$$dq = -x\frac{dy\,d(dx) - dx\,d(dy)}{dy^2} - \frac{dx}{dy}\,dx - 12y\,dy \qquad \text{quotient rule on the left term}$$

So, what is $d(dx)$ and $d(dy)$? They are differentials of differentials. If you wanted to, you *can* leave them like that. However, since dx is already an abbreviation for $d(x)$, that means that what we really have is $d(d(x))$. The double-application of $d()$ to a variable x is often notated as $d^2(x)$. This *does not* mean that we are squaring anything. Since the 2 is raised above the d it means that we are *applying* $d()$ twice.[1] Therefore, we can write this as:

$$dq = -x\frac{dy\,d^2x - dx\,d^2y}{dy^2} - \frac{dx}{dy}\,dx - 12y\,dy$$

This is the differential. To get the derivative, we just divide both sides by dy, since we are taking the derivative with respect to y:

$$\frac{dq}{dy} = -x\frac{dy\,d^2x - dx\,d^2y}{dy^3} - \frac{dx}{dy}\frac{dx}{dy} - 12y$$

---

[1] What is really confusing is that, with other functions, such as $\sin(x)$, $\sin^2(x)$ means to square the result, not to apply $\sin(x)$ twice. One of the results of the fact that mathematics has developed over several centuries across multiple continents and cultures is that the notation is not always consistent.

That, then, is the second derivative of z with respect to y. There are a number of ways that this could be simplified, but this is the essence of the answer.

Another way to write this would be:

$$\frac{\mathrm{d}q}{\mathrm{d}y} = -x\frac{\mathrm{d}^2 x}{\mathrm{d}y^2} + x\frac{\mathrm{d}x}{\mathrm{d}y}\frac{\mathrm{d}^2 y}{\mathrm{d}y^2} - \left(\frac{\mathrm{d}x}{\mathrm{d}y}\right)^2 - 12y$$

In any case, as you can see, the process is actually a straightforward application of all of the existing rules. It's just that the numerous multiplications and quotients cause the number of steps to increase dramatically (and the example chosen was done to *minimize* the number of steps).

The one thing to keep in mind is that the differential of the differential of x is $\mathrm{d}^2 x$, while $\mathrm{d}x^2$ means the first differential of x squared.

Review

In this chapter, we learned:

1. The process of taking a differential of a multivariable equation is exactly the same as for a single variable equation.

2. The primary difference is that at the end there will be more variables and more differentials than before.

3. The process for taking the derivative of a multivariable equation is exactly the same as for a single variable equation.

4. The only difference in the process of taking the derivative is that you have a larger choice as to what differentials you choose to put into ratio with each other.

5. The phrase "take the derivative of u with respect to v" means that you need to take the differential and solve for $\frac{\mathrm{d}u}{\mathrm{d}v}$.

6. When taking the derivative of an equation of more than two variables, you will usually wind up with a result that includes the derivatives of other variables, but usually with respect to the same variable.

7. If your derivative equation includes the derivatives of other variables, that means that the slope between the two variables in your derivative is dependent upon the slopes between the other variables.

8. You can take the derivative with respect to a variable that is not present within the equation. This works by dividing both sides by the differential of that variable (like you always do for the derivative). The fact that the variable is not present in the equation doesn't matter, though doing the operation presumes that the new variable is tied in some way to the existing variables.

9. In Leibniz notation, the second derivative can be taken by creating a new variable (q is often a good choice) and setting it to the result of taking the first derivative. Then, take the derivative of q with respect to the same variable as before.

10. Third and higher derivatives can be found by repeating the same process continually.

11. When performing differentials for multivariable derivatives, you will often be in a situation where you need to take the differential of a differential. The differential of the differential of u is notated as either $\mathrm{d}(\mathrm{d}(u))$, $\mathrm{d}(\mathrm{d}u)$, or $\mathrm{d}^2 u$, all of which are equivalent. This is known as the second differential of u.

12. The third differential of u (the differential of the differential of the differential of u) can be notated in similar ways, with d^3u being the preferred way. Higher order differentials can be written out in similar ways.

13. For more information on notations for the second derivative, see Appendix B.

Exercises

Find the differential:

1. $z = x + y$

2. $m^2 = 4q + \sin(b)$

3. $\sin(xy) = z^2$

4. $jkb = r^3$

Find the derivative:

5. Find $\frac{dy}{dx}$ for $\sin(y) = x^2$.

6. Find the derivative of w with respect to y for $\cos(w) = x^2 + y^2$.

7. Find the derivative of q with respect to m for $b^2 - c^2 = mq$.

8. Find the derivative $\frac{dh}{dk}$ for $\frac{k}{h} = \sin(hq)$.

9. Find the derivative of r with respect to v for $3r^5 = 5x^2$.

10. Find the derivative $\frac{dy}{dt}$ for $\sin(xy) = r^3$.

11. Find the second derivative of y with respect to x of $3y = x^3$.

12. Find the second derivative of h with respect to g for $e^g = \sin(h)$.

13. Find the third derivative of y with respect to x for $y = x \sin(x)$.

Chapter 14

Relating Rates Using Differentials

Since we know how to use the differential and how to take the differential of composite functions, we can now look at some of the more advanced uses of the derivative.

14.1   Converting Between Static and Dynamic Relationships

Differentials can be thought of as a method of converting static relationships into dynamic ones. That is, when you take a differential, what you are doing is converting a previously established relationship (i.e., the original equation) and showing how the *differences in the variables* relate to each other.

Thus, while the original equation tells you about the static relationships between the variables (if x is this then y is that), the differential gives you an equation that tells you about the *dynamic* relationships between the variables. In other words, how does the change in x impact the way that y is changing.

All that dx and dy mean are the relative changes of the variables to each other. When we find a differential, we convert an equation that relates x and y directly to an equation that relates the *changes* in x and y (i.e., dx and dy) to each other at any point on the graph.

Calculus is useful in the sciences precisely because it manages this conversion from static relationships to dynamic relationships. Sometimes you are given a static relationship and asked to find the dynamic one. For instance, if you take the Pythagorean theorem ($A^2 + B^2 = C^2$), this gives a static relationship between each of the sides of a right triangle.

However, let's say that we want to know how much impact a *change* in the lengths in one of those sides will have? If we take the differential, it will convert our static relationship to a dynamic one:

$$A^2 + B^2 = C^2 \qquad \text{pythagorean theorem}$$
$$d(A^2 + B^2) = d(C^2) \qquad \text{differentiate both sides}$$
$$2A\,dA + 2B\,dB = 2C\,dC \qquad \text{power rule}$$
$$A\,dA + B\,dB = C\,dC \qquad \text{simplify}$$

From here, we can solve for any differential we like. If we want to know how much C is impacted by changes, we solve for dC. If we want to know how much B is impacted by changes, we solve for dB.

So, let's solve for dB:

$$A\,\mathrm{d}A + B\,\mathrm{d}B = C\,\mathrm{d}C$$

$$B\,\mathrm{d}B = C\,\mathrm{d}C - A\,\mathrm{d}A$$

$$\mathrm{d}B = \frac{C\,\mathrm{d}C - A\,\mathrm{d}A}{B}$$

What this equation says is that the changes in B (i.e., $\mathrm{d}B$) are based on not only the actual values of A, B, and C, but also how much A and C themselves are changing.

Differentials are useful conceptually to understand dynamic relationships, but they are hard to *use* in practice. That is, how would I be able to measure an infinitely small value? However, differentials *do* produce measure values when put into ratio with each other. That's the power of the derivative—by putting differentials in ratio with each other, we achieve a quantity that is no longer an infinitesimal, but is a real, measurable quantity.

So, for this equation, we might want to solve for a derivative. That is, if we want to know the ratio of the changes in B to the changes in C at any given point, we can solve for $\frac{\mathrm{d}B}{\mathrm{d}C}$:

$$\mathrm{d}B = \frac{C\,\mathrm{d}C - A\,\mathrm{d}A}{B}$$

$$\frac{\mathrm{d}B}{\mathrm{d}C} = \frac{\frac{C\,\mathrm{d}C - A\,\mathrm{d}A}{B}}{\mathrm{d}C}$$

$$\frac{\mathrm{d}B}{\mathrm{d}C} = \frac{C\,\mathrm{d}C - A\,\mathrm{d}A}{B\,\mathrm{d}C}$$

$$\frac{\mathrm{d}B}{\mathrm{d}C} = \frac{C}{B} - \frac{A}{B}\frac{\mathrm{d}A}{\mathrm{d}C}$$

What this equation tells us is that the ratio of changes of B and C in our right triangle depends not only on the actual lengths A, B, and C, but also on the ratio of changes between A and C.

An even more practical ratio of changes that are important (especially for physical quantities) is the *rate* of change—in other words, the ratio of change of our values to the *change in time*. A rate is merely the ratio of the change in a variable to the *change in time*. Note that time is not a quantity in our original equation, but, as we learned in the previous chapter, it is completely legitimate to take a derivative with respect to a variable not in the equation. As long as we do the same thing to both sides of the equation, we can do anything we want.

Therefore, if we want to know how the *rates of change* of each of these sides are impacted by each other, then we simply take the original differential, and divide by the differential of time (usually written as $\mathrm{d}t$):

$$A^2 + B^2 = C^2 \qquad\qquad \text{the original equation}$$

$$A\,\mathrm{d}A + B\,\mathrm{d}B = C\,\mathrm{d}C \qquad\qquad \text{the differential}$$

$$A\frac{\mathrm{d}A}{\mathrm{d}t} + B\frac{\mathrm{d}B}{\mathrm{d}t} = C\frac{\mathrm{d}C}{\mathrm{d}t} \qquad\qquad \text{divide both sides by } \mathrm{d}t$$

What this equation does is to relate the *rates of change* in each of the variables. This is known as a **related rate** equation. If someone tells you A, B, C, and two of the rates, you can solve for the third rate.

Let's say that $A = 3$ft, $B = 4$ft, and $C = 5$ft. Let's also say that the length of B is not changing. Note that *not changing* means that the differential is *zero*, so $\frac{\mathrm{d}B}{\mathrm{d}t}$ will also be zero. Let's say that A is changing at the rate of $2\frac{\text{ft}}{\text{sec}}$. Given all of this, what is the rate that C is changing with respect to time?

Given our related rate equation, it is really easy to just plug and chug:

$$A\frac{dA}{dt} + B\frac{dB}{dt} = C\frac{dC}{dt} \qquad \text{the related rates equation}$$

$$3\text{ft} \cdot 2\frac{\text{ft}}{\text{sec}} + 4\text{ft} \cdot 0\frac{\text{ft}}{\text{sec}} = 5\text{ft} \cdot \frac{dC}{dt} \qquad \text{substituting in our values}$$

$$6\frac{\text{ft}^2}{\text{sec}} + 0 = 5\text{ft} \cdot \frac{dC}{dt} \qquad \text{simplify the left}$$

$$\frac{6\frac{\text{ft}^2}{\text{sec}}}{5\text{ft}} = \frac{dC}{dt} \qquad \text{solve for } \frac{dC}{dt}$$

$$\frac{6}{5}\frac{\text{ft}}{\text{sec}} = \frac{dC}{dt} \qquad \text{simplify}$$

So, given these conditions, the rate at which C is changing is $\frac{6}{5}$ feet per second.

Note that when doing calculations with units, it is important to either (a) keep the units with the numbers at all times, or (b) make sure everything is in consistent units before starting. With (a) you can treat units just as if they were variables (constant variables, actually—they are treated as constants for the purpose of the differential). Units cancel just like variables, they square just like variables, etc. You can think of a quantity like 2ft as being "two times whatever quantity a foot is." Unless you are really familiar with the equation, I recommend that you stick to (a), as there are fewer avenues for mistakes, and, in fact, when you do make mistakes it is more obvious because your units will often be obviously wrong.

You should note that, because the rate depends on the values of the sides of the triangle itself, this rate is known as an **instantaneous rate of change**, because the rate itself is continually fluctuating as the conditions change.

That is how to convert between from a static relationship to a dynamic one. In later chapters, you will learn to go in the reverse direction, and take dynamic relationships and convert them into static ones.

— Example 14.1

Find the dynamic relationship between the radius of a sphere and its volume. Then, determine the related rate equation. If the radius is 3in and it is increasing at a rate of $1\frac{\text{in}}{\text{sec}}$, how fast is the volume of the sphere increasing?

The first part of this problem is to find the dynamic relationship between the volume of a sphere and its radius. To do that, we just take the volume equation for a sphere and find the differential:

$$v = \frac{4}{3}\pi r^3$$

$$d(v) = d(\frac{4}{3}\pi r^3)$$

$$dv = 4\pi r^2 \, dr$$

The second part of the problem is to convert the equation into a related rate equation. This allows us to take our differentials (which are hard to deal with in physical terms) and convert them into rates of change. To convert our differential equation to a related rate equation we divide both sides by dt:

$$\mathrm{d}v = 4\pi r^2 \, \mathrm{d}r$$

$$\frac{\mathrm{d}v}{\mathrm{d}t} = 4\pi r^2 \frac{\mathrm{d}r}{\mathrm{d}t}$$

The final part of the problem is to find out how fast the volume is increasing. Which derivative is the rate of volume increase? It is $\frac{\mathrm{d}v}{\mathrm{d}t}$. We are given the rate of radius increase. That is $\frac{\mathrm{d}r}{\mathrm{d}t}$. We are also given the current radius. Therefore, all we have to do is substitute in our values and solve for $\frac{\mathrm{d}v}{\mathrm{d}t}$:

$$\frac{\mathrm{d}v}{\mathrm{d}t} = 4\pi r^2 \frac{\mathrm{d}r}{\mathrm{d}t}$$

$$\frac{\mathrm{d}v}{\mathrm{d}t} = 4\pi (3\text{in})^2 \cdot 1\frac{\text{in}}{\text{sec}}$$

$$\frac{\mathrm{d}v}{\mathrm{d}t} = 4\pi \cdot 9\text{in}^2 \cdot \frac{\text{in}}{\text{sec}}$$

$$\frac{\mathrm{d}v}{\mathrm{d}t} = 36\pi \frac{\text{in}^3}{\text{sec}}$$

For our set of conditions, the volume of the sphere is increasing at a rate of 36π (or 113.09733) cubic inches per second.

14.2   Related Rates Problems

Now that we know how to convert from a static representation to a dynamic one, and then convert that representation to a related rate equation, we should look how to solve related rates problems.

Related rates problems are very similar to the problem given in Example 14.1. The main difference is that, in most related rate problems, you have to do a lot more interpreting and setup to get it to the form of the problem as listed in that example. For instance, in Example 14.1 you are *given* the radius. In most related rate problems, it will be something like, "the sphere started off at a point and increased at a rate of $1\frac{\text{in}}{\text{sec}}$ for three seconds." Then, you would have to calculate what the actual radius was after three seconds yourself.

Additionally, physical objects are often substituted for abstract geometries. For instance, instead of a sphere, it might be a spherical baloon. Instead of the problem giving you the increase of the radius, it is more likely to give you the rate of increase of the volume and ask for the increase of the radius. But, rather than call it the volume, the problem might tell you about the flow of water into the baloon. You then have to know that an amount of water *is* a volume, and, since (unlike air) water is essentially uncompressable, a flow of water with a specific rate will affect the volume directly.

You can usually solve a related rate problem with these steps:

1. Figure out the abstract geometry of the equation. Are we dealing in spheres? Triangles? Cylinders?

2. Generate an equation (often a standard geometry equation, such as a volume equation) relating the different static relationships in the problem.

3. Identify any fixed values in the equation, and substitute for those values.

4. Convert the equation to a related rate equation (as in Section 14.1).

5. Identify which rates you are given and which rates you need to solve for in this equation.

6. Note that anything that is *not changing* is the same as having a zero for the derivative. The problem will not always *tell* you that something isn't changing, you may have to figure that out for yourself. Is a particular length fixed? Then it can't change, so its rate of change is zero.

7. Identify which static values need to be computed in order to solve the equation (i.e., do we need to know the volume before we figure out the rate of change of the radius?). Usually, you have to use one of the given rates to figure out the static unknowns for the question. For instance, if we are given a rate of change in the volume, and we need the value for the volume to compute the rate of something else, then we use the rate of change of the volume to find its value at the time we need to solve for the other rate(s) in question.

8. Solve for the unknown rates.

9. Double-check to make sure that you have solved for precisely what is asked for. Do any additional conversions or clean-ups to make sure you have finished the problem precisely.

Related rate problems are essentially there as a full-system test of your understanding of the differential. Do you know how to think about a problem in terms of a static equation? Do you know how to convert a static equation to a dynamic equation using differentials? Do you realize that dividing by d*t* converts these differentials to rates? Do you realize that when something doesn't change that its rate of change (derivative with respect to time) is zero? Do you recognize the physical rates that you are given in the related rate equation you generated? Do you see how to convert a value that is not quite what you need into the value you do need using basic logic and arithmetic manipulations?

If you can do related rate problems, then you have a pretty thorough and practical knowledge of what differentials and derivatives are and how to apply them.

14.3   Solving a Related Rate Problem

This section will focus on solving a single related rate problem.

Let's say that a man is standing on a ladder fixing a gutter. The ladder is 11ft long, leaning against the house, with the top of the ladder touching the exterior wall of the house. On the ground, the ladder is 3ft away from the wall. The man is standing at the very top of the ladder. That's not very safe, but it does make the problem simpler.

Figure 14.1 shows a picture of the scene (note that if you weren't given a picture, it often helps to draw one).

The man's young son decides to play a prank on him. He decides to push the base of the ladder away from the house, such that the top of the ladder continues to be touching the wall of the house the whole time. He is able to push the ladder *away* from the house at a rate of $2\frac{\text{ft}}{\text{sec}}$. After the child pushes the ladder for half a second, how fast is the man (i.e., the top of the ladder) descending?

So, in this problem, we have two rates—one given, and one we have to solve for. The first rate is the rate that the child is pushing the ladder. We are given that one, it is $2\frac{\text{ft}}{\text{sec}}$. The second rate is the rate that the man is descending after half a second.

The question is, how do we relate these rates to each other?

Figure 14.1: Picture of a Child Pushing His Dad's Ladder

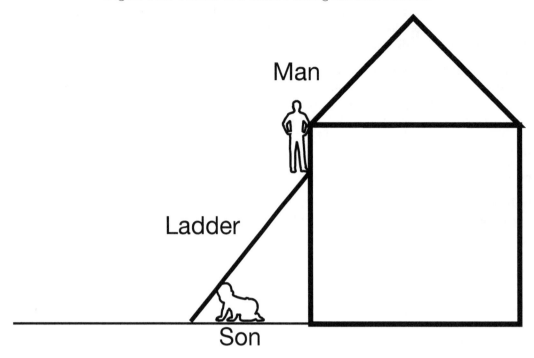

Since we are trying to determine the relationship between these two rates, this is known as a related rate problem. Therefore, we will use the steps in Section 14.2 to solve the problem.

The first step is to figure out the abstract geometry of the problem. What are we dealing with? If you don't already have a drawing of the problem, it helps to draw it out on paper. The essential geometrical figure in Figure 14.1 is a triangle. Not only that, it is a right triangle. Additionally, we can see that even as the ladder moves, the corner between the house and the ground is going to stay at a right angle, and therefore the triangle, even as the other angles change, will remain a right triangle.

So, since we are dealing with a right triangle (and specifically with the lengths of the sides) we can use the Pythagorean Theorem to relate the lengths of the sides. However, before we do this, we need to label which length is which so we don't get confused going forward.

Figure 14.2 shows our abstract geometry with the sides labelled. We are using H for the height, B for the base, and L for the ladder itself.

Note that while L does not change (because the ladder is a fixed entity), the sizes of H and B will change as the ladder moves.

Since all of the sides form a right triangle with L as the hypotenuse, we can use the Pythagorean theorem to say that

$$H^2 + B^2 = L^2$$

Now that we have the geometry, the next step is to look for any fixed values in the equation, and substitute for them. Since $L = 11$, the equation can be simplified to

$$H^2 + B^2 = 11^2$$

which can be further simplified to

$$H^2 + B^2 = 121$$

Figure 14.2: The Abstract Geometry of the Ladder Problem

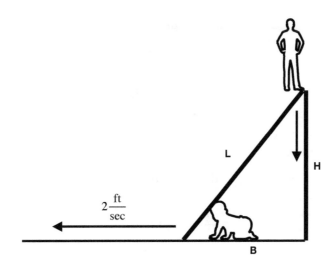

That is the static relationship between the pieces of the problem. Next we need to identify the dynamic relationships by taking a differential:

$$H^2 + B^2 = 121 \qquad \text{the original equation}$$

$$2H\,\mathrm{d}H + 2B\,\mathrm{d}B = 0 \qquad \text{the differential}$$

$$H\,\mathrm{d}H + B\,\mathrm{d}B = 0 \qquad \text{simplified}$$

Since we are talking about *rates* (the change in quanties vs. the change in time), we can convert this to a related rate equation by dividing it through by $\mathrm{d}t$:

$$H\,\mathrm{d}H + B\,\mathrm{d}B = 0 \qquad \text{the differential}$$

$$H\,\frac{\mathrm{d}H}{\mathrm{d}t} + B\,\frac{\mathrm{d}B}{\mathrm{d}t} = 0 \qquad \text{related rate equation}$$

Now that we know the pieces and the basic relationships, what are we given and what are we looking for? We are told that the child is pushing the ladder at $2\frac{\text{ft}}{\text{sec}}$. What does this quantity represent? Looking at the drawing, you can see that moving the bottom of the ladder will increase the length of the base (B) by however far we move the ladder. Therefore, B is increasing at $2\frac{\text{ft}}{\text{sec}}$. In other words, $\frac{\mathrm{d}B}{\mathrm{d}t} = 2\frac{\text{ft}}{\text{sec}}$.

Now consider the value we are trying to discover—the instantaneous rate of change of the height (H). Since $\frac{\mathrm{d}B}{\mathrm{d}t}$ was the rate of change of B, then $\frac{\mathrm{d}H}{\mathrm{d}t}$ will be the rate of change of H. This is the unknown that we are solving for.

This is a good place to stop and note where we have gone. We started by picturing the problem in our mind (Figure 14.1). Next, we converted that picture to an abstract geometry and labelled the pieces (Figure 14.2). Then, we filled in the quantities that were known, and looked at the known relationships between the known values. Finally, we established what final quantity that we were seeking.

So, how would we find a formula for $\frac{dH}{dt}$? We just need to take our related rate equation and solve for it:

$$H\frac{dH}{dt} + B\frac{dB}{dt} = 0$$

$$H\frac{dH}{dt} = -B\frac{dB}{dt}$$

$$\frac{dH}{dt} = \frac{-B}{H}\frac{dB}{dt}$$

Now we have a formula that will give us $\frac{dH}{dt}$. We can simplify this further, because we were given $\frac{dB}{dt}$ in the problem. So we can substitute that into the formula like this:

$$\frac{dH}{dt} = \frac{-B}{H}\frac{dB}{dt}$$

$$\frac{dH}{dt} = \frac{-B}{H}(2\frac{\text{ft}}{\text{sec}})$$

$$\frac{dH}{dt} = \frac{-2B}{H}\frac{\text{ft}}{\text{sec}}$$

Now we have a formula for $\frac{dH}{dt}$ given the just the static values B and H. Now, we know what B and H are *at the start of the problem*. However, the question was not to determine what $\frac{dH}{dt}$ is at the beginning of the problem. The question was to determine what the rate is *after a half of a second*. Therefore, we need to compute what all of these pieces will be after the half second.

So, if we know $\frac{dB}{dt}$, we can compute what the new base will be after a half of a second. It will change by:

$$2\frac{\text{ft}}{\text{sec}} \cdot 0.5\text{sec} = 1\text{ft}$$

Therefore, since B started at 3ft, the new B after one second is 4ft.

Now we need to know what H is. This can be solved using the Pythagorean theorem. Since we know that L is 11, we know that:

$$H^2 + B^2 = L^2$$

$$H^2 + (4)^2 = (11)^2$$

$$H^2 + 16 = 121$$

$$H^2 = 105$$

$$H = \sqrt{105}$$

$$H \approx 10.2470$$

Now we have all of the pieces of the formula we need to find $\frac{dH}{dt}$:

$$\frac{dH}{dt} = \frac{-2B}{H}\frac{ft}{sec}$$

$$\frac{dH}{dt} = \frac{-2(4ft)}{10.2470ft}\frac{ft}{sec}$$

$$\frac{dH}{dt} = \frac{-8}{10.2470}\frac{ft}{sec}$$

$$\frac{dH}{dt} = \frac{-8}{10.2470}\frac{ft}{sec}$$

$$\frac{dH}{dt} \approx -0.7807\frac{ft}{sec}$$

So, after the boy pushes on the ladder for a half of a second, the distance between the man and the ground ($\frac{dH}{dt}$) is changing at a rate of $-0.7807\frac{ft}{sec}$.

While this example (as well as most related rates equations) has a lot of *steps*, each of the steps are usually straightforward applications of tools you already know how to do. You just have to be able to connect the dots between the pieces.

14.4   Making a General Formula

Way back in Section 9.4 we discussed the general method for converting a specific problem with a specific solution into a general problem with a general solution. We will now apply that method to the ladder problem from Section 14.2. The goal is to find a general formula that we can use to solve similar problems no matter what the specific values are, and to make that formula algebraic so that one does not need calculus to *use* the formula, only to create it.

If you remember from Section 9.4, the way to do this is to replace all of the constants in the equation with *constant variables*, meaning that we assign them a letter to look like a variable, but, since they are going to be given constant values in any given problem statement, we will treat them like constants when we take the derivative.

In Section 14.3, the ladder was $11ft$ long, which we will substitute with L. The ladder was $3ft$ from the house (side B of the triangle), which we will substitute with D (starting distance). The ladder was being pushed at a rate of $2\frac{ft}{sec}$, which we will call R. Finally, we wanted to know what the rate was after being pushed for a certain length of time, which we will call T.

Now, using these constant variables, let us evaluate the problem. These will be the same steps we used in Section 14.2, but we will go through them faster and with less explanation.

To start with, because the ladder forms a triangle with the ground and the house, we can say that $H^2 + B^2 = L^2$. The only difference is that we will not simplify L^2 into a number, but keep it as L^2.

So, next, we convert this into a related rate equation:

$$L^2 = H^2 + B^2 \qquad\qquad \text{the triangle equation}$$

$$2L\,dL = 2H\,dH + 2B\,dB \qquad\qquad \text{the differential}$$

$$L\,dL = H\,dH + B\,dB \qquad\qquad \text{simplifying}$$

$$L\frac{dL}{dt} = H\frac{dH}{dt} + B\frac{dB}{dt} \qquad\qquad \text{convert to related rate}$$

Then, because L is fixed (it is the size of the ladder itself, which is not changing), dL will always be zero. So we can simplify this equation to:

$$0 = H\frac{dH}{dt} + B\frac{dB}{dt}$$

Now, the goal is to find $\frac{dH}{dt}$. So let's solve for that:

$$H\frac{dH}{dt} + B\frac{dB}{dt} = 0$$

$$H\frac{dH}{dt} = -B\frac{dB}{dt}$$

$$\frac{dH}{dt} = \frac{-B}{H}\frac{dB}{dt}$$

Because R is our rate (given in the problem), we can simplify this to:

$$\frac{dH}{dt} = \frac{-BR}{H}$$

The rate we are looking for, $\frac{dH}{dt}$, will depend on the length of the sides of the triangle and the rate that the person is pushing the ladder. So, to find out what B is, we simply take the starting position of the ladder (D) and then find the distance it has moved. The distance will just be the rate that it is moving (R) multiplied by the time (T). Therefore $B = D + RT$. We can then substitute that in for B in our equation:

$$\frac{dH}{dt} = \frac{-BR}{H} \qquad\qquad \text{the formula so far}$$

$$\frac{dH}{dt} = \frac{-(D + RT)R}{H} \qquad\qquad \text{substituting for } B$$

$$\frac{dH}{dt} = \frac{-DR + -R^2 T}{H} \qquad\qquad \text{simplifying}$$

Now, the only value we have left to discover is the value of H. We can use our original triangle equation for that:

$$H^2 + B^2 = L^2 \qquad\qquad \text{the equation for the triangle}$$

$$H^2 = L^2 - B^2 \qquad\qquad \text{solve for } a$$

$$H = \sqrt{L^2 - B^2}$$

$$B = D + R \cdot T \qquad\qquad \text{our previous solution for } b$$

$$H = \sqrt{L^2 - (D + R \cdot T)^2} \qquad\qquad \text{substituting}$$

Then, if we substitute that definition of H into our final equation, we get:

$$\frac{dH}{dt} = \frac{-DR + -R^2 T}{H} \qquad \text{our solution so far}$$

$$\frac{dH}{dt} = \frac{-DR + -R^2 T}{\sqrt{L^2 - (D + R \cdot T)^2}} \qquad \text{substituting for } H$$

Now we have a formula that is entirely in terms of our original numbers! It isn't an easy equation, but it is definitely workable by anyone with basic mathematical ability.

To test out the formula, let's plug in the numbers from the original example, and see if it gives us the same result:

$$\frac{dH}{dt} = \frac{-DR - R^2 T}{\sqrt{L^2 - (D + R \cdot T)^2}} \qquad \text{the equation}$$

$$\frac{dH}{dt} = \frac{-(3\text{ft})(2\frac{\text{ft}}{\text{sec}}) - (2\frac{\text{ft}}{\text{sec}})^2(0.5\text{sec})}{\sqrt{(11\text{ft})^2 - (3\text{ft} + (2\frac{\text{ft}}{\text{sec}})(0.5\text{sec}))^2}} \qquad \text{using our values}$$

$$\frac{dH}{dt} = \frac{-6\frac{\text{ft}^2}{\text{sec}} - 4\frac{\text{ft}^2}{\text{sec}^2}(0.5\text{sec})}{\sqrt{121\text{ft}^2 - (3\text{ft} + (1\text{ft})^2}} \qquad \text{simplifying}$$

$$\frac{dH}{dt} = \frac{-6\frac{\text{ft}^2}{\text{sec}} - 2\frac{\text{ft}^2}{\text{sec}}}{\sqrt{121\text{ft}^2 - 16\text{ft}^2}}$$

$$\frac{dH}{dt} = \frac{-8\frac{\text{ft}^2}{\text{sec}}}{\sqrt{105\text{ft}^2}}$$

$$\frac{dH}{dt} = \frac{-8\frac{\text{ft}^2}{\text{sec}}}{\sqrt{105}\text{ft}}$$

$$\frac{dH}{dt} = \frac{-8}{\sqrt{105}} \frac{\text{ft}}{\text{sec}}$$

$$\frac{dH}{dt} \approx -0.7807 \frac{\text{ft}}{\text{sec}}$$

Notice that units are treated just like constant variables—they can be squared, added, multiplied, and divided. This provides an important check on your work—if the equation works, it will give you the correct units.

14.5 Related Rates with Fluid Flows

Another common usage of related rates problems is with fluid flow. The idea behind it is that you have a container of some shape that you are filling with water at a certain rate. The question is, at a given time t, what is the instantaneous rate that the liquid is rising, or the radius is changing, etc..

Here is the example we will work with for this section:

Water is being pumped into a spherical baloon at a rate of $30\frac{\text{cm}^3}{\text{hr}}$. In other words, the baloon will always be a sphere, but the radius will expand based on the total volume of water. After 2 hours, what is the rate that the radius of the sphere is increasing?

So, as with any math problem, the first thing to do is to see what we know. We have a sphere. What do we know about spheres? Since this problem is about volumes, we probably will want the volume equation for a sphere. If you don't remember this from geometry, the volume of a sphere is $v = \frac{4}{3}\pi r^3$ (we will actually derive this equation ourselves in Section 20.1).

What else are we given? We know that water is being pumped in at a *rate* of $30\frac{\text{cm}^3}{\text{hr}}$. What is a rate? It is the change of a quantity over time. What quantity is being changed by this rate? The *volume* of the sphere. That means that $30\frac{\text{cm}^3}{\text{hr}}$ represents $\frac{dv}{dt}$.

So what are we trying to find? We are trying to find the rate of increase of the radius. If it is a *rate* of increase, that means that we are trying to find the *change* in the increase divided by the *change* in time. In other words, we are trying to find $\frac{dr}{dt}$.

So, we have the equation for the volume, so what do we do to find the rates? Since a rate is simply the ratio of a differential of a variable to the differential of another variable (usually time), then the first thing we need to do is find the relevant differentials. Because the variables are already related to each other through the volume equation ($v = \frac{4}{3}\pi r^3$), then we can find out the relationship between the differentials by taking the differential of the equation:

$$v = \frac{4}{3}\pi r^3 \qquad\qquad \text{original equation}$$

$$dv = 3\frac{4}{3}\pi r^2 dr \qquad\qquad \text{differentiating with the power rule}$$

$$dv = 4\pi r^2 dr \qquad\qquad \text{simplifying}$$

Now we have an equation relating the differentials. However, what we want is an equation relating the *rates*. To do this, we merely divide both sides by the differential of time, dt:

$$dv = 4\pi r^2 dr \qquad\qquad \text{the differential}$$

$$\frac{dv}{dt} = 4\pi r^2 \frac{dr}{dt} \qquad\qquad \text{divide both sides by } dt$$

Now, if you look back at the problem, you will see that $\frac{dv}{dt}$ (the rate at which water—the volume—is being added to the sphere) is actually one of our givens. It is $30\frac{\text{cm}^3}{\text{hr}}$. Therefore, the equation can be rewritten as:

$$30\frac{\text{cm}^3}{\text{hr}} = 4\pi r^2 \frac{dr}{dt}$$

Now the quantity we want to solve for is $\frac{dr}{dt}$. Therefore, we should rearrange the equation to solve for it:

$$\frac{dr}{dt} = \frac{30\frac{cm^3}{hr}}{4\pi r^2}$$

Now we only need to solve for what r is at the time in question (2 hours). This can be done using the original volume equation. Since $v = \frac{4}{3}\pi r^3$, and we know that we get 30cm^3 water per hour, then after two hours, we know that our volume will be 60cm^3. Therefore, we can quite simply solve for r:

$$v = \frac{4}{3}\pi r^3 \qquad\qquad \text{volume equation}$$

$$60\text{cm}^3 = \frac{4}{3}\pi r^3 \qquad\qquad \text{the volume after two hours}$$

$$\frac{60\text{cm}^3}{\frac{4}{3}\pi} = r^3 \qquad\qquad \text{solve for } r$$

$$\sqrt[3]{\frac{60\text{cm}^3}{\frac{4}{3}\pi}} = r$$

$$2.4286\text{cm} \approx r$$

Now we can use the relationship between the rates to solve for $\frac{dr}{dt}$:

$$\frac{dr}{dt} = \frac{30\frac{cm^3}{hr}}{4\pi r^2} \qquad\qquad \text{rate equation}$$

$$\frac{dr}{dt} = \frac{30\frac{cm^3}{hr}}{4\pi(2.4286\text{cm})^2} \qquad\qquad \text{substitute for } r$$

$$\frac{dr}{dt} \approx \frac{30\frac{cm^3}{hr}}{74.1177\text{cm}^2} \qquad\qquad \text{simplifying}$$

$$\frac{dr}{dt} = \frac{30}{74.1177}\frac{\text{cm}^3}{\text{cm}^2\text{hr}}$$

$$\frac{dr}{dt} = \frac{30}{74.1177}\frac{\text{cm}}{\text{hr}}$$

$$\frac{dr}{dt} \approx 0.4048\frac{\text{cm}}{\text{hr}}$$

Therefore, after filling with water for two hours, the balloon's radius will be increasing at a rate of approximately $0.4048\frac{cm}{hr}$.

Review

In this chapter, we learned:

1. Taking a differential is used to convert an equation that shows a static relationship into an equation that shows a dynamic relationship.

2. Derivatives tend to be more useful than just the differentials when there is a value to be measured or calculated.

3. The derivative with respect to time is useful because it expresses differentials as rates of change—the ratio of the change in a variable to the change in time.

4. To convert a differential to a derivative with respect to time, you need only divide a given equation of differentials by the differential of time (usually represented as dt), even if the original equation did not have a time component in it.

5. Derivatives of multiple variables with respect to time is known as a related rates equation, because it relates the rates of change of different variables.

6. Finding a related rate involves finding one or more equations governing the static relationships between the variables, differentiating them to get the dynamic relationships, dividing by dt to get the related rates equation, determining the remaining variables needed to perform the calculation for the unknown rate, and then plugging the numbers in to get a solution.

7. A general list of steps for a related rate equation can be found in Section 14.2.

8. Related rates problems can be applied to anything where rates are related to each other.

Exercises

Solve the following problems:

1. Imagine you have a trough shaped like an extruded isosceles triangle (with the angle at the bottom) that you are filling with a liquid. The trough has a 90° angle at the vertex, and is 20 centimeters long. Find an equation that relates the height of the liquid in the trough with the volume of the liquid in the trough. Use the variable h to represent the height of the liquid, and the variable v to represent the volume.

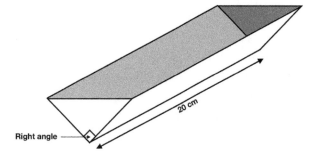

2. Find the differential of the previous equation.

3. Divide the entirety of the previous equation by dt (the differential of time).

4. Solve the previous equation for the change in height with respect to time.

5. If you are filling the trough from empty at a rate of 5 milliliters per minute (1 milliliter equals 1 cubic centimeter), after 16 minutes, what is the rate of change of the height of the liquid?

6. Two cars start at the same point. One travels South at 60 miles per hour and the other travels East at 15 miles per hour. After two hours, what rate is the distance between the cars increasing?

7. Look at the example in Section 14.3. Calculate the rate of change of the *angle* between the ladder and the ground after a half a second of pushing. Remember (from Section 11.1) to use radians for angle measures, but also remember that radians are an implied unit, and do not normally have a unit name attached (i.e., instead of saying $1 \frac{radian}{sec}$ you would normally just say $\frac{1}{sec}$ for one radian-per-second). Therefore, you don't need to keep track of the radian unit during your calculation (and, in fact, it might lead to confusing results if you tried).

8. A pebble is dropped into a pond, generating circular ripples. The radius of the largest ripple is increasing at a constant rate of 2 inches per second. After 5 seconds, what is the rate that the *circumference* of the largest ripple is increasing?

9. A hose is inflating a spherical baloon which begins empty. The water is coming out of the hose at a rate of $4\frac{mL}{sec}$ ($1mL = 1mm^3$). After 10 seconds, what is the rate of the radius of the baloon increasing?

10. A plane is flying at a constant altitude of 3 miles down a straight road at 150 miles per hour with a radar gun to catch speeding vehicles. The radar gun, however, only determines the speed of the vehicle *with relation to the airplane* (i.e., how fast the distance between the plane and the vehicle is increasing or decreasing) and the distance to the vehicle. If a vehicle headed *the same direction of the plane* is clocked by the radar gun as coming toward you at 80 miles per hour at a distance of 5 miles, how fast is the vehicle going?

11. A radar gun manufacturer has asked you to develop an algorithm for the previous problem using only arithmetic operations, so that the operator only has to enter in the plane's speed and altitude, and it will calculate the speed of cars based on the measured distance and the measured relative speed. Develop a formula that will allow for this. You can assume that the car is headed in the same direction as the plane.

Chapter 15

Working with Problems Involving Differentials

In Chapter 2, I said that "step 1 of math is philosophy." What I meant by that is that you have to first think about what a problem *means* before you can correctly solve it. In fact, most of the developments of this whole part of the book are based on carefully examining the meanings of words, and how they can be written out mathematically.

The derivative *means* a slope of a graph at a particular point. Thinking about the way that slopes and graphs look, we figured out that smooth, continuous graphs can *only* have local minimas and maximas where the derivative is zero. We also thought about exceptions to this—when the graph isn't smooth or continuous, there may be other minimas and maximas lurking about. Additionally, the global minimum or maximum may occur at the tail ends of the graph at infinity.

We didn't prove these things with numbers and theorems (though you could). Instead, we used basic ideas about the nature of things (i.e., philosophy) to show that it is true.

Most of the time, the success or failure in working with calculus is about being able to *think* successfully about derivatives and differentials.

15.1   Reviewing the Meaning of Differentials and Derivatives

In simple terms, we have learned that the derivative is simply an equation that tells the slope between two variables at any particular point. $\frac{dy}{dx}$ just means the slope between x and y at any given point. While finding the slope seems trivial, even this basic idea can be used to great effect to find maximas and minimas of equations. When the slope is zero, we have found a top or a bottom (at least locally). Therefore, finding the slope is helpful, because finding where the slope is zero helps us to find optimized points.

We then generalized our ideas about derivatives into differentials. Differentials can be trivially converted into derivatives if needed, but, by themselves, they give us information about the relative amounts of change of each variable. This simplifies the process of taking a derivative, and allows us to easily generalize the process to multiple variables.[1]

When you find a differential equation, what you have found is an equation which relates the *changes* of

---

[1]When I say it "simplifies the process" I am referring both to the fact that it provides a simple way of finding complex derivatives, but also it is simplified compared to other derivative-finding methods taught in other books.

variables to each other. In the book, we have called these *dynamic* relationships. Differentiating an equation converts static relationships to dynamic ones. Thus, all of the static relationships that you know (geometry formulas, etc.) can be automatically converted to dynamic relationships using the differential.

The differential has limited *practical* use because a differential value is infinitely small. Thus, the differential is primarily a mental construct.[2]

However, differential equations can become much more practical and quantifiable by transforming them into related rates equations, which give us information about how these changes happen within time, relating different rates of change to each other. We found these equations by taking our differential equations and dividing by the differential of time, dt.

In support of these processes, we learned the rules of differentiation. The rules of differentiation we have learned applies to innumerable functions and equations. Pretty much any function that you can conceive of using standard continuous functions can be differentiated using the rules we have established. While it may not be *easy*, finding a differential using the rules is straightforward and mechanical.

15.2   Recognizing the Presence of the Derivative

The key to applying calculus is to *recognize* when you have a situation that depends on rates, or where an optimization is needed, or somewhere else where you are interested in changes or dynamic relationships. Once you recognize the relationship, applying calculus is merely correctly applying labels to things, and recognizing what can be solved for.

Some keywords that should trigger you to start thinking about calculus include:

maximize When you hear that you need to maximize something, you should think about finding maximas and minimas. In other words, finding places where the slope is zero. In order to do this successfully, you need to be sure that the vertical axis (i.e., y-value) is the value you are trying to maximize, and the horizontal axis (i.e., x-value) is the thing that you can vary to affect the vertical axis. Once you have an equation that can relate changes in x to changes in y, you can use the derivative to find the locations where the derivative is zero—these are your local extremas, one of which is probably your maximum value.

minimize This is the same as maximize, except that you are looking for the smallest extrema, not the largest.

change When someone is describing a changes in a value or values, they are usually describing differentials. A differential is merely the smallest form of a difference. Differences are the result of changes. Therefore, a change in something usually implies that a differential can be used to model the change. So, if I am talking about the change in the number of cats in the pound, I can use c as the number of cats, and describe the change using the differential dc. If I want to relate the change in temperature (i.e., dT) to the change in cats in the pound, I can describe this as $\frac{dC}{dT}$.

difference If something differs, what does it do? It *changes*. Differences in something can usually be approximated using differentials (see Section 15.3).

slope Any time a problem deals with slopes, this is the comparison (i.e., division) of two differentials.

---

[2]Even though the differential itself is primarily a mental construct (we cannot perform infinitely small measurements), the differential can be used to *approximate* the effects of small changes. That is, if I have an equation that includes dy and dx, I can approximate the result of changing dx by a tiny amount by solving for dy and substituting that tiny amount for dx. In other words, if I have the equation $dy = 5x\,dx$, then I can approximate the change in y for a tiny change in x. I can say that, if my change in x at $x = 3$ is 0.001, then my change in y will probably be approximately 5(3)(0.001) = 0.015. Practical applications of this fact can be found in Appendix D.1.

rate If a problem includes a rate, then it is talking about the derivative of something with respect to time. In other words, it is the *change* in some variable divided by the *change* in time. For instance, if I want to talk about how fast I read a book, I can express that as $\frac{\mathrm{d}pages}{\mathrm{d}t}$. In other words, the rate for which I read a book is the change in the number of pages I have read over the change in time. The rate at which a lumberjack cuts down trees is given by $\frac{\mathrm{d}trees}{\mathrm{d}t}$. Any rate that is given can be described by differentials.

speed The speed of something is just another word for "rate."

fast Yet another word for "rate."

velocity Yet another word for "rate." This is usually specifically referring to the rate of change in position to the change in time (i.e., $\frac{\mathrm{d}p}{\mathrm{d}t}$).

acceleration The acceleration of something is merely the rate of change *of* the rate of change. For example, when dealing with velocity, we have said that $v = \frac{\mathrm{d}p}{\mathrm{d}t}$, so acceleration can be given as $a = \frac{\mathrm{d}v}{\mathrm{d}t}$. It is the second derivative, or the derivative of the derivative. When you are driving and put your foot on the "accelerator," you are changing your vehicle's velocity.

does not change If something in an equation does not change, you can say that its differential or derivative is zero. This can be a simplification (if something doesn't change, we can treat it as a constant when taking differentials and derivatives), or it can be something to solve for. If someone asks you to balance something so that some quantity does not change, it means to solve for the condition where the derivative is zero.

keeps steady This is another way that "does not change" is stated. It just means that either the differential is zero (and therefore allows simplification) or we need to solve for the case where the differential is zero.

The point of all of this is that when you see word problems, you need to learn to be comfortable assigning differentials to the quantities for which they apply. You need to make a habit of seeing these words, and having them trigger in your mind two things:

1. The fact that we are probably dealing in differentials

2. What those differentials are

The second part of this seems to be the most tricky for the most people. However, if you can rephrase the terms so that it literally says "the change in ___ divided by the change in ___," then you now have the sepecific variables and differentials that you need.

— Example 15.1

Bob has noticed that for every 2 degree of change in temperature, the pressure in his tires change by 0.2 PSI. Create a differential equation to represent this.

In this problem, we are talking about a *change* in temperature. Remember that changes indicate differentials. So, what are the things that are changing? The *temperature* is changing. How can we represent that? We can use T for temperature (I usually use a capital T for temperature because the lower-case t is so often used for "time"). Therefore, the change in temperature is just $\mathrm{d}T$.

The pressure can be given using the variable p, so the change in pressure will just be $\mathrm{d}p$.

The problem now can be written like this: "for every 2 $\mathrm{d}T$, Bob gets 0.2 $\mathrm{d}p$." In other words, the ratio between $\mathrm{d}p$ and $\mathrm{d}T$ (i.e., $\frac{\mathrm{d}p}{\mathrm{d}T}$) is $\frac{0.2}{2}$ or just 0.1.

Written as an equation, we can say:

$$\frac{\mathrm{d}p}{\mathrm{d}T} = 0.1$$

In this lesson, we are mostly concerned with just writing down the equations correctly.

— Example 15.2

A company has a manufacturing process that takes in a particular gaseous compound and uses it to produce a liquid which they sell. The rate that this process consumes a particular volume of gas is ten times the rate at which this process produces a volume of liquid. Write this as a differential equation.

Because the gas is being consumed, that is *changing* the total amount of gas. Because it is happening at a particular *rate*, then that means that we are talking about a derivative with respect to time. If we use g to represent the total volume of gas available, then we can say that changes in this volume are represented by $\mathrm{d}g$. The rate of change in this volume is represented by $\frac{\mathrm{d}g}{\mathrm{d}t}$.

Likewise for the liquid. If we say that L is the total liquid produced, then $\mathrm{d}L$ is the change in the amount produced, and $\frac{\mathrm{d}L}{\mathrm{d}t}$ is the rate at which the total produced liquid is changing.

Now, before we go further, notice that the gas is being *consumed* and the liquid is being *produced*. That means that $\frac{\mathrm{d}g}{\mathrm{d}t}$ will be negative and $\frac{\mathrm{d}L}{\mathrm{d}t}$ will be positive. Being consistent on your signs is very important! Which way to put your signs will depend on practical issues of the problem itself, but whichever way you roll, just be sure that you know what sign conventions you are using.

Now, the problem says that it takes 10 volumes of gas to produce 1 volume of liquid. In other words, the rate of volume of gas consumed is ten times the volume of liquid produced. This means that $-10\frac{\mathrm{d}L}{\mathrm{d}t}$ is the same rate as $\frac{\mathrm{d}g}{\mathrm{d}t}$. Or, as an equation:

$$\frac{\mathrm{d}g}{\mathrm{d}t} = -10\frac{\mathrm{d}L}{\mathrm{d}t}$$

The negative sign is there because we are comparing a consuming process to a producing process.

15.3   Making Discrete Things Continuous

So far, we have generally discussed differentials and derivatives as applying to only smooth, continuous functions. However, there are a large class of problems which are not continuous, but they act as if they were continuous under certain circumstances.

For instance, let's look at population growth. Population growth is not continuous. Babies are quite discrete units. You either have a baby or you don't. You are either a creature or you aren't.

However, for populations that are sufficiently large, population growth acts as if it were continuous. For instance, we can give a birth rate that is given as a fraction $\frac{\text{babies}}{\text{year}}$. In a tiny population, this ratio will be very jagged and discontinuous. If there is a population of two, they may decide to wait for 10 years to have babies, and then have a baby each year. Then, we have to wait for those children to mature before they start having babies.

However, as the population grows, the changes in these variables start to smooth out. It never becomes perfectly smooth, but eventually the process becomes sufficiently smooth that calculus can be used to describe it.

Instead of talking about babies in particular, we can talk about the change in population over time as a differential $\frac{dp}{dt}$.

You will find that many equations have been developed from differentials which talk about discrete processes. This is simply because as you have more and more samples, the discrete processes start to look more and more continuous, allowing for analysis in terms of calculus.

Additionally, small values can be used as "approximate" differentials. That is, even though dx is infinitely small, we can recognize that a small change in x can substitute as an approximation for dx. We can then solve for dy. Again, this will be an approximation, because the actual differential formulas are based on infinitely small changes. Nonetheless, for sufficiently small values, these approximations can work quite well. For more information on this idea, see Appendix D.

15.4   Multicomponent Differentials

In the previous section, we talked about changes in a population size due to birth, and we called that $\frac{dp}{dt}$. However, in calculus, it is important to note when a particular change has more than one cause, and which quantity in particular is changing. Is birth the only cause of population size changes?

Unfortunately, no. There is also death. Therefore, the birth rate is not the *equivalent* of $\frac{dp}{dt}$ (the change in population over time), but merely one *component* of it.

Therefore, we can speak of the change in population over time as being the combination of the birth rate and the death rate. In other words:

$$\frac{dp}{dt} = \frac{d\mathit{babies}}{dt} - \frac{d\mathit{deaths}}{dt}$$

Now, we usually don't speak about a "change in babies" or a "change in deaths" (even though that's really what they are), but merely "births" meaning a change in the total number of babies that have been born and "deaths" meaning a change in the total number of deaths. So we would probably write the equation as:

$$\frac{dp}{dt} = \frac{\mathit{babies}}{dt} - \frac{\mathit{deaths}}{dt}$$

It is important to recognize that the language of math is much more specific than everyday language. Interpreting quantities back and forth is sometimes difficult.

The important thing to realize is that a differential is the *total* change in a quantity from all causes under consideration.[3] If p is the total population size, $\frac{dp}{dt}$ has *exactly one* meaning—the total change in population size over time from *all considered causes*.

If there are multiple causes for a particular differential or derivative, each individual cause needs to be labelled with its own variable, differential, or derivative.

---

[3]In mathematics, we often simplify equations by leaving certain things out of consideration. So, for instance, an equation for $\frac{dp}{dt}$ probably won't include the changes in population due to alien abduction.

—   Example 15.3

A large jug of water has an open top, but has leak in the bottom. If we are adding water to the jug, write an equation describing the changes in the amount of water in the jug.

In this case, there are two components to the change in the amount of water—the amount of water being poured in and the amount of water draining.

So, we will use w as being the total amount of water in the jug. Therefore, the total rate of change in w can be given as $\frac{dw}{dt}$. Since $\frac{dw}{dt}$ represents the total rate of change, it will be the sum of its component changes.

That means that we need variables to represent the water leaving through the leak and the water entering through the top. We can call the water coming in as $\frac{dE}{dt}$, where e is the amount of water that enters the jug. We can call the water going throught the leak as $\frac{dL}{dt}$.

Now, there are actually two ways to write this equation, depending how how we want to account for the water draining out of the leak. We can either say that we are account for water flow through the leak, in which case positive values of $\frac{dL}{dt}$ will cause us to lose water in w, or we can say that we are doing everything from the perspective of water in the jug, so that when water leaks out, it counts as a negative flow. In this case, the values of $\frac{dL}{dt}$ will be negative when it leaks.

I prefer the latter, because it makes the math simpler on more difficult equations. Therefore, we can just write up the changes in w as being the total of all of the causes of the changes:

$$\frac{dw}{dt} = \frac{dE}{dt} + \frac{dL}{dt}$$

The other way, considering water flowing through $\frac{dL}{dt}$ is positive, would be to say:

$$\frac{dw}{dt} = \frac{dE}{dt} - \frac{dL}{dt}$$

The reason to use this latter equation would be for engineering purposes. If you had a water flow detector on the leak, it might report positive values for the flow rate of the liquid, because the flow detector might not know which direction is "positive."

Therefore, while the first version is preferred in general, there are many reasons why you might need to use the second one instead. The main point is to keep clear in your mind what positive and negative values for each differential *really means*, because the first step in solving a math problem is to get the philosophy right!

15.5   Derivatives in Physics

Physics is largely based on derivatives and integrals. The way that physicists often look at the world is in terms of position and time. Objects are always moving around (otherwise life would be very boring). The change in an object's position relative to the change in time is called *velocity* in physics. I hope that you recognized the language there—*change*. Anytime you hear the word change, you should think about differentials. And, in this case, it is change in position relative to the change in time—a rate.

Thus, we can see that velocity (often written using the variable v) is the first derivative of position with respect to time. This is often written as $v = \frac{dp}{dt}$ or $v = p'$ (to use Newtonian notation).

Going further, the change in velocity over time is known as acceleration. This is essentially the derivative of the derivative. Thus, we can write $a = \frac{dv}{dt}$ (to recognize that acceleration is the derivative of velocity) or we can write it as $a = p''$ (to use Newtonian notation). There is also a Liebniz notation for the second derivative, but it is a somewhat complicated subject. If you are interested, information on that is found in Appendix B.

Other derivatives of position exist, but are lesser used. Jerk is the third derivative of position. The fourth, fifth, and sixth derivatives of position are sometimes affectionately referred to as "snap, crackle, and pop," though the fourth also goes by the somewhat more technical name of "jounce."

For second derivatives (and higher derivatives), we will use the method outlined in Chapter 13 where we will simply substitute in a new variable for the first derivative, and then take the derivative of that new variable.

— Example 15.4

The position p (in feet) of an object on a line at time t (in seconds) is given by the equation $p = t^4 - \sin(t) + 5$. What is the acceleration of this particle at time $t = 5$ seconds?

Acceleration is simply the second derivative of position. Therefore, we will start by calculating the first derivative:

The first derivative is:

$$p = t^4 - \sin(t) + 5 \qquad\qquad \text{original equation}$$

$$d(p) = d(t^4 - \sin(t) + 5) \qquad\qquad \text{differentiate}$$

$$dp = 4t^3\,dt - \cos(t)\,dt$$

$$\frac{dp}{dt} = 4t^3 - \cos(t) \qquad\qquad \text{first derivative}$$

$$v = 4t^3 - \cos(t) \qquad\qquad \text{velocity is the first derivative}$$

Acceleration is the derivative of velocity:

$$v = 4t^3 - \cos(t) \qquad\qquad \text{the equation for velocity}$$

$$d(v) = d(4t^3 - \cos(t)) \qquad\qquad \text{differentiate}$$

$$d(v) = 12t^2\,dt + \sin(t)\,dt$$

$$\frac{dv}{dt} = 12t^2 + \sin(t) \qquad\qquad \text{the derivative of velocity}$$

$$a = 12t^2 + \sin(t) \qquad\qquad \text{acceleration is the derivative of velocity}$$

Therefore, the acceleration of this object at time $t = 5$ seconds will be found by substituting 5 for t:

$$a = 12t^2 + \sin(t) \qquad\qquad \text{acceleration equation}$$
$$= 12(5)^2 + \sin(5)$$
$$= 300 + -0.9589$$
$$= 299.0411$$

The units on this are $\frac{in}{sec^2}$ (inches per second squared). The unit on the bottom is "seconds squared" because we have divided by seconds twice—once for each derivative. You can also think of it as "inches per second per second", or $\frac{\frac{in}{sec}}{sec}$.

15.6   An Advanced Example in Engineering

Engineering is one area where differentials and derivatives are used most often and most directly. This is because engineers often have to deal with moving around heat, concentrations, and other quantities, and have to do it relative to other factors, especially time.

For instance, if you have a tank of water that is being used to wash a series of components, you may need to know how much clean water needs to be added and how much dirty water needs to be removed in order to keep the total amount of dirtiness of the water in check.

Being able to think in terms of derivatives helps us to formulate such problems of rates. Such a problem has a number of rates:

- The rate of clean water entering
- The rate of dirty water leaving
- The rate of dirt entering the water
- The total change of dirt in the water

Each of these can be represented by some sort of rate, and a rate is simply a differential.

In the given scenario in this section (a cleaning tank with dirt entering, dirty water draining, and clean water incoming), let's say that we have a tank of 100 gallons, and the dirt is entering at a rate of 1 pound per hour. We will assume that the tank has a mechanism that keeps the water well-mixed. In other words, we will assume that the concentration of dirt will be equivalent everywhere. We will have no pockets of especially clean or dirty water.

Now, let's say that our specifications say that we cannot allow more than 4 pounds of dirt in the water at any given time. What can we do to achieve this? Well, one thing we could do would be to completely empty and refill the tank whenever the tank accumulates 4 pounds of dirt. However, that is both wasteful of water, and requires stopping production to empty and refill the tank. Is there a way to accomplish this without having arduous manual processes?

Well, we could be continually draining the tank and adding fresh water. This way, the water level in the tank never changes, but we are continually removing dirty water and adding clean water—essentially continuously cleaning the tank. Therefore, we need to find an equation that tells us at what rate we need to do this in order to keep the dirt in the water steady at 4 pounds.[4]

Now, we need to write an equation for how the dirt in the water changes. In order to do this, we will assume that the dirt doesn't add anything to the volume of the water, so we will assume that the amount of water coming in is the same as the amount of water going out, and the dirt adds weight but not volume.[5]

For this problem, there are two systems which are affecting the dirt in the water—dirt coming in and dirt going out. However, the rate of the dirt going out is going to depend on both the rate at which the water leaves as well as the concentration of the dirt in the water. Let's let w be the number of gallons of water, p be the number of pounds of dirt particles, and k be the rate at which we remove water from the tank (which is the same as the rate which we are filling it).

Note that because we are filling the tank at the same rate we are emptying it, w does not change (it can be treated as a constant variable). However, p (the poundage of the dirt particles) does change. Additionally, we can represent the concentration of dirt in the tank as a ratio between the number of particles in the tank, p, divided by the gallons of water in the tank, w. Therefore, $\frac{p}{w}$ will be the number of pounds of dirt for each gallon of water.

The number of dirt particles *leaving* is based on this number. Since we are removing *dirty water* at some rate k, the rate of just dirt that we remove will be $k \cdot \frac{p}{w}$ (note that we could also write this as $-k$ to indicate that the dirt is leaving, but leaving it as-is just means that we will get a negative number at the end, and should remember that this is because the dirt is leaving).

But, we are also gaining dirt at a rate of 1 gallon per hour from cleaning the objects. We will call this rate q, so it is easy to identify in the equations. So, since we are gaining dirt at the rate q and losing dirt at a rate of $k \cdot \frac{p}{w}$, that means that the total change in dirt particles in our tank can be given by the formula:

$$\frac{\mathrm{d}p}{\mathrm{d}t} = q + k \cdot \frac{p}{w}$$

Because q is 1 gallon per second, and w is 100 gallons, we can rewrite this with numbers as:

$$\frac{\mathrm{d}p}{\mathrm{d}t} = 1\frac{\text{pound}}{\text{hr}} + \frac{kp}{100 \text{ gallon}}$$

Now, the question asked to find the rate (k) at which the amount of dirt will stay steady at 4 pounds. To solve this, we need to remember what a derivative *is* (step 1 of math is philosophy!). The derivative is the amount of *change* in a variable compared to another variable (in this case, time). If we want the variable p to "stay steady" that means we want it to *not change*. Or, to put another way, we want the change to be zero.

Therefore, we can rewrite the equation as:

$$0 = 1\frac{\text{pound}}{\text{hr}} + \frac{kp}{100 \text{ gallon}}$$

Because we know we want p to be 4 pounds, we can simplify this further to:

$$0 = 1\frac{\text{pound}}{\text{hr}} + \frac{k \cdot 4 \text{ pound}}{100 \text{ gallon}}$$

---

[4]You may wonder why we chose to keep it steady at 4 pounds (the maximum allowed) and not some lower number. The 4 pounds gives us a target that uses the minimum amount of water. We can always flush more clean water in, but this gives us the limit for how little water we can use to get by.

[5]These sorts of simplifying assumptions help not only because it makes the equations easier for a book like this, but also makes the equations easier in real life. Dirt does take up volume, but water actually has a huge carrying capacity, and doesn't increase volume very much when dissolvable substances are added in.

Now we just need to solve for k:

$$-1\frac{\text{pound}}{\text{hr}} = \frac{k \cdot 4 \text{ pound}}{100 \text{ gallon}}$$

$$-\frac{1\frac{\text{pound}}{\text{hr}}}{\frac{4 \text{ pound}}{100 \text{ gallon}}} = k$$

$$-1\frac{\text{pound}}{\text{hr}} \cdot \frac{100 \text{ gallon}}{4 \text{ pound}} = k$$

$$-1 \cdot 25 \cdot \frac{\text{pound}}{\text{hr}} \cdot \frac{\text{gallon}}{\text{pound}} = k$$

$$-25\frac{\text{gallon}}{\text{hr}} = k$$

Therefore, in order to keep the amount of dirt steady at 4 pounds, the amount of dirty water that needs to be drained and replaced with clean water is 25 gallons per hour (the negative sign means that it is being drained).

Using techniques that you will learn in the next part of the book, we will be able to determine that, if we start out with a clean tank, the amount of dirt in the tank at any point in time can be calculated by the following formula:

$$p = \frac{qw}{k}\left(e^{\frac{kt}{w}} - 1\right)$$

This is evaluated in Example 23.2.

15.7   Going the Other Way

The derivative is actually used even more often going the other way—finding relationships which *are* derivatives and using them to find static relationships.   Doing that is the reverse of differentiation—integration, which will be the subject of the next part of the book. Knowing the differential is key to not only being able to perform integration, but also to *recognize* when you are looking at a differential. Are you measuring the static size of something or its dynamic state—its relationship with time or with other quantities? If you are measuring its dynamic state, then you are probably measuring a derivative of some sort or another.

For instance, bank savings accounts are often advertised by their interest yield. What is interest yield? Interest yield is the change in account value over time.

Therefore, if a bank says that the account yields 2% interest per year (compounded continuously), that means that the *change in money* is occurring at a rate of 0.02 times the amount of money currently in the account per year.[6] In other words, if m is money and t is time, the equation reads:

$$\frac{dm}{dt} = 0.02m$$

---

[6]Note that since it is compounded *continously*, you will actually get more than 2% interest in this way. The point is that the *rate* is always 2%, not that the total amount that you get is 2%. You get more than that because, as the year goes by, there is more in the account (from prior interest) that continues to get interest payments.

You may have learned that the equation for continually compounded interest is the following:

$$m = p \cdot e^{rt}$$

where m is the total amount of money at the end of a given period, p is the starting amount of money (known as the "principal"), r is the yearly percentage rate, and t is the number of years. You may have wondered where this comes from. It actually comes from *reversing* the process of differentiation, which we will learn in the next part of the book.

But, for now, we can see that this is the case by taking the differential and solving for $\frac{dm}{dt}$ (keep in mind that p and r are both constants):

$$m = p \cdot e^{rt} \qquad \text{the equation for compound interest}$$
$$d(m) = d(p \cdot e^{rt}) \qquad \text{differentiate both sides}$$
$$dm = p \cdot e^{rt} r \, dt$$
$$\frac{dm}{dt} = r \cdot p \cdot e^{rt} \qquad \text{solve for } \frac{dm}{dt}$$

Now, this might not seem like the same equation that we had before, until you realize that in the first equation, it says that $m = p \cdot e^{rt}$. Thus, we can perform that substitution in the last equation:

$$\frac{dm}{dt} = r \cdot p \cdot e^{rt} \qquad \text{the starting derivative}$$
$$\frac{dm}{dt} = r \cdot m \qquad \text{substituting in } m$$

This is the same equation as we started with! The difference being that we used a specific r as 0.02, giving us $\frac{dm}{dt} = 0.02m$.

Now, it is interesting to note that the compound interest equation is not something that is intuitively obvious to most people, but the differential formula came *directly* from just talking about what we were meaning by our words. Thus, calculus allows us to start with intuitively obvious building blocks, and from there develop larger scale equations which were not immediately or intuitively obvious.

Much of physics, economics, biology, and other sciences are developed from this sort of mindset. If a problem can be broken down into its simplest, most intuitive form, more complicated formulas and equations can be built from that.

One of the great things about calculus is that it can be used to develop formulas that can be performed using only arithmetic and calculators. The interest formula here is a great example. You probably learned the interest formula in Algebra, but it was developed using calculus. You can often use calculus to *build* the formulas that you need, and then afterwards the formulas can be applied using only arithmetic.

Additionally, knowing calculus can help you re-build existing formulas for your own needs. Knowing calculus helps you see where other formulas are constructed from. Therefore, if a formula doesn't quite fit your needs, you can deconstruct it and reconstruct it as needed. You will need much more calculus practice to employ this idea effectively, but hopefully you can see that this is where these ideas are leading.

Review

In this chapter, we learned:

1. Finding the slope between variables in an equation allows us to find out all sorts of information about the equation that was difficult to do beforehand.

2. Finding where slopes are zero allow us to find tops (maximas), bottoms (minimas), and points of stasis (i.e., where nothing changes).

3. Taking a differential allows us to convert static relationships among entities into dynamic ones.

4. When a differential is divided by the differential of time (usually dt), it yields a rate.

5. When a relationship (i.e, an equation) of differentials is divided by the differential of time, the result is a relationship (an equation) of rates, with the equation being known as a related rate equation.

6. Recognizing the presence of differentials and derivatives in word problems is a key part to successfully applying calculus in real life.

7. Several keywords that indicate that calculus may be applicable are maximize, minimize, change, difference, slope, rate, speed, fast, velocity, acceleration, does not change, and keeps steady.

8. Learning to be comfortable in speaking, writing, and thinking in differentials is essential to applying calculus to problems.

9. Even though calculus deals with continuous entities, some discrete (i.e., non-continuous) entities act relatively continuous with a large enough number of items (i.e., populations).

10. Very small values can be used as stand-ins for differentials in equations. However, since differentials are assumed to be infinitely small, such substitutions (and the result results) should only be considered approximations.

11. Given a quantity x, the differential (i.e., dx) refers to the total of *all* of the changes to x for any reason. If dx is composed of distinguishable causes, none of the individual causes alone should be listed as dx because dx should only refer to the total change in the variable for all considerations.

12. Calculus helps us create equations that can be used over and over again—the calculus itself is often used once to help create a new algebraic formula.

13. Large portions of physics are based on derivatives and integrals.

14. The derivatives of position with respect to time are known as: velocity, acceleration, jerk, snap (or jounce), crackle, and pop.

15. Engineers often use the derivative to relate flows of heat, particles, liquids, and gasses, in order to balance out the results of different processes happening within a system.

16. One important use of differentials and derivatives is in going the other way—we can recognize that a quantity that we are looking at is a derivative of some sort, and then we can recognize that reversing the derivative (which is the subject of the next part of the book) will tell us more about the static relationships that exist.

Exercises

1. Jan has a jug full of water. The amount of water in the jug is w. What term would you use to refer to the total rate of change in the amount of water in the jug?

2. In the previous question, let's say that no water was being added, but water was leaving through (a) a leak, and (b) evaporation. Write an equation for the total rate of change of water that incorporates these causes.

3. The speed of gas flowing into a factory is twice the the speed of liquid leaving the factory. Write out this relationship using derivative notation.

4. The bank account pays 4% interest per year (compounded continuously) on savings accounts. Write this out in differential notation.

5. If my position p along a road (in meters) after t seconds is given by the equation $p = t^2$, what is my velocity after 10 seconds.

6. The number of students at the school is given by S. The number of students change throughout the year due to enrollment (which adds students), graduation (which removes them), and drop-outs (which also removes them). Write an equation for the change in students over time.

7. If my position p along a road (in meters) after t seconds is given by the equation $p = t^3$, what is my velocity after 10 seconds?

8. If my position p along a road (in meters) after t seconds is given by the equation $p = 5t$, what is my acceleration?

9. In a given engine, there is usually an optimal speed at which the engine runs (given as revolutions-per-minute, or RPM), such that its ability to convert energy into work is maximized. If I had an equation which related RPM to the ability to convert energy to work, how would I (in general terms) find the maximum value?

Part III

The Integral

The integral is the second major operation of calculus, and it is defined as being the inverse of the derivative. In its essence, the integral is an infinite sum of infinitely small values. The integral can be used for a variety of purposes, including finding areas and volumes defined by curves.

Chapter 16

The Integral as an Antidifferential

In Part II of this book, we spent a lot of time learning about differentials and differentiation. In this part, we are going to focus on the reverse process—**integration**.

In Chapter 6, we introduced the integral as the area under the curve. In this part, we are going to see that that is just one of the many *applications* of the integral, though it is a powerful one, as many problems can be modeled as the area under the curve.

We will be looking at the integral using two basic but related approaches:

1. The integral as an antidifferential operator (this chapter)

2. The integral as an infinite sum (Chapter 17)

After understanding what an integral *is*, we will look at how the integral can be applied to geometrical questions such as areas, lengths, and volumes. Then, we will look at specific techniques for computing integrals. Finally, we will look at how the integral can be applied in a wide variety of fields to model large-scale relationships.

In this chapter, we will focus on the integral as an antidifferential operator.

16.1   Antidifferentiation with the Integral

The most general way of thinking about the integral is that *the integral is simply the operator that reverses differentiation.* The integral is basically the "undo" operation of the differential.

Every mathematical tool you have encountered so far as a "reverse" (technically known as an *inverse*) operation. For addition it is substraction; for multiplication it is division; for exponentiation it is the logarithm. For the differential it is the integral. The integral operator is usually written as $\int$, which is merely an elongated "S," the reason for which will be explained in Chapter 17.

For instance, if we have the expression x^2, the differential is $2x \, dx$. Therefore, the integral of $2x \, dx$ is x^2 (technically, as we will see in Section 16.2, it is actually $x^2 + C$). Therefore, we would write, $\int 2x \, dx = x^2$, and read it as "the integral of two-ex dee-ex is ex-squared."

So, for a given function $f(x)$, we can essentially say that:

$$\int d(f(x)) = f(x)$$

This says that the integral of the differential of a function is the function itself. In other words, if we take the differential, and then reverse it with the integral, we will get back the original function. As we will see in Section 16.2, there are some caveats to this, but it is a good way to think about it.

Alternatively, we can go in the other direction as well. We can say that:

$$d\left(\int f(x)\, dx\right) = f(x)\, dx$$

Note that since integration is the reverse process of differentiation, it only makes sense to use on functions, formulas, and equations which contain some form of differential. Additionally, it only works on the kinds of functions that calculus generally works with (i.e., smooth and continuous functions).

— Example 16.1

What is $\int dx$?

Since the integral is the reverse process of differentiation, you simply need to ask yourself, what would the original expression have been which, when differentiated, would give dx? The answer is simple—x.

Since $d(x) = dx$ then $\int dx = x$.

— Example 16.2

What is $\int e^x\, dx$?

Since the integral is the reverse process of differentiation, you simply need to ask yourself, what would the original expression have been which, when differentiated, would give $e^x\, dx$? The answer is simple—e^x.

Since $d(e^x) = e^x\, dx$ then $\int e^x\, dx = e^x$

— Example 16.3

What is $\int \frac{v\, du - u\, dv}{v^2}$?

You might recognize the formula we are integrating as being the result of the quotient rule. The quotient rule says:

$$d\left(\frac{u}{v}\right) = \frac{v\, du - u\, dv}{v^2}$$

Therefore, integrating will give us back the original formula:

$$\int d\left(\frac{u}{v}\right) = \frac{u}{v}$$

The integral is a simple enough concept, but, as we will see in the forthcoming chapters, there are a lot more practical issues that come up when performing complicated integrals than there were for differentials. Nonetheless, for the most part, you are halfway to being proficient at integration from your study of differentials.

16.2   The Integral is a Family of Functions

In the previous section we said that since the differential of x^2 is $2x\,dx$, then the integral of $2x\,dx$ is x^2. That is not entirely true. The fact, is, we cannot know *exactly* what the integral of any differential is.

To see what the problem is, think about what the differential of $x^2 + 5$ is:

$$d(x^2 + 5) = d(x^2) + d(5)$$
$$= 2x\,dx + 0$$
$$= 2x\,dx$$

So, you can see, *both* x^2 and $x^2 + 5$ have the differential $2x\,dx$! In fact, because the differential of *any* constant becomes zero, there are an infinite number of functions that have the differential $2x\,dx$, one for each constant that could be added. Therefore, if we have the differential $2x\,dx$, we don't know which of those infinite functions it came from! Therefore, to represent this fact, the integral of $2x\,dx$ is not written not as x^2, but $x^2 + C$. This C represents the following facts:

1. the original function could have had any constant added to it, and it would have the same derivative

2. we have no idea from looking at the derivative which constant it should be

Therefore, we are using C to indicate a constant value (i.e., it never changes), but it is a constant for which *we don't know what the value of it is.*

Therefore, for every integral you do, you *must* add $+C$ to the end in order to represent the fact that the integral could have any constant added to it and it would remain a valid result of integration.

This value, C, is known as the *constant of integration.*

Another way of stating this is that the differential is a "lossy" operation. You actually throw away information about the original equation when you perform a differential. This is different than most other mathematical operations you have encountered. You don't lose any information when adding that you can't get back by subtracting. You don't lose any information when multiplying that you can't get back by dividing (except when multiplying by zero). However, you do lose information when differentiating. Therefore, when doing the reverse process (integration), the $+C$ at the end represents the fact that we simply can't tell what the original constant would have been.

Figure 16.1: Basic Integral Rules

Rule Name	Differential Rule	Related Integral Rule
Simple Variable Rule	$d(u) = du$	$\int du = u + C$
Addition Rule	$d(u + v) = d(u) + d(v)$	$\int (du + dv) = \int du + \int dv$
Constant Multiplier Rule	$d(n \cdot u) = n \cdot d(u)$	$\int n \cdot du = n \int du$
Power Rule	$d(u^n) = n \cdot u^{n-1} du$	$\int u^n du = \frac{u^{n+1}}{n+1} + C$
Natural Logarithm Rule	$d(\ln(u)) = \frac{du}{u}$	$\int \frac{du}{u} = \ln(|u|) + C$
Exponential Rule	$d(e^u) = e^u du$	$\int e^u du = e^u + C$

If there are multiple integrations involved (such as the result of splitting an integral using the addition rule), you only need to add a single $+C$ at the end. The reason for this is that, although each integral operation could have a constant of integration, since each constant is an arbitrary constant, the result of adding them together is also an aribtrary constant.

So, instead of saying $\int dx + \int dy = x + C_1 + y + C_2$, we can just say:

$$\int dx + \int dy = x + y + C$$

Since we didn't know C_1 and C_2 anyway, $C_1 + C_2$ is just as arbitrary, and, since it is a constant, can just be represented as C.

16.3   Basic Integration Rules

The basic rules of integration are simply the rules of differentiation in reverse. The biggest difference (that we will encounter in a later chapter) is that the chain rule on the integral, while based on the same premises, is much more difficult to apply on integrals, but we will save that discussion for Chapter 19.

So, for instance, using the power rule, we can see that $d(x^4) = 4x^3 dx$. That means that $\int 4x^3 \, dx = x^4 + C$. The power rule for differentials has us taking the exponent and moving it out front as a multiplier, and then decreasing the exponent by one. Therefore, to perform the integral we just do the reverse process. First, we *increase* the exponent by one. Then, we take the new exponent, and use it as a divisor.

So, as a general form, we would write this rule as:

$$\int u^n du = \frac{u^{n+1}}{n + 1}$$

A short set of basic integral rules is given in Figure 16.1. A more complete listing can be found in Appendix H.7. This table can be used just like the table of differentials in Appendix H.6. If you hit upon an integral form that you don't know how to integrate, don't forget to check the appendix.

If you have memorized the rules of differentiation, then the basic rules of integration should be no problem, since they are simply the reverse process. Let's turn to a few example problems.

— **Example 16.4**

Find $\int x^5 \, dx$.

For this example, we simply use the power rule, which states $\int u^n \, du = \frac{u^{n+1}}{n+1} + C$. Therefore, the power increases from 5 to 6, and we divide it by our new power, 6. Therefore, it becomes:

$$\int x^5 \, dx = \frac{x^6}{6}$$

Adding the constant of integration, we get:

$$\int x^5 \, dx = \frac{x^6}{6} + C$$

— **Example 16.5**

Find $\int 2x^2 \, dx$.

This is very similar to the previous problem, except that we have a constant multiplier out front. According to the constant multiplier rule, we can rewrite this expression as:

$$2 \int x^2 \, dx$$

So, the solution to this problem can be obtained as follows:

$$\int 2x^2 \, dx = 2 \int x^2 \, dx \qquad \text{constant multiplier rule}$$

$$= 2 \cdot \frac{x^3}{3} \qquad \text{power rule}$$

$$= \frac{2}{3} x^3 \qquad \text{simplified}$$

$$= \frac{2}{3} x^3 + C \qquad \text{add in constant of integration}$$

— **Example 16.6**

Find $\int (x^3 \, dx + 3 \, dx)$.

This can be solved by first applying the addition rule, and then using the power rule and the constant multiplier rule.

$$\int (x^3\,dx + 3\,dx) \qquad\qquad \text{the original integral}$$

$$= \int x^3\,dx + \int 3\,dx \qquad\qquad \text{addition rule}$$

$$= \frac{x^4}{4} + C_1 + \int 3\,dx \qquad\qquad \text{power rule for integrals}$$

$$= \frac{x^4}{4} + C_1 + 3\int dx \qquad\qquad \text{constant multiplier rule}$$

$$= \frac{x^4}{4} + C_1 + 3x + C_2 \qquad\qquad \text{simple variable rule}$$

$$= \frac{x^4}{4} + C_1 + 3x + C_2 \qquad\qquad \text{simple variable rule}$$

$$= \frac{x^4}{4} + 3x + C_1 + C_2 \qquad\qquad \text{rearranging}$$

$$= \frac{x^4}{4} + 3x + C \qquad\qquad \text{combining unknown constants}$$

Notice how each integrals yields its own additional constant, C_n. They are listed it as C_n so you could tell which integral the constant came from.

Even though each integral has its own constant, since we don't know the value of the constant anyway, we can combine them all together at the end into a single unknown constant. In other words, since C_1 and C_2 are arbitrary values, then when they are added together, we get another arbitrary value. Therefore, we can combine them all into a single arbitrary value, C.

In the future, we will not show every C_n produced by every integration, but instead just add a $+C$ at the end of the process to represent them all.

—   Example 16.7

Find $\int (7x^5 + \frac{1}{x} - 12)\,dx$.

This is very similar to the previous example, except that we will need to first multiply dx through the equation before solving. Additionally, the first term will use both the power rule and the constant multiplier rule.

$$\int (7x^5 + \frac{1}{x} - 12)\,dx \qquad\qquad \text{original integral}$$

$$= \int (7x^5\,dx + \frac{1}{x}\,dx - 12\,dx) \qquad\qquad \text{multiple } dx \text{ through}$$

$$= \int 7x^5\,dx + \int \frac{1}{x}\,dx - \int 12\,dx \qquad\qquad \text{addition rule}$$

$$= 7\int x^5\,dx + \int \frac{1}{x}\,dx - 12\int dx \qquad\qquad \text{constant multiplier rule}$$

$$= 7\frac{x^6}{6} + \int \frac{1}{x}\,dx - 12\int dx \qquad\qquad \text{power rule}$$

$$= 7\frac{x^6}{6} + \ln(|x|) - 12\int dx \qquad\qquad \text{natural logarithm rule}$$

$$= 7\frac{x^6}{6} + \ln(|x|) - 12x \qquad\qquad \text{simple variable rule}$$

$$= 7\frac{x^6}{6} + \ln(|x|) - 12x + C \qquad\qquad \text{add in the constant of integration}$$

Note that $\frac{1}{x}$ looks like a power rule (because it is x^{-1}), but it is actually the differential of the natural logarithm.

16.4   Using the Differential to Validate an Integral

By this point in the book, you should be a pro at differentiation. Because integration is the opposite of differentiation, you should be able to check your integrals fairly easily by simply reversing the process (i.e., finding the differential of your integral) and checking to see if it matches the original differential that you were integrating.

— Example 16.8

Find $\int(\frac{1}{x}\,dx + x^2\,dx)$ and check your answer using differentiation.

For this problem, we first notice that the outermost function is addition. Therefore, we can use the addition rule to separate this into two integrals: $\int \frac{1}{x}\,dx + \int x^2\,dx$. The first one is simply the logarithm rule, which yields $\ln(|x|) + C$, and the second one is a power rule, which yields $\frac{x^3}{3} + C$.[a] Combining them together (and combining the constants of integration), we get:

$$\ln(|x|) + \frac{x^3}{3} + C$$

Now we neeed to check this by differentiation:

$$d\left(\ln(|x|) + \frac{x^3}{3} + C\right) =$$

$$d(\ln(|x|)) + d\left(\frac{x^3}{3}\right) + d(C) \qquad \text{addition rule}$$

$$d(\ln(|x|)) + \frac{1}{3}\,d(x^3) + 0 \qquad \text{constant multiplier rule}$$

$$\frac{1}{x}\,dx + \frac{1}{3}\cdot 3x^2 \qquad \text{logarithm rule and power rule}$$

$$\frac{1}{x}\,dx + x^2 \qquad \text{simplifying}$$

This is the differential we started out with, so that means that our integration was correct.

---

[a]Note that while the differential of $\ln(x)$ is $\frac{dx}{x}$, the integral of $\frac{dx}{x}$ is actually $\ln(|x|)$—the natural log of the *absolute value* of x. This asymetry between the differential and the integral may seem strange. The reason for this is that $\ln(|x|)$ is valid for a larger set of x values than is $\ln(x)$, which is not valid for negative values of x. $\ln(|x|)$ is valid for both positive and negative values, and the derivative is correct. In other words, previously, when dealing with functions having a logarithm of x, we were implicitly assuming that $x > 0$. However, with $\ln(|x|)$ we don't have to assume that, and we only have to assume that $x \neq 0$. It isn't necessarily wrong to integrate $\frac{dx}{x}$ to $\ln(x)$, but it just means your result is only valid for a restricted range of x (i.e., $x > 0$).

16.5   Integrating Both Sides of an Equation

The basic reason for performing an integral is to take a relationship between differentials (which we have often referred to as a "dynamic relationship") and find the static relationships among the original variables. That is, if we have an equation which tells us how dy and dx relate to each other, then integrating that equation show us how y and x relate to each other by themselves.

When dealing with equations, the rule is always—"you can do whatever you want to an equation, *as long as you do the same thing to both sides!*" The same is true with integrals.

So, let's say that I have a simple equation:

$$dy = 5x\,dx$$

If I want to know the original relationshp between y and x, I can simply integrate both sides:

$$dy = 5x\,dx \qquad \text{the original differential}$$

$$\int dy = \int 5x\,dx \qquad \text{integrate both sides}$$

$$\int dy = 5\int x\,dx \qquad \text{constant multiplier rule}$$

$$y + C_1 = 5\frac{x^2}{2} + C_2 \qquad \text{simple variable rule and power rule}$$

$$y = 5\frac{x^2}{2} + C_2 - C_1 \qquad \text{put constants of integration on the same side}$$

$$y = 5\frac{x^2}{2} + C \qquad \text{coalesce our two constants of integration}$$

Note that even though each side generated a constant of integration, we easily coalesced them into a single constant. Since they were both arbitrary constants, subtracting one from the other still yields an arbitrary constant.

Now, let's say I am given a derivative (i.e., $\frac{dy}{dx}$) and I want to find the original relationship between x and y. Before integrating this I would need to convert it into differential form.

For instance, let's say I have the following derivative:

$$\frac{dy}{dx} = 4x^3 - 2$$

To find the original relationship between the variables, we have to integrate the equation. However, before we integrate it, we have to multiply both sides by dx so that each side is a differentiable that can be integrated.

$\frac{dy}{dx} = 4x^3 - 2$	the original equation
$dy = 4x^3\,dx - 2\,dx$	separating differentials
$\int dy = \int (4x^3\,dx - 2\,dx)$	integrate both sides
$\int dy = \int 4x^3\,dx - \int 2\,dx$	addition rule
$\int dy = 4\int x^3\,dx - 2\int dx$	constant multiplier rule
$y = 4\frac{x^4}{4} - 2x + C$	integrating
$y = x^4 - 2x + C$	simplifying

Note that if you are given a derivative ($\frac{dy}{dx}$) and asked to "integrate" it, then what that really means is that you are supposed to first get it into differential form, and *then* integrate both sides.

— Example 16.9

Find the integral of $\frac{dy}{dx} = \ln(x) + x^3$.

For this one, we will have to look in the back of the book (Appendix H.7). Don't forget to look there for integral rules if you need to!

We know how to take the *differential* of a natural log, but not its integral. The back of the book says that:

$$\int \ln(u) = u\ln(u) - u + C$$

So we will use that rule for this example.

$$\frac{dy}{dx} = \ln(x) + x^3$$

$$dy = \ln(x)\,dx + x^3\,dx$$

$$\int dy = \int (\ln(x)\,dx + x^3\,dx)$$

$$\int dy = \int (\ln(x)\,dx) + \int (x^3\,dx)$$

$$y = x\,\ln(x) - x + \frac{x^4}{4} + C$$

16.6   Things That You Cannot Yet Integrate

It may seem from the examples that you now know how to do integration as completely as differentiation. This is not the case. The goal of this section isn't to scare you, but merely to point out things that you cannot yet do with the tools that you have.

One of the biggest issues that I find with calculus students is that they are tempted to gloss over important subtleties, which leads them to wrong answers. For differentials, the biggest problem is to remember to use u-substitution in order to get the form of the differential to match the form in the table. If they don't match, you can't use the formula in the table.

Similarly, with integration, it is very important to be sure that the forms match *exactly* before performing the integral.

Let's say you want to solve $\int \cos(x^2)dx$. This is actually a very difficult integral. You might be tempted to say that the answer is $\sin(x^2)$, but that would be wrong. The reason is that the form that you can integrate is $\int \cos(u)\,du$. While you could set $u = x^2$, that only gives you $\int \cos(u)\,dx$, which is *not the same thing*. As a matter of fact, this may be surprising, but $\int \cos(x^2)\,dx$ doesn't have *any* solution in terms of our standard functions! For the standard functions, any smooth, continuous function has a derivative that also can be expressed using the standard functions. However, integrals are not the same, as we will discover in Chapter 19.

For now, however, you should focus on the fact that, for the integral to work, the forms must line up precisely. Therefore, until we get to Chapter 19, we cannot handle composite functions very well.

The main thing is to realize the limits of what the tools do, so that if you are posed with something that you cannot solve (or that is even completely unsolveable) you will be aware of it. In those cases, all is not lost—you can still often find numeric approximations. We will cover those techniques in Chapter 24.

Review

In this chapter, we learned:

1. The inverse process of differentiation is integration.

2. All integrals are actually a family of functions that all differ by a constant, known as the constant of integration, written as $+C$. This constant of integration should be added to all integrals.

3. Because the constant of integration is both arbitrary and constant, all constants of integration can be added together into a single $+C$ at the end.

4. When integrating both sides of an equation, you only need to add the constant of integration to one side.

5. The rules for integrating basic functions are merely the reverse of the rules for differentiating them.

6. Because the integral is the inverse process of differentiation, an integral can usually be verified by differentiating it and verifying that you wind up with the original expression.

7. Even though integrating is simply the reverse process of differentiation, as we will see in the future, it has some intrinsic issues that make it more difficult than differentiation on composite functions.

8. Integrating an equation allows you to convert an equation for differentials (what we have called "dynamic relationships") into an equation for the basic variables themselves (what we have often called "static relationships").

9. For equations, you can take the integral as long as you take the integral of both sides of the equation.

10. If an equation is in derivative form (i.e., $\frac{dy}{dx} = something$), then you first need to convert the equation into differential form before applying the integral (i.e., multiply both sides by dx).

11. Appendix H.7 lists out many integrals you may need to know. If you don't know how to do a particular simple integral, check in this table.

12. Remember that the integral must match the formula exactly in order to use an integral from the table. The chain rule in integration is much more difficult to apply than in differentiation, and will be covered in Chapter 19.

13. Even though you can take the differential of any equation that uses standard functions and have the result be in terms of standard functions, this is not true for integrals. Many integrals (even very simple ones) cannot be expressed in terms of standard functions.

Exercises

Integrate the following:

1. $\int dx$

2. $\int x \, dx$

3. $\int x^7 \, dx$

4. $\int (x \, dx + x^2 \, dx)$

5. $\int 3e^x \, dx$

6. $\int \frac{1}{x} \, dx$

7. $dy = 3x^2 \, dx$

8. $y \, dy = \sin(x) \, dx$

9. $\frac{dy}{dx} = \cos(x) + 2^x$

10. $\frac{dy}{dx} = \tan(x) - e^x - x^4$

11. $\cos(y) \, dy - y^2 \, dy = \sin(x) \, dx + 5x^2 \, dx$

Chapter 17

The Integral as an Infinite Sum

In Chapter 16 the integral was introduced as the antidifferential. But does the operation itself have a meaning? When we are taking an integral, what are we actually finding?

This chapter will focus on the meaning of the integral as an infinite sum of infinitely small values.

This explanation is a little complicated, so it is explained twice in the first two sections. The third section boils it all down for what you need to be able to *do* to solve problems. Therefore, even if after reading the first two sections you don't understand *why* the integral works as an infinite sum, the third section will tell you how to make use of this fact anyway.[1]

You may be wondering why we would want to have an infinite sum of infinitely small values. The short answer is, trust me—we will find ample use for it in the coming chapters. There are an unlimited number of problems that we can model as infinite sums of infinitely small values.

Like most things in calculus, the performance of this operation assumes that the thing we are trying to find an infinite sum of is smooth and continuous over the range we are looking at.

17.1 The Integral as an Infinite Sum

17.1.1 Total Changes in Value

Have you ever had an older person tell you, "When I was your age I used to walk to school in the snow—uphill both ways!" The obvious nature of the joke is that a path cannot be uphill both ways and arrive back at the same point. To get back to the same point, you have to go uphill just as much as you go downhill.

This is true no matter how complicated the slope is. If you have five separate hills going to school, you have to retrace all five in order to get back home. In fact, even if you took a different route home, your total change in elevation will be exactly the same as it is with any other route.

If the school is 10 feet higher in elevation than your house, then, ultimately, to get to the school the grand total of your elevation changes have to be 10 feet, no matter what. Then, to get back home, the grand total of your elevation changes have to be −10 feet.

---

[1]Sometimes, for difficult subjects, learning the process itself will help reserve a place in your mind for figuring out why the process works at a later date.

The same thing is true in graphs. Let's say that I have a simple graph, where the y value goes straight from 2 to 6.

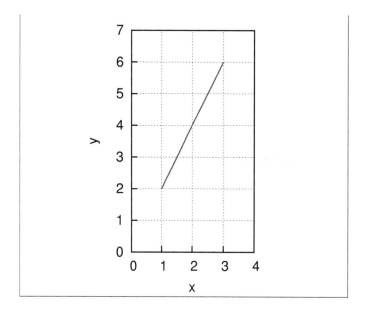

Now, the total change of the y value of this graph (from $x = 1$ to $x = 3$) is 4.

Let's look at a wavier graph:

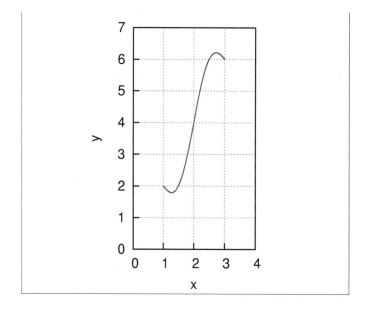

Now, even though the road is bumpier, the total change in y from $x = 1$ to $x = 3$ is *still* 4.

17.1.2   Total Changes are the Sums of Differentials

What does 4 represent in the graph above? It is the *sum total* of all of the changes in y that happens while x moves from 1 to 3.

So, being a *sum total* of the changes, that means that it is, in fact, a *sum*. What is it a sum of? It is the sum of *all of the changes* in y.

However, if you think about it, on a smooth graph, all of the changes are gradual, meaning that each individual change of the graph is infinitely small.

Now, think back to Chapter 10 (and, frankly, most of Part II of this book). What did we call an infinitely small change in y? We called it dy.

Therefore, the total change in y over a portion of the graph is the *sum* of all of the values of dy over that portion of the graph. Since dy is infinitely small, then the number of changes that are being summed is infinite. But, even though we are summing an infinite number of values, since the changes themselves are infinitely small, they add up to a finite value.

Therefore, on a given graph, the total change in the y values between two points is the infinite sum of all of the infinitely small changes in y.

To be more technical, let's call the starting point on our graph P_0 and the ending point P_1.

1. P_0 is located at the coordinates (x_0, y_0).
2. P_1 is located at the coordinates (x_1, y_1).

If y is a function of x (i.e., $y = F(x)$), then we can substitute $F(x)$ for the y value in each case. Therefore, we can say that:

1. P_0 is located at $(x_0, F(x_0))$.
2. P_1 is located at $(x_1, F(x_1))$.

Now, the total of all of the changes in y is simply $y_1 - y_0$. Since y is a function of x, then we can also say that $F(x_1) - F(x_0)$ gives us the sum total of all of the changes in y between x_0 and x_1.

If you think about it, "the sum total of all of the changes in y between x_0 and x_1" means the exact same thing as "the sum of every value of dy between x_0 and x_1." Therefore, we can say that:

$$\text{"the sum of all } dy \text{ values from } x_0 \text{ to } x_1 \text{"} = F(x_1) - F(x_0)$$

17.1.3 The Evaluation Bar

Another way of writing $F(x_1) - F(x_0)$ is using the evaluation bar. Instead of saying $F(x_1) - F(x_0)$ we can instead say $F(x)\Big|_{x_0}^{x_1}$, which reads as "the difference between F of x evaluated at x_0 and x_1."

We can write this as:

$$F(x)\Big|_{x_0}^{x_1} = F(x_1) - F(x_0) \tag{17.1}$$

Therefore, we can write our equation as:

$$\text{the sum from } x_0 \text{ to } x_1 \text{ of all } dy = F(x)\Big|_{x_0}^{x_1}$$

17.1.4   Using Antidifferentials (Integrals) to Find Infinite Sums

Now, do we know a way to get an equation for dy? Well, dy can be found by taking the differential of the equation. Therefore, if $y = F(x)$ then $dy = d(F(x))$.

So, we can rewrite this as:

$$\text{the sum from } x_0 \text{ to } x_1 \text{ of all } d(F(x)) = F(x) \Big|_{x_0}^{x_1}$$

Since $d(F(x))$ is a differential (by definition of what $d()$ means), then the antidifferential of $(d(F(x))$ is $F(x)$ by definition. Because the antidifferential *is* the integral, we can say that:[2]

$$\int (d(F(x))) = F(x)$$

Therefore, the difference between the integral evaluated at two different x-values gives us the sum of all of the changes of the y-values between those two x-values.

So, we can now say:

$$\text{the sum from } x_0 \text{ to } x_1 \text{ of all } d(F(x)) = \int d(F(x)) \Big|_{x_0}^{x_1}$$

or

$$\text{the sum from } x_0 \text{ to } x_1 \text{ of all } dy = \int d(F(x)) \Big|_{x_0}^{x_1}$$

When doing this, the constant of integration doesn't really matter—it more or less disappears. If we factor the constant of integration in, it gives us $F(x_1) + C - (F(x_0) + C)$, which becomes $F(x_1) + C - F(x_0) - C$, and the C's cancel out, yielding just $F(x_1) - F(x_0)$.

This makes sense graphically, because the total change in $F(x)$ doesn't matter if the graph is shifted up and down. If the total change in y value is 4, that will still be the same even if we shift the graph up or if we shift the graph down.

When looking at the sum of all dy values between two specific x-values, the integral is written as $\int_{x_0}^{x_1} dy$. This is called a **definite integral**, since we are looking for a specific amount of change within a defined (definite) range. The definite integral is merely the combination of the the indefinite integral and the evaluation bar.

In other words:

$$\int_{x_0}^{x_1} dy = \int dy \Big|_{x_0}^{x_1} = y \Big|_{x_0}^{x_1}$$

The lower and upper boundaries for the x values appearing on the integral are known as the **limits of integration**. Most of the time, these are just numbers, but you can also say specifically which variable is getting the limits of integration. This doesn't matter in simple cases, but later on, especially in upper-level calculus courses, it makes it easier to keep track of what you are doing.

---

[2]More technically, the integral is $F(x) + C$, because of the constant of integration, but we will see shortly that the constant of integration doesn't matter in this case.

So, if I was looking for the integral of $2x\,dx$ from $x = 2$ to $x = 5$, I could write that as:

$$\int_2^5 2x\,dx$$

Alternatively, I could write it as:

$$\int_{x=2}^{x=5} 2x\,dx$$

The former form is helpful because it is easier to write and read, the latter form is helpful because it is more specific.

— Example 17.1

Let's say that we have the differential $dy = 2x\,dx$ but not the original equation. What is the total change in y from $x = 3$ to $x = 5$?

To find the solution, remember that the total change in y will be the difference between the antidifferential of $2x\,dx$ evaluated at $x = 3$ and $x = 5$. Therefore, we can take the integral of both sides, from $x = 3$ to $x = 5$. We would write this as:

$$\int_3^5 dy = \int_3^5 2x\,dx$$

First, we need to convert the right-hand side to use the evaluation bar:

$$\int_3^5 dy = \int 2x\,dx \Big|_3^5$$

Next, we find the integral of $2x\,dx$ is $x^2 + C$, using the power rule. Therefore, the integral from $x = 3$ to $x = 5$ is going to be the difference between the antidifferential at those two places. Therefore, the right-hand side becomes:

$$\int_3^5 dy = x^2 + C \Big|_3^5$$

That vertical line means to evaluate the given expression at those two x values and subtract. Therefore, this becomes:

$$\int_3^5 dy = ((5)^2 + C) - ((3)^2 + C) = 25 - 9 = 16$$

Therefore, the sum of all dys from $x = 3$ to $x = 5$ is 16.

Notice again that since we are subtracting the two evaluations, the Cs cancel each other out. In other words, given any specific constant of integration, the constant of integration will cancel itself out when the two evaluations are subtracted, and therefore can be ignored.

To review, to find an infinite sum of infinitesimal changes in y (i.e., dy) between two values of x, you simply take the integral and evaluate it at the start and end values of x; then, subtract the value at the beginning from the value at the ending.

— **Example 17.2**

Find the total changes in dy from $x = -2$ to $x = 7$ when d$y = \cos(x)$dx.

To find the total changes in dy, we simply integrate dy and evaluate it at $x = -2$ and $x = 7$. Therefore, to solve, we apply the integral to both sides. This yields:

$$\int_{-2}^{7} dy = \int_{-2}^{7} \cos(x)dx$$

To solve this, we evaluate the antidifferential of $\cos(x)$dx and evaluate it at $x = -2$ and $x = 7$. The antidifferential of $\cos(x)$dx is simply $\sin(x)$. Therefore, this becomes:

$$\int_{-2}^{7} dy = \int_{-2}^{7} \cos(x)dx \qquad \text{the original integral}$$

$$= \sin(x) + C \Big|_{-2}^{7} \qquad \text{the antidifferential}$$

$$= \sin(7) + C - (\sin(-2) + C) \qquad \text{evaluating at } x = -2 \text{ and } x = 7$$

$$= \sin(7) + C - \sin(-2) - C \qquad \text{simplifying}$$

$$= \sin(7) - \sin(-2) + C - C$$

$$= \sin(7) - \sin(-2) \qquad \text{the constant of integration gets cancelled}$$

$$\approx 0.657 - 0.909 \approx -0.252$$

17.2   Another Way to Think About It

I often find that some ways of explaining a concept work for some students and not for others. Therefore, if you are still lost after the previous explanation, this section will attempt to explain it in a slightly different way.

The integral is the opposite of the differential, correct? So, if we have an equation in terms of differentials, we can get the original function that these were differentials for by integrating.

If we solve a differential for dy, so that dy is on the left hand side of the equation by itself, it will integrate to y, correct? In other words, $\int dy = y$.

If we wanted to know the total amount of change that happens in y from one point on the graph to another, then we simply just subtract the y at one point from the y at the other, correct? In other words:

$$\text{total change in } y = y_1 - y_0 \tag{17.2}$$

dy is an *infinitely small* change in y. If you were to be able to add up all of the values for dy between two points, it would tell you the total amount that y changed during this period.

In other words, the sum total of all dy between two points is the same as the difference in y values between these points. We can write this as follows.

Given two points, (x_0, y_0) and (x_1, y_1):

$$\text{the sum of all values of } dy \text{ between these points} = y_1 - y_0 \tag{17.3}$$

We can also express y as a function of x (let's call it $F(x)$)and say:

$$\text{the sum of all values of } dy \text{ between } x_0 \text{ and } x_1 = F(x_1) - F(x_0) \tag{17.4}$$

So, what is the relationship between dy and y? $y = \int dy$

In other words, $F()$ is just the integral of dy, which is also equal to the integral of the right-hand side of the equation.

Let's use an example. Let's say that $dy = 5x^2\, dx$. We want to know the sum of every value of dy from $x = 6$ to $x = 8$. How do we do this?

Well, according to Equation 17.3, all we need to do is to find the differences in y itself at these points. How do we find a formula for y? We simply integrate the equation.

$$dy = 5x^2\, dx$$

$$\int dy = \int 5x^2\, dx$$

$$y = \frac{5}{3}x^3 + C$$

Now it is easy to find the total change in y from $x = 6$ to $x = 8$. We just substitute them into the equation:

$$y = \frac{5}{3}x^3 + C \qquad\qquad \text{the equation for } y$$

$$y_0 = \frac{5}{3}(6)^3 + C \qquad\qquad \text{how to find } y_0$$

$$y_1 = \frac{5}{3}(8)^3 + C \qquad\qquad \text{how to find } y_1$$

Now, to find the total change, we just subtract these values:

$$\text{total change in } y = y_1 - y_0 \qquad\qquad \text{formula for the total change in } y$$

$$= \frac{5}{3}(8)^3 + C - (\frac{5}{3}(6)^3 + C) \qquad\qquad \text{substituting for } y_1 \text{ and } y_0$$

$$= \frac{5}{3}(8)^3 + C - \frac{5}{3}(6)^3 - C \qquad\qquad \text{simplifying}$$

$$= \frac{5}{3}(8)^3 - \frac{5}{3}(6)^3$$

$$= \frac{5}{3} \cdot 512 - \frac{5}{3} \cdot 216$$

$$\approx 853.3333 - 360$$

$$\approx 493.3333$$

Remember that the "total change in y" is the same as the infinite sum of all values of dy. Therefore, we can also say that "the sum total of all values of dy from $x = 6$ to $x = 8$ is 493.3333."

Note that we found the total sum of dy values by looking at the difference between the y values, and we got the formula for y by *integrating* the differential equation. Therefore, the integral of a differential evaluated at two points is the same as the sum of every value of the differential (all infinity of them) between those two points.

So, whenever we need an infinite sum of infinitely small values, we should look to the integral to give us the solution.

17.3   The Most Important Bits

If the previous two explanations didn't work, here are the important parts that you need to know for actually doing problems. Once you have done enough problems to be comfortable with the idea, you might come back and look harder at the theory behind it to see if you can understand it on a deep level.

In short, if you want to sum up an infinite number of infinitely small values, you use a definite integral.

To perform a definite integral, you perform the following steps:

1. Write out the definite integral. The definite integral should include the differential that you are wanting to sum up, and the limits of integration for the sum (i.e., the starting and ending x values).

2. Convert the definite integral to an indefinite integral with an evaluation bar. The limits of integration simply move from the definite integral to the evaluation bar.

3. Perform the indefinite integration (i.e., find the antiderivative), but you can ignore the constant of integration (i.e., the $+C$ is unnecessary).

4. Evaluate this result at the beginning (at the bottom) and end (at the top) values of the evaluation bar. Subtract the beginning value from the ending value.

5. Compute the resulting value.

For instance, to sum up all of the values $3x^2 \, dx$ from $x = -1$ to $x = 2$, we simply take the definite integral of the original formula from -1 to 2. In other words, we would write:

$$\int_{-1}^{2} 3x^2 \, dx$$

$$= \int 3x^2 \, dx \Big|_{-1}^{2}$$

$$= x^3 \Big|_{-1}^{2}$$

$$= (2)^3 - (-1)^3$$

$$= 8 - -1$$

$$= 8 + 1$$

$$= 9$$

Or, written another way:

Definite Integral		Indefinite Integral w/ Evaluation Bar		Integration Result		Evaluation		Evaluation Result
$\int_{-1}^{2} 3x^2 \, dx$	$=$	$\int 3x^2 \, dx \Big|_{-1}^{2}$	$=$	$x^3 \Big|_{-1}^{2}$	$=$	$(2)^3 - (-1)^3$	$=$	9

Every definite integral you solve should contain those steps.

— Example 17.3

Find the sum of all of the values of $x \, dx$ from $x = 6$ to $x = 10$.

The "sum of all values" is the same as the definite integral. The definite integral is simply written as:

$$\int_6^{10} x \, dx$$

The definite integral is merely the combination of the indefinite integral and the evaluation bar:

$$\int_6^{10} x \, dx = \int x \, dx \Big|_6^{10}$$

The integral of $x \, dx$ is $\frac{x^2}{2} + C$ using the power rule. However, the $+C$ can be ignored for definite integrals because it would get cancelled out in the next step anyway. Therefore, the equation can be written as:

$$\int_6^{10} x \, dx = \frac{x^2}{2} \Big|_6^{10}$$

The evaluation bar just says to find the difference of the function evaluated at the two points.

$$\int_6^{10} x \, dx = \frac{(10)^2}{2} - \frac{(6)^2}{2}$$

This becomes:

$$\int_6^{10} x \, dx = \frac{(10)^2}{2} - \frac{(6)^2}{2}$$
$$= \frac{100}{2} - \frac{36}{2}$$
$$= 50 - 18$$
$$= 32$$

Therefore, the sum of all of the values of $x \, dx$ from $x = 6$ to $x = 10$ is 32.

17.4 Two Cases of Summation

There are really two different cases where you might want an infinite sum of infinitely small values—when you have an equation containing the term you want to sum, and when you have only an expression you want to sum.

When you have an equation that contains a term that you would like to sum, in order to perform the summation properly, you have to *isolate* the term that you want to sum on one side of the equation. Then, you can perform a definite integral on both sides.

For instance, let's say I have the equation $\frac{dy}{x} = x^2 \, dx$ and I want to know the sum of all of the values of dy from $x = 2$ to $x = 10$. In order to solve this problem, I need to first isolate dy by itself on one side of the equation. This is easy enough to do, and it gives the equation $dy = x^3 \, dx$. Then, to perform the sum, we integrate both sides and evaluate.

The full set of steps is as follows:

$$\frac{dy}{x} = x^2\, dx \qquad\qquad \text{original problem}$$

$$dy = x^3\, dx \qquad\qquad \text{isolate the term we want to sum } (dy)$$

$$\int_2^{10} dy = \int_2^{10} x^3\, dx \qquad\qquad \text{integrate both sides}$$

$$= \int x^3\, dx \Big|_2^{10} \qquad\qquad \text{convert limits of integration to evaluation}$$

$$= \frac{x^4}{4} \Big|_2^{10} \qquad\qquad \text{perform integration}$$

$$= \frac{(10)^4}{4} - \frac{(2)^4}{4} \qquad\qquad \text{evaluate}$$

$$= 2500 - 4 \qquad\qquad \text{simplify}$$

$$= 2496$$

So the sum of all of the infinitely small values of dy from $x = 2$ to $x = 10$ is 2496.

Sometimes, instead of getting a full equation, we are just given an expression and asked for a sum. For instance, if we want to know the sum of all of the values of $\sin(x)\, dx$ from $x = 0$ to $x = \pi$, we would simply write it as an integral expression:

$$\int_0^\pi \sin(x)\, dx = \int \sin(x)\, dx \Big|_0^\pi \qquad\qquad \text{the integral and the evaluation bar}$$

$$= -\cos(x) \Big|_0^\pi \qquad\qquad \text{performing the integral}$$

$$= -\cos(\pi) - -\cos(0) \qquad\qquad \text{applying the evaluation bar}$$

$$= -\cos(\pi) + \cos(0) \qquad\qquad \text{simplifying}$$

$$= -(-1) + 1$$

$$= 2$$

Therefore, the sum of all of the infinitely small values $\sin(x)\, dx$ from 0 to π is 2. Or, another way to put it, is that the total change in the function $-\cos(x)$ from 0 to π is 2.

17.5 The Foundational Principles of Calculus

Here, we should take a moment and lay out what I consider the foundational principles of calculus.[3] These principles lay out the relationships between the differential and the integral in a straightforward way. The **principles of indefinite integration are:**

1. The differential and the indefinite integral are almost-inverses of each other.[4]

2. The indefinite integral is an entire family of possible functions, each differing by a constant. This is represented by adding in an abitrary constant C to the result of integration.

3. A specific constant of integration can usually be found by knowing a point at which the integral passes through, and solving for the constant of integration.

Likewise, there is a set of **principles of definite integration:**

1. On a smooth, continuous function, the definite integral represents the sum total of all differentials between the start and end values of the independent variable(s).

2. The beginning and ending values of the independent variable(s) are known as the limits of integration.

3. The definite integral can be found by first finding the indefinite integral (i.e., the inverse of the differential) and then evaluating the difference of the value of the function between the beginning and ending values of the limits of integration (i.e., applying the evaluation bar).

4. When doing definite integrals, the constant of integration can be ignored, because, whatever the value happens to be, it will be subtracted out when applying the evaluation bar.

These principles govern the relationship between differentials and integrals, and between indefinite and definite integrals.

17.6 Multiple Variables

It is also possible to do definite integrals with equations involving multiple independent variables. The only difference between having a single independent variable and multiple independent variables is that, with multiple variables, the limits of integration are more complicated.

Let's say that we have the differential expression: $du + dv - dx$ and we want to find the sum of all of these values between two points. With three variables, the starting and ending points will not just have an x value, but also starting and ending values for u and v.

So, if we wanted to know the total sum of all the values of $du + dv - dx$ from $u = 1, v = 3, x = 6$ to $u = 2, v = -1, x = 7$, we would write that as:

$$\int_{u=1, v=3, x=6}^{u=2, v=-1, x=7} (du + dv - dx)$$

---

[3]Most calculus books lay out what are known as the Fundamental Theorems of Calculus. These are very similar to what is laid out here, but I think these provide a better means of thinking about calculus. The First and Second Fundamental Theorems of Calculus are laid out in Appendix C.

[4]"Almost" because the differential loses information (all constants differentiate to zero), while the integral adds back in a constant of integration to compensate.

We would then solve it like this:

$$\int_{u=1,v=3,x=6}^{u=2,v=-1,x=7} (du + dv - dx) = \int (du + dv - dx) \Big|_{u=1,v=3,x=6}^{u=2,v=-1,x=7}$$

$$= \int du + \int dv - \int dx \Big|_{u=1,v=3,x=6}^{u=2,v=-1,x=7}$$

$$= u + v - x \Big|_{u=1,v=3,x=6}^{u=2,v=-1,x=7}$$

$$= (2) + (-1) - (7) - ((1) + (3) - (6))$$

$$= -6 - (-2)$$

$$= -4$$

So the infinite sum of all of the values $du + dv - dx$ between those points is -4.

This also works with full equations. If we have the equation $1 = 3\frac{dy}{dz} + 4x\frac{dx}{dz}$, and we want to know the sum of all of the values of dz from $x = 2$, $y = 7$ all the way to $x = 3$, $y = -1$, we can solve that by first isolating dz (the thing we want to sum) and then performing the integration.

The operation looks like this:

$$1 = 3\frac{dy}{dz} + 4x\frac{dx}{dz} \qquad\qquad \text{the original equation}$$

$$dz = 3\,dy + 4x\,dx \qquad\qquad \text{isolate } dz$$

$$\int_{x=2,y=7}^{x=3,y=-1} dz = \int_{x=2,y=7}^{x=3,y=-1} 3\,dy + 4x\,dx \qquad\qquad \text{integrate both sides}$$

$$= \int 3\,dy + 4x\,dx \Big|_{x=2,y=7}^{x=3,y=-1} \qquad\qquad \text{convert to evaluation bar}$$

$$= 3y + \frac{4x^2}{2} \Big|_{x=2,y=7}^{x=3,y=-1} \qquad\qquad \text{perform integration}$$

$$= 3y + 2x^2 \Big|_{x=2,y=7}^{x=3,y=-1} \qquad\qquad \text{simplify}$$

$$= (3(-1) + 2(3)^2) - (3(7) + 2(2)^2) \qquad\qquad \text{apply evaluation bar}$$

$$= -3 + 18 - 21 - 8 \qquad\qquad \text{simplify}$$

$$= -14$$

Therefore, the total change in dz over this range is -14.

Review

In this chapter, we learned:

1. Infinite sums can be found of infinitely small values, which may yield a value in terms of a real number.

2. The **definite integral** is just the regular indefinite integral, but evaluated at two points using the evaluation bar.

3. The evaluation bar specifies two points for evaluation of an expression, and then the evaluation of the expression using the bottom value is subtracted from the evaluation of the expression using the top value.

4. The two points where the definite integral is evaluated at are known as the **limits of integration**.

5. When performing a definite integral, the constant of integration can be safely ignored, as it is cancelled out by the subtraction of the two evaluations.

6. The definite integral can be used to calculate the infinite sum of infinitely small values.

7. Being asked to "find the value for a definite integral" and to "find an infinite sum of infinitely small values" are the same thing. Asking someone to "find the value for a definite integral" is used more often because it sounds less abstract.

8. The definite integral can be easily calculated for multiple variables as long as the limits of integration specify all of the needed variables

9. Finding an infinite sum of infinitely small values sounds weird, but it actually has numerous applications.

10. Don't forget that "an infinitely small change in x" usually simply means dx!

Exercises

Find the following definite integrals:

1. $\int_1^2 x \, dx$

2. $\int_7^{10} 6x^2 \, dx$

3. $\int_{-6}^{-2} (3x^2 - 4x + 3) \, dx$

4. $\int_0^1 e^x \, dx$

5. $\int_0^{2\pi} \cos(x) \, dx$

6. $\int_{-1}^4 e^x \, dx \quad \int_{x=2,z=3}^{x=5,z=6} x^2 \, dx - 2^z \, dz$

Find the given infinite sums:

7. Find the infinite sum of every value of $5x \, dx$ from $x = 2$ to $x = 8$.

8. Find the infinite sum of every dy from $x = -3$ to $x = 4$ where d$y = \sin(x) \, dx + x \, dx$

9. Find the infinite sum of every dy from $x = 1$ to $x = 2$, where $\frac{dy}{dx} = \frac{9}{x}$.

10. Find the sum of every dx from $y = 2, z = 3$ to $y = 6, z = 8$ for the equation d$x = y \, dy - 2z \, dz$

11. Find the sum of every dq from $x = 2, y = 1$ to $x = -1, y = 3$ for the equation $\frac{dq}{dx} + \frac{dy}{dx} = 5$

Chapter 18

Using the Integral to Find the Area Under the Curve

We introduced the integral in Chapter 6 as an *area* under a curve. Indeed, that is probably what it is best known for. However, I think that this is a bit of a misleading idea.

While the integral *is* antidifferentiation (Chapter 16) and the definite integral *is* an infinite sum (Chapter 17), the integral is merely *used to find* the area under the curve. This is a subtle difference but one that I think is important.

Finding areas under curves is not *what* the integral is, but it is an *application* of the concept of an integral.

In Chapter 17, you may have found the idea of infinite summation interesting (I certainly do!), but maybe you had trouble figuring out how it might be applied. This chapter shows the beginnings of how infinite sums can be used to solve a more concrete mathematical problem—finding the area beneath a curve.

18.1   Thinking About the Area Under a Curve

Let's say that we have the curve $y = \frac{x^2}{3}$:

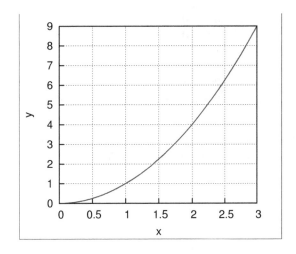

Note that this graph is drawn with x and y having different scales so it would be easier to see.

Now, let's say we want to find out the area *under* the curve from $x = 0$ to $x = 3$. How do we find such a number?

Let's say that we only wanted to estimate the area. What could we do then? If we were only interested in estimation, we could start by dividing the curve into small regions, and then using rectangles to estimate the area.

So, let's start by breaking up the curve into segments that are 0.5 wide, and then we will estimate the areas underneath each section:

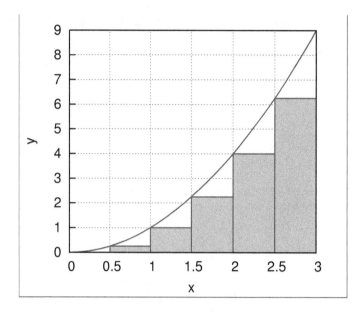

As you can see, by breaking it up into rectangles, we can approximate the area under the curve by simply adding up the areas of the rectangles. Remember, the area of a rectangle is simply *width · height*. Since the widths will all be 0.5, and the heights will be the y value, then the rectangles are simply $0.5y$. So, at $x = 0$, $y = 0$, so the rectangle is $0.5 \cdot 0 = 0$ square units. At $x = 0.5$, $y = 0.25$, so the rectangle is $0.5 \cdot 0.25 = 0.125$ square units. All of the measurements are given below:

x	y	**area** $(0.5y)$
0	0	0
0.5	0.25	0.125
1	1	0.5
1.5	2.25	1.125
2	4	2
2.5	6.25	3.125

These areas all add up to 6.875 square units. However, we can get a better estimate by making the change in x smaller. This time, instead of going by increments of 0.5, we will go by increments of 0.25:

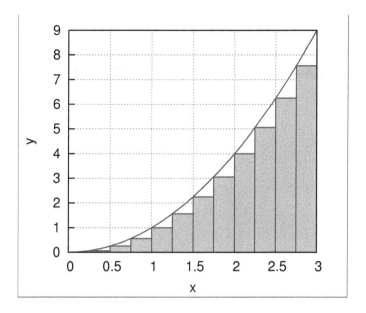

The location and areas for each rectangle is listed below:

x	y	**area** $(0.25y)$
0	0	0
0.25	0.0625	0.03125
0.5	0.25	0.125
0.75	0.5625	0.140625
1	1	0.25
1.25	1.5625	0.390625
1.5	2.25	0.5625
1.75	3.0625	0.765625
2	4	1
2.25	5.0625	1.265625
2.5	6.25	1.5625
2.75	7.5625	1.890625

If you add up the sizes of these rectangles, you get 7.96875. As the widths of the rectangles get smaller, the value gets closer and closer to the real area.

18.2   Finding the Real Area

So, we have a nice method of finding an estimate for the area, and we can get this estimate closer and closer to the "real" area by simply making the base of the boxes (i.e., the change in x values) smaller and smaller.

So how does one get to the "real" area? Exactly?

Let's take this process to completion. If we make the widths smaller and smaller, then we are eventually going to wind up at an infinitely small width. The width is the change in x. So, if the change in x is infinitely small, what do we call that?

Think back to the previous part of the book. What did we call infinitely small changes in x?

An infinitely small change in x is called dx.

Therefore, if we break this up into an infinite number of rectangles, each rectangle will have a base of dx. What will the height of the rectangle be? Just like before, the height will be y.

The area of a rectangle is simply width times height. The area of each rectangle, then, is $y\,dx$.

This value will be infinitesimal (infinitely small) because the rectangle itself is infinitesimal in width. But, what we want is the *sum* of all of the rectangles. What we have is an infinite sum of infinitely small quantities. As we learned in Chapter 17, that's exactly what an integral is!

Therefore, we can represent the area under the curve as:

$$\text{total area} = \int y\,dx$$

That is the general formula. However, since the curve goes on and on forever, what we really need is the area of the curve between certain points—the origin ($x = 0$) and our final destination ($x = 3$).

Therefore, we need a definite integral:

$$\text{area within between 0 and 3} = \int_{x=0}^{x=3} y\,dx$$

Unfortunately, we can't solve this as written.[1] We have a y and a dx. By themselves, they don't really mix using known integration formulas.

However, the original equation gives us a *formula* for y, so we can substitute that in! The original equation was $y = x^2$, so we can use x^2 to stand in for y.

Therefore, the new, *solvable* equation is:

$$\text{area} = \int_{x=0}^{x=3} x^2\,dx$$

This says that we want to know the infinite sum of the areas of the infinitely small rectangles formed by x^2 and dx from $x = 0$ to $x = 3$. To solve such an integral, we simply evaluate the antidifferential at $x = 0$ and $x = 3$. The antidifferential can be found simply with the power rule.

---

[1] I want to make a quick note about unsolvable formulas. In mathematics, it is actually *more important* to setup the equations correctly than to be able to work them. Even when an equation can't be solved, if you at least have it set up correctly, you can usually deduce truths about your equation, even if you can't find the exact answer. Knowing how to set up the equation means knowing the logical structure of the problem. Just having the insight to formulate a problem correctly is the largest part of the mathematical enterprise.

Therefore, this becomes:

$$\text{area} = \int_{x=0}^{x=3} x^2 \, dx$$

$$= \frac{x^3}{3} \Big|_{x=0}^{x=3}$$

$$= \frac{(3)^3}{3} - \frac{(0)^3}{3}$$

$$= 9 - 0$$

$$= 9$$

So the area between the curve, the x axis, $x = 0$ and $x = 3$ is 9 square units.

The general formula for this is given below:

$$\text{area} = \int_{x=\text{start}}^{x=\text{finish}} y \, dx \tag{18.1}$$

Then, in order to be able to perform the integration, you substitute y with its formula in terms of x. Then the equation is solved by finding the antidifferential, and solving for the given starting and ending points.

— Example 18.1

Find the area under the curve $y = e^x - \cos(x)$ from $x = 2$ to $x = 4$.

In order to solve this, we start with Equation 18.1:

$$\text{area} = \int_{x=\text{start}}^{x=\text{finish}} y \, dx$$

Now, we substitute y with our formula for y and evaluate it:

$$\text{area} = \int_{x=\text{start}}^{x=\text{finish}} y \, dx \qquad\qquad \text{Equation 18.1}$$

$$\text{area} = \int_{x=2}^{x=4} (e^x - \cos(x)) \, dx \qquad\qquad \text{substitute with the formula for } y \text{ and our own integration limits}$$

$$\text{area} = \int (e^x - \cos(x)) \, dx \Big|_{x=2}^{x=4} \qquad\qquad \text{convert integration limits to evaluation bar}$$

$$\text{area} = \int e^x \, dx - \int \cos(x) \, dx \Big|_{x=2}^{x=4} \qquad\qquad \text{addition rule}$$

$$\text{area} = e^x - \sin(x) \Big|_{x=2}^{x=4} \qquad\qquad \text{exponential and cosine rules}$$

$$\text{area} = (e^4 - \sin(4)) - (e^2 - \sin(2)) \qquad\qquad \text{apply the evaluation bar}$$

$$\text{area} = e^4 - \sin(4) - e^2 + \sin(2) \qquad\qquad \text{simplify}$$

area $\approx (54.5982) - (-0.7568) - (7.3891) + (0.9093)$

area ≈ 48.8752

The area under the curve between $x = 2$ and $x = 4$ is approximately 48.8752 square units.

18.3   The Area Between Two Curves

Once you know how to find the area under a curve, the next thing to consider is that sometimes you will need to find an area when have a curve on both the top *and* the bottom. This is actually very straightforward if you have grasped the idea of calculating the area beneath a curve.

The area between two curves is merely the area under the top curve subtracted from the area under the bottom curve.

So, let's say we wanted to find the area between the two curves $y = e^x$ and $y = x^2$ from $x = 1$ to $x = 2$. If you graphed these two equations, e^x is on the top, and x^2 is on the bottom. To find the area *between* them, you just subtract the areas from each other. You can either (a) calculate each area independently, then subtract, or (b) subtract the equations, then calculate the area. Because you are integrating both curves with the same limits of integration, these two methods give identical answers. We will use the first method.

To begin with, we will find the area under the top curve:

$$\text{area} = \int_1^2 e^x \, dx$$

$$= \int e^x \, dx \bigg|_1^2$$

$$= e^x \bigg|_1^2$$

$$= e^2 - e^1$$

$$\approx 4.6708$$

Next, we will find the area under the bottom curve:

$$\text{area} = \int_1^2 x^2 \, dx$$

$$= \int x^2 \, dx \bigg|_1^2$$

$$= \frac{x^3}{3} \bigg|_1^2$$

$$= \frac{(2)^3}{3} - \frac{(1)^3}{3}$$

$$= \frac{8}{3} - \frac{1}{3}$$

$$= \frac{7}{3}$$

$$\approx 2.3333$$

Therefore, the area between these curves is $4.6708 - 2.3333 = 2.3375$ square units.

18.4 The Relationship Between the Derivative and the Area Under the Curve

In Chapter 6, we demonstrated that the derivative was the equation for the slope of a curve at any point and that the integral was the area under a given curve. Not only that, but the derivative and the integral were essentially the opposite of each other. This relationship between slope and area has baffled many students. In fact, in the history of mathematics, the discovery of this relationship was quite a surprise—until the development of calculus, this relationship was largely unknown.

The question most people have is *why* are these two operations opposite of each other?

Let's look at the process for finding the slope of an equation and the area under the curve of an equation and see if we can understand this relationship.

The process for finding the slope (i.e., the derivative) of an equation where y is written as a function of x (i.e., $y = f(x)$) is as follows:

1. Start with the original equation solved for y in terms of x.

2. Take the differential of the equation.

3. Divide both sides by dx.

4. This new equation is the derivative.

The process for finding the area under the curve of an equation where y is written as a function of x is as follows:

1. Start with the original equation solved for y in terms of x.

2. Multiply both sides by dx in order to get an equation for infinitesimal rectangles.

3. Integrate both sides to find the infinite sum of those rectangles.

4. This new equation is the integral.

As you can see, these processes are opposite of each other. For the derivative, we take the differential and then divide by dx. For the integral, we first multiply by dx and then integrate. They are the exact opposite processes.[2]

---

[2]This relationship between the equations for area under the curve and the slope is known as the First Fundamental Theorem of Calculus. It is known as the "first" theorem because its discovery was first and more critical to the initial understanding of calculus. I don't give it as much prominence because I recognize it as an outgrowth of the *application* of the integral, not an intrinsic part of integration. I don't really like it that much because it limits our view of the integral to the case of two dimensions, while, as we learned in Chapter 17, viewing it as a sum of differentials does not limit the number of variables involved. It was certainly the first fundamental theorem in the *development* of calculus, but I would view the relationship between infinite sums of incremental changes and the antidifferential to be more fundamental.

18.5   The General Technique

We will revisit this several times in this part of the book, but I wanted to take a moment to talk about the general method that was used here. Since integration is the same as infinite summation of infinitely small values, we were able to convert our problem into just that form.

In our case, we were looking for the area under a curve. Therefore, we took the curve and divided it into infinitely small boxes. We then found the formula for each box (i.e., $y \, dx$). We then summed the formula over the desired range by performing a definite integral. In order to actually perform the definite integral, we had to replace y with the equation of y which we were given.

So, in general terms, we should:

1. Think about the original problem.

2. See if the problem is disible into infinitely small subproblems.

3. Find a formula for the infinitely small subproblem. Remember to use dx and dy (or whatever differential) to represent any infinitely small change in your variable you need.

4. Sum the formula over the desired range using a definite integral.

5. You may need to replace variables such as y with their formula in terms of other variables to be able to perform the integral.

18.6   Getting Terminology Straight

Throughout the book, we have thrown around a number of terms. The goal of this section is to make sure that they are being thought about consistently. In Chapter 6, we were not careful to be consistent because the goal was to introduce a number of new concepts. However, now that the main concepts are introduced, we should focus more on defining our terms consistent.

I almost titled this section "Getting Terminology Correct." The problem with the word "correct" is that different schools of thought use different terms for different things. Therefore, while there is no such thing as *correct* terminology, we can at least aim for *consistent* and *helpful* terminology.

The four main concepts that I want to be sure are distinguished in your mind are the following:

The Differential The differential of a variable or function is the infinitesimal change of that variable or function at a given point. Differentials are essentially almost zero (known as infinitesimals), but the ratios between differentials can yield real numbers.

The Derivative The derivative of a function is an equation where one side is the ratio of two differentials (i.e., $\frac{dy}{dx}$), which gives the the instantaneous slope between the base variables (i.e., y and x) at any given point.

The Integral The integral is the opposite of the differential, and it is synonymous with the idea of an antidifferential. It represents the total change of differentials over an unspecified region. This is also referred to as the Indefinite Integral.

The Definite Integral The definite integral is an integral with a specified region over which the total change in differentials is being measured. This region is specified using the limits of integration. While the definite integral is used to measure the total change in differentials, the term "definite integral" usually refers more to the *process* than to what you are trying to do with it.

The Area Under the Curve The area under a function's curve is the integral of the individual infinitesimal areas created by multiplying the function by the differential of the independent variable (usually dx).

Within these, there are two sets of operations that are inverses of each other. The first set of inverses is the differential and the integral. The differential operator takes a function and produces a differential function. The integral takes a differential function and produces the original function (though possibly differing by a constant).

The other set of operations that are inverses of each other are the derivative and the area under the curve. The derivative is obtained by taking the differential of a function and dividing by a differential of a variable (usually dx), and the integral is obtained by taking a function, multiplying by dx to produce a differential, and integrating it.

You can see this in the notation that is used:

- To take the differential of a function, the d() operator is used.

- To find the integral of a differential, the $\int$ operator is used.

- To take the derivative of a function, the $D_x()$ (also notated as $\frac{d}{dx}()$) operator is used.

- To find the area under a curve $y = f(x)$, we multiply by dx and then use the integral, giving $\int f(x)\,dx$.

The Integral	— is the opposite of —	The Differential
The Area Under the Curve	— is the opposite of —	The Derivative

Other books have slightly different usage for these terms, so if you take an advanced calculus course, pay careful attention to what they are calling things. For instance, many books use the term "integral" to refer to *both* the antidifferential *and* the area under the curve. You have to find out which one they are talking about from context. Other books refer to the indefinite integral as the antiderivative, and only the definite integral as the integral.

In short, the list of definitions I have given above are intended to be clear both in their usage and in their relationship to one another within this book, but you may find other definitions and usages elsewhere.

Review

In this chapter, we learned:

1. The integral can be used to find the area under a curve within a specific range.

2. To estimate the area of a region under a curve, the region can be broken up into equal-width boxes where the top of the box touches the curve, and the areas of each of these boxes can be summed up.

3. This estimate gets closer and closer to the true value as the width of each box decreases.

4. The estimate is *equal* to the true area when the width of each box is infinitely small (i.e., the width becomes dx).

5. Therefore, to find the area under a curve:

   (a) Begin with a function of some variable (i.e, x).

   (b) Multiply the function by that variable's differential (i.e., dx). This yields a function that tells the area of any single infinitely small box for a given x value.

   (c) Sum all of the areas of all of the infinitely small boxes over the required range by performing a definite integral of the new function using the specified limits.

6. The technique of infinite summation of differentials can be used to solve all sorts of problems.

7. Just as integration and differentiation are inverses of each other, so are finding the derivative and finding the area under a given curve.

8. Different books can use slightly different meanings for these words, but their meanings can usually be judged based on context.

Exercises

1. Find the area under the curve $y = 4$ from $x = 0$ to $x = 3$ using the method specified in this chapter. Then, draw the equation and see if there is some other way that you know of obtaining the area.

2. Find the area under the curve $y = 4x - 2$ from $x = 2$ to $x = 4$. What shape does this form on the graph?

3. Find the area under the curve $y = x^2 - 2x$ from $x = -1$ to $x = 0$

4. Find the area under the curve $y = e^x - \sin(x)$ from $x = 0$ to $x = \pi$.

5. Find the area under the curve $y = \frac{1}{x}$ from $x = 2$ to $x = 3$

6. Find the area under the curve $y = \frac{1}{x^2}$ from $x = 1$ to $x = 5$. You may need to think about other ways to write this in order to solve it.

7. Find the area under the curve $y = \ln(x)$ from $x = 1$ to $x = 7$. Note that this integral is not one that you would already know from differentiation, so you need to look it up in Appendix H.7.

8. Find the area under the curve $y = -x^2 - 2x - 1$ from $x = 2$ to $x = 4$.

9. Find the area *between* the curves $y = \sin(x)$ and $y = -x^2$ from $x = 0$ to $x = \pi$.

10. Which of the following operations are inverses of each other: differentiation, finding a derivative, integration, finding the area under a curve.

Chapter 19

Integration and u-Substitution

In Chapter 11 we learned how to do u-substitution in order to differentiate functions within functions. This is also known as the "chain rule." This concept also applies to the integral, but in reverse. However, as we will see, while the chain rule for the differential is straightforward and mechanical to apply, the same rule for integrals requires a lot more thought and effort, and sometimes trial and error.

19.1 Review of u-substitution

In Chapter 11, we learned the rules for differentiating a composite function. Anytime we want to find a differential of a composite function, the first step is to take the inner function and assign it a new variable name (usually u) and replace the inner function with u. Then we can take the differential normally.

Therefore, if I have the function $\sin(x^2)$, to take the differential I would first set $u = x^2$ and then take the differential of $\sin(u)$. This results in $\cos(u)\,du$ from our basic table of differentials. However, this introduces a new term, du, which needs to be found.

However, since we set $u = x^2$, we can find out what du is supposed to be by simply differentiating both sides of *that* equation, giving $du = 2x\,dx$.

Therefore, substituting back in for du, we find that $d(\sin(x^2)) = \cos(x^2)2x\,dx$.

19.2 Applying u-substitution to Integration

Remember, however, that integration is the reverse of differentiation. Therefore, if we have $d(\sin(x^2)) = \cos(x^2)2x\,dx$ then that means that the reverse is also true:

$$\int \cos(x^2)\,2x\,dx = \sin(x^2) + C$$

The problem is this—how would anyone recognize that the mess on the left is equivalent to the formula on the right?

What you have to do is be comfortable and efficient enough with derivatives to recognize them on sight.

In the expression we are supposed to integrate, the cos() function has an "inner" function (x^2) and it is multiplied by an "outer" differential expression ($2x\,dx$). In order to do this kind of integral, you have to be able to recognize on sight that the outer differential expression is equal to the differential of the inner function.

In other words, you have to be able to see $\int \cos(x^2)\,2x\,dx$ and say, "Hey! The inside and outside of that cosine function are related! I wonder if I set u to the inner function, will du wind up being the outside function (or something close to it)?"

So, then, you set u to be the inside of the cosine function (i.e., x^2), and see what du becomes. Well, if $u = x^2$ then $du = 2x\,dx$, which is exactly what the outer function is. If we do both of these substitutions, we get:

$$\int \cos(u)\,du$$

That's easy to integrate! This just becomes $\sin(u)$. Of course, after integrating, we need to back-substitute in for u, which will give us $\sin(x^2)$.

In your mind, when you see something like $\cos(x^2)\,2x\,dx$, the expression $2x\,dx$ should just jump out at you as being the differential of x^2. If you have practiced your differentials enough, your mind should pick this up automatically. If it doesn't, I would suggest going back and reworking problems from Part II, and copying the table in Appendix H.6 several times.

Never forget that you must replace *both* the expression for x as well as the expression for dx! If you wind up with a mix of xs and us at the end then you have probably done it wrong. You have to be able to substitute for both the xs and the dxs or it doesn't work.

—   Example 19.1

Find $\int e^{x^3}\,3x\,dx$.

Hopefully when you looked at the problem it immediately popped out at you that $3x\,dx$ is the differential of x^3. Therefore, we can set $u = x^3$ and therefore $du = 3x\,dx$. This can be substituted back into the equation to become:

$$\int e^u\,du$$

This is a super-easy integral:

$$\int e^u\,du = e^u + C$$

We are almost done—we just need to back-substitute in for u. $u = x^3$, therefore, this becomes:

$$e^{x^3} + C$$

Putting it all together, we have:

$$\int e^{x^3}\,3x\,dx = e^{x^3} + C$$

If you are worried about any of the steps, just go back and differentiate your results to see if you get the original expression back.

— Example 19.2

Find $\int \sin(x+3)\,\mathrm{d}x$.

Here, the inner function is very simple. Since the inner function is $u = x + 3$, then the differential is merely $\mathrm{d}u = \mathrm{d}x$ because the constant goes to zero upon differentiating.

Therefore, the integral becomes:

$$\int \sin(u)\,\mathrm{d}u$$

When integrated, this just becomes:

$$\int \sin(u)\,\mathrm{d}u = -\cos(u) + C$$

Backsubstituting in for u yields:

$$-\cos(x+3) + C$$

— Example 19.3

Find $\int \frac{\mathrm{d}x}{x-1}$.

Here, we can set $u = x - 1$. Therefore, $\mathrm{d}u = \mathrm{d}x$. Therefore, the integral expression becomes:

$$\int \frac{\mathrm{d}u}{u}$$

This becomes:

$$\int \frac{\mathrm{d}u}{u} = \ln(u) + C$$

When we backsubstitute in for u, this becomes:

$$\ln(x-1) + C$$

— Example 19.4

Find $\int (x+4)^5 \, dx$.

Now, we *could* solve this by actually expanding out the expression. However, we would be here all day. An easier way to handle this is to just set $u = x + 4$. Differentiating, we find that $du = dx$.

That makes the problem become:

$$\int u^5 \, du$$

When integrated, that becomes:

$$\int u^5 \, du = \frac{u^6}{6} + C$$

Backsubstituting in for u, this becomes:

$$\frac{(x+4)^6}{6} + C$$

— Example 19.5

Find $\int \frac{\cos(x)}{\sin(x)} \, dx$.

It should immediately jump off the page at you that $\cos(x)dx$ is the differential of $\sin(x)$. But how does this help?

Because you have to "see" the integral correctly in order to solve it, sometimes it helps to rewrite it in different ways, and see if one of them brings you closer to the solution. In this case, let's rewrite this integral as $\int \frac{1}{\sin(x)} \cos(x) dx$.

Now, using u-substitution, let's set $u = \sin(x)$, which means $du = \cos(x)dx$. If we rewrite the integral with this substitution, we get $\int \frac{1}{u} du$. This matches one of the basic integral rules in Appendix H.7, which says:

$$\int \frac{1}{u} du = \ln(u) + C$$

Therefore, if $u = \sin(x)$, then the final answer is:

$$\int \frac{1}{\sin(x)} \cos(x) dx = \ln(\sin(x)) + C$$

19.3   Being Off by a Constant Factor

Sometimes when one rule alone backs you into a corner, another rule can come to the rescue. If asked to find $\int \sin(x^2)\, x \, dx$, you might recognize that $x\,dx$ is *almost* the derivative of x^2, and so this *almost* follows the form of $\sin(u)du$. However, it is off by a constant factor—it is missing a 2.

We can solve this in two ways. I prefer the first way, because it is more straightforward, but the other way is used often enough that it is worth teaching. Ultimately, both methods do the same thing.

19.3.1 Solving for the Differential that is There

When we look at $\sin(x^2)\,x\,dx$, we see that there is definitely an inner function, which is x^2. We can see that the differential is *almost* the same as the outer function. Even though they are different, let's not give up yet.

Let's start by doing our *u*-substitution and set $u = x^2$.

Now, let's differentiate for *u*. This gives us $du = 2x\,dx$.

Now, when doing algebraic manipulations, if two things are equal to each other (i.e., there is an equal sign between them), then they can be *substitutes* for each other. Now the right-hand side of our du equation does not *quite* match up with $x\,dx$. However, if we divide both sides by 2, they *will* match:

$$du = 2x\,dx$$

$$\frac{du}{2} = x\,dx$$

Now we have a replacement formula! Since the right-hand side matches what is in the original expression, then we can substitute for it. It's just that instead of substituting in du, we will be substituting in $\frac{du}{2}$:

$$\int \sin(x^2)\,x\,dx = \int \sin(u)\frac{du}{2}$$

Now, what makes this work is that we are dividing by a constant. Dividing by 2 is the same as multiplying by the constant $\frac{1}{2}$. The nice thing about a constant, is that a constant can move outside the integral. That means that our integral has reduced to:

$$\frac{1}{2}\int \sin(u)\,du$$

And *this* is a very easy integral to solve!

$$\frac{1}{2}\int \sin(u)\,du = \frac{1}{2}\cdot -\cos(u) + C = -\frac{1}{2}\cos(u) + C$$

Now, we just backsubstitute in for *u* for the final answer:

$$-\frac{1}{2}\cos(2x) + C$$

19.3.2 Manipulating the Integral to Make Life Easier

We can also manipulate this another way using the constant multiplier rule.

Remember, the integral we are trying to solve is:

$$\int \sin(x^2)\,x\,dx$$

If we set $u = x^2$, then $du = 2x\,dx$. This is similar to the multiplier $(x\,dx)$, but not exactly equal.

The constant multiplier rules states that $\int n\,du = n\int du$. In other words, a constant multiplier can bounce back and forth across the integral barrier whenever you want it to.

Additionally, based on the simple rules of multiplication, we can *introduce* any constant multiplier we want by also multiplying by its inverse. In other words, we can always multiply something by 2 if we divide it by 2 at the same time, because $\frac{2}{2}$ is just 1, which is the identity multiplier.

In this case, we need to add an additional 2 multiplier into the equation to make the integral work with our du, which is $2x\,\mathrm{d}x$ (the equation only has $x\,\mathrm{d}x$). Therefore, we will multiply our integral by $\frac{1}{2} \cdot 2$. This is just a creative way of multiplying by one. However, it gives us all the tools we need to solve the integral.

First, the integral now looks like this:

$$\int \sin(x^2)x\,\mathrm{d}x = \frac{1}{2} \cdot 2 \int \sin(x^2)x\,\mathrm{d}x$$

Both sides are equal, because all we really did was multiply by $\frac{2}{2}$.

Now, because constants can jump back-and-forth across the integral sign, we will simply move the 2 to the other side of the integral, but leave the $\frac{1}{2}$ outside the integral. Now the problem becomes:

$$\frac{1}{2} \int \sin(x^2)\,2x\,\mathrm{d}x$$

The integral is *now* in the form that the outer function is equivalent to the differential of u. Therefore, we can rewrite this as:

$$\frac{1}{2} \int \sin(u)\,\mathrm{d}u$$

This then becomes:

$$\frac{1}{2} \cdot (-\cos(u) + C)$$

This simplifies to the following (notice that the C just stayed as C because half of an arbitrary constant is still an arbitrary constant):

$$-\frac{1}{2}\cos(u) + C$$

Note that both this method and the previous one yield the same result.

Also note that neither of these methods work for cases where the differential term is off by terms more complicated than a constant. The reason for this is that, if an x or dx wound up on the du side of the equation, then the result would not be integratable, because it would have a mix of xs and us in the same term, rendering it difficult or impossible to integrate.

19.4   Multiple Substitutions

You can see even greater difficulty if you take a differential that is composed of functions that are multiple levels deep, like $(\sin(x^2))^3$. We can solve for the differential like this:

$$d(\sin(x^2)^3)$$

$u = \sin(x^2)$	create a substitution
$d(u^3) = 3u^2 du$	substituting and using the power rule
$v = x^2$	another substitution
$u = \sin(v)$	substituting
$du = \cos(v) dv$	cos() rule
$dv = 2x\, dx$	power rule
$d(\sin(x^2)^3) = 3(\sin(x^2))^2 \cos(x^2)2x\, dx$	putting it all back together
$d(\sin(x^2)^3) = 6(\sin(x^2))^2 \cos(x^2)x\, dx$	simplifying

Now, suppose someone gave you the equation $dy = 6(\sin(x^2))^2 \cos(x^2)x\, dx$ and asked you to integrate it. Is there any way to know from looking at it that the original equation was $(\sin(x^2))^3$?

The answer is yes and no. In the case of differentials, we had a short, simple rulebook that allowed us to easily find the differential. In the case of integrals, you have to know differentials well enough to "see" them. That is, you have to be able to take a look at the function $6(\sin(x^2))^2 \cos(x^2)x\, dx$ and recognize that this is actually in the form of $u^2 du$, where $u = \sin(x^2)$ and $du = \cos(x^2)2x\, dx$.

If you have worked enough differentials to know them on sight, this actually isn't incredibly hard. However, it does take a lot of time and practice. Being able to do this kind of integral is not nearly as important as just recognizing the fact that these types of integrals exist and this is how they are solved.

One final note—sometimes when doing substitutions, it is good to actually write out the variable for the limits of integration. The reason for this is to help you remember to backsubstitute for u and not to try to use the limits of integration *on u*.

Review

In this chapter, we learned:

1. While u-substitution (also known as the "chain rule") in integration is based on the *same principle* as for differentiation, it is not as straightforward and mechanical to use.

2. The key insight is to recognize when the *multiplier* of a function is the same as the *differential* of the inner function. This is when u-substitution is most appropriate.

3. u-substitution requires that you substitute for both the xs in the expression as well as the dxs. If you wind up with a mix of us and xs then you did not do it correctly.

4. If your u-substitution is off by a constant factor, you can manipulate either the equation or the du differential to make the substitution work correctly.

5. An integral may consist of multiple layers of u-substitutions that have to be recognized.

6. You must remember to backsubstitute for u after performing the integral. The limits of integration are in terms of x, not u.

Exercises

Find the indefinite integrals:

1. $\int (1+x)^2 \, dx$

2. $\int \cos(2x) \, dx$

3. $\int \cos(x^2) 2x \, dx$

4. $\int \sin(x^3) x^2 \, dx$

5. $\int \sqrt{2x-1} \, dx$

6. $\int \frac{e^{x^2} x}{3} \, dx$

Find the definite integral:

7. $\int_2^7 (x-34)^2 \, dx$

8. $\int_3^{3.25} \sin(x^4 + 6) x^3 \, dx$

Integrate the following equations:

9. $\frac{dy}{dx} = (x-3)^5$

10. $e^{2y} \, dy = \cos(x-5) \, dx$

Find the area under each curve:

11. $y = (x-10)^7$ from $x = 12$ to $x = 14$

12. $y = \sin(x^3) \, x^2 \, dx$ from $x = 0$ to $x = 1$.

Chapter 20

Other Geometric Uses of the Integral

The integral appears in many surprising places. It takes a while to wrap your mind around the different places where an integral can be used. The ones given here are no more special or important than any other application of the integral, but the goal is for them to inspire your imagination to think about ways that the integral might be used, and how you might use integration to create new formulas.

In Chapter 18, we found the area under the curve by noting that the area could be *estimated* using rectangles. Then, that estimate could be improved by continuing to reduce the width of the rectangles we were using. Eventually, when the area was subdivided into an infinite number of rectangles, the solution went from an estimate to the precise result.

We can use this sort of technique for finding all sorts of applications of the Integral. In this chapter, we will focus primarily on *geometric* applications since they are straightforward, but the technique can apply to any number of areas.

In short, we can use a definite integral to solve a problem if the following conditions are met:

1. The problem can be estimated by some formula.

2. The problem can be divided into subproblems.

3. The estimation formula (from condition 1) and subdivision method (from condition 2) have to follow the following rules:

   (a) Each subproblem has the same form/formula.

   (b) The total result is achieved by *adding* together the results of the subproblems.

   (c) Increasing the number of subdivisions (i.e., making the subdivisions smaller) *improves* the accuracy of the estimation.

The key is to choose an estimation formula that is "regular" enough so that the final result gets more and more accurate as the problem size gets smaller and smaller. Also note that because the integral is an infinite *sum*, the subproblems have to be able to add together for a final result.

When those conditions are met, the exact result can be found by:

1. Making infinitely small subdivisions, and

2. Adding them up using the definite integral

This chapter presents specific types of problems that you should learn how to solve, but you should be thinking in the back of your mind how the above criteria apply to those problems and how they lend themselves to using the integral to solve them. The larger goal is not just to be able to solve these particular problems, but to gear your mind to see a problem and recognize that an integral could be used for a solution.

20.1   Finding the Volume of a Solid of Revolution

In Chapter 18, we learned how to use the integral to find the area under a curve. However, the integral can be used for much more complicated geometric uses as well.

Look at the line $y = \frac{x}{2}$:

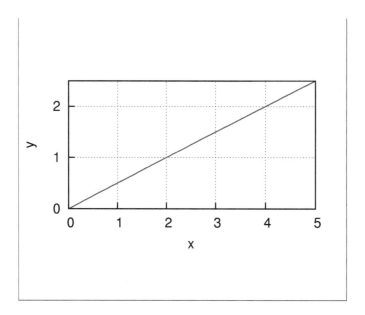

Now, imagine that line spun around the x-axis. What shape would that make?

It makes a cone with the height along the x-axis:

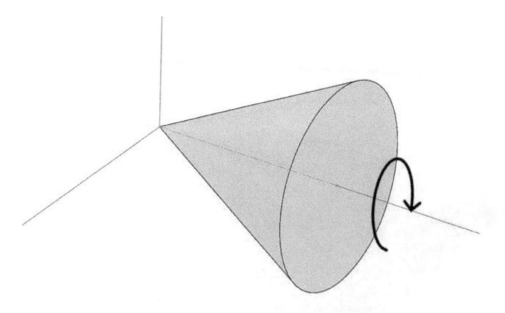

Let's say we wanted to know the volume of that cone from $x = 0$ to $x = 3$.

While you might already know how to compute the volume of a cone, let's think of how we could do it with calculus if we didn't already know the formula.

Think about how we solved the question about the area under the curve—we developed a method of approximating the solution, and then expanded our approximation to infinity.

Therefore, since this figure was made by turning around the x-axis, we can think of it as making a bunch of discs for each point along the line:

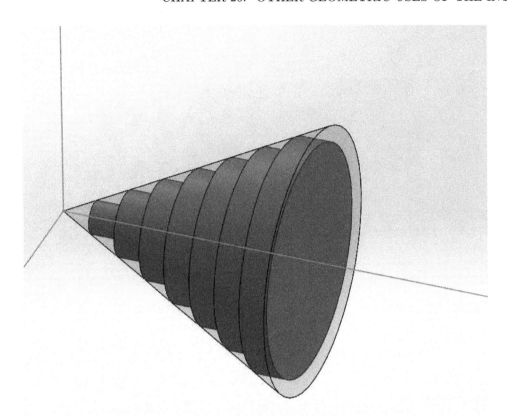

Now, we can approximate the volume of any of these by treating them as a cylinder with a height along the x-axis.

Just like for rectangles, the volume of a cylinder is very regular and easy to calculate. Therefore, to get the total volume of the cone, we just have to add up the volumes of all of these cylinders.

So what is the volume of each cylinder? You can look up the equation for the volume of a cylinder in Appendix H.3, but I will also give it below. In the equation below, v is the volume, r is the radius, and h is the height (which is along the x-axis in this type of problem):

$$v = \pi r^2 h$$

In this case, since the cylinder is on its side, the y-value is the radius of the circle, and the distance along the x-axis is the height.

Now, a set of cylinders is only an approximation to the volume of a cone. However, we can improve our approximation by making the cylinders shorter and shorter on the x axis. To get infinitely good resolution, we will shrink the height of each cylinder until the height is only an infinitesimal amount on the x axis. What is an infinitesimal amount on the x axis called? We call that dx.

Therefore, since the radius of each cylinder is y, and the height of each cylinder is dx, using the volume equation we know that the volume of *each* cylinder will be:

$$v = \pi y^2 \, dx \qquad\qquad\qquad (20.1)$$

Now, each of these cylinders will be infinitely small. However, we have an infinite number of them. And we need to add them together. However, they each have the same basic form: $\pi y^2 \, dx$.

What do we do when we need to add an infinite number of infinitely small things together that all have the same form? We use a definite integral!

Therefore, to find the sum of all of the cylinders formed in this way we would use the following integral:

$$\text{volume} = \int_{x=\text{start}}^{x=\text{finish}} \pi y^2 \, dx \tag{20.2}$$

In fact, this is not just the formula for finding the volume of a cone, Equation 20.2 is the equation for *any* solid formed by rotating a curve around the x axis. What will change with any particular solid is the equation for y.

As it stands in Equation 20.2, we cannot integrate this yet because we have y and dx together. However, the original equation for the line tells us that $y = \frac{x}{2}$. Therefore, we can substitute $\frac{x}{2}$ in for y. If we also add in our bounds of integration ($x = 0$ and $x = 3$) that gives the equation:

$$\text{volume} = \int_0^3 \pi \left(\frac{x}{2}\right)^2 dx$$

Now this is in a form that can be easily solved using standard definite integration techniques!

$$\begin{aligned}
\text{volume} &= \int_0^3 \pi \left(\frac{x}{2}\right)^2 dx \\
&= \int \pi \left(\frac{x}{2}\right)^2 dx \Big|_0^3 \\
&= \int \frac{\pi}{4} x^2 \, dx \Big|_0^3 \\
&= \frac{\pi}{4} \int x^2 \, dx \Big|_0^3 \\
&= \frac{\pi}{4} \frac{x^3}{3} \Big|_0^3 \\
&= \frac{\pi x^3}{12} \Big|_0^3 \\
&= \frac{\pi (3)^3}{12} - \frac{\pi (0)^3}{12} \\
&= \frac{27\pi}{12} - 0 \\
&= \frac{9\pi}{4} \\
&\approx 7.0686
\end{aligned}$$

This works for any solid that is made by rotating a curve around the x-axis.

The basic steps are as follows:

1. When a shape is formed by rotating a curve around the x axis, its volume can be estimated by breaking it up into infinitesimal cylinders.

2. The volume of each infinitesimal cylinder will be $\pi y^2 \, dx$.

3. The total volume can be found by adding together all of these infinitesimal cylinders, which can be done using the integral from Equation 20.2: $\int \pi y^2 \, dx$.

4. For the specific curve, substitute in the equation for y, and add in the limits of integration to make a definite integral.

5. Solve the definite integral.

The result will be the volume of the shape.

Example 20.1

Find the volume of the shape formed by rotating $y = x^2 - 10x$ around the x axis from $x = 5$ to $x = 10$.

To do this, we will begin with Equation 20.2:

$$\text{volume} = \int_{x=\text{start}}^{x=\text{finish}} \pi y^2 \, dx$$

Now, we will substitute in our equation for y in for y above, and use the limits of integration specified in the problem:

$$\text{volume} = \int_{x=5}^{x=10} \pi (x^2 - 10x)^2 \, dx$$

Now we just have to solve the integral. To simplify, since π is a constant, it can be moved outside of the integration. Then we can further simplify the problem by expanding $(x^2 - 10x)^2$. This will yield an integral that is readily solvable:

$$\text{volume} = \int_{x=5}^{x=10} \pi (x^2 - 10x)^2 \, dx \qquad \text{starting equation}$$

$$= \pi \int_{x=5}^{x=10} (x^2 - 10x)^2 \, dx \qquad \text{move } \pi \text{ outside the integral to simplify}$$

$$= \pi \int_{x=5}^{x=10} x^4 \, dx - 20x^3 \, dx + 100x^2 \, dx \qquad \text{expand the exponent}$$

$$= \pi \int x^4 \, dx - 20x^3 \, dx + 100^2 x \, dx \Big|_{x=5}^{x=10} \qquad \text{convert to an indefinite integral with evaluation}$$

$$= \pi \left(\frac{x^5}{5} - 5x^4 + \frac{100x^3}{3} \right) \Big|_{x=5}^{x=10} \qquad \text{perform indefinite integration}$$

At this point, we now just need to plug in our numbers:

$$\text{volume} = \pi \left(\frac{(10)^5}{5} - 5(10)^4 + \frac{100(10)^3}{3} \right) - \pi \left(\frac{(5)^5}{5} - 5(5)^4 + \frac{100(5)^3}{3} \right) \qquad \text{apply evaluation bar}$$

$$= \pi \left(20000 - 50000 + \frac{100000}{3} \right) - \pi \left(625 - 3125 + \frac{12500}{3} \right)$$

$$= \pi \left(20000 - 50000 + \frac{100000}{3} - 625 + 3125 - \frac{12500}{3} \right)$$

$$= \pi \left(-27500 + \frac{87500}{3} \right)$$

$$\approx 5235.9878$$

You may be wondering why this method *looks* so different than the standard formula for the volume of a cone. It's actually not that different—what is different is that this method uses the equation of a line to find the volume while the standard formula uses the radius and the height. Appendix E.3 shows how to derive the standard formula for the volume of a cone using the techniques discussed here.

20.2 Rotating Around the y Axis

Another method of generating three dimensional shapes is to rotate a curve around the y axis, where you are still using the area *under* the curve as the "filled-in" volume of the shape.

For instance, let's start with the same line given in the previous section:

$$y = \frac{x}{2}$$

The volume generated by revolving this line around the y axis looks like this:

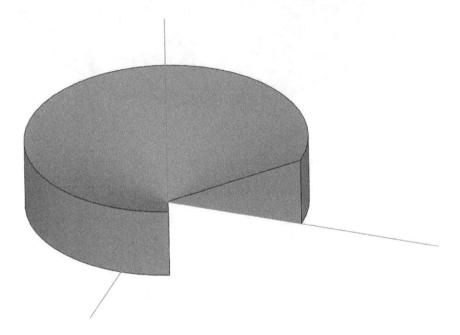

In order to calculate this volume, we need a different approach. This is because, previously, the *area* being rotated was between the function and the x axis, which was also the axis of rotation. In this case, the area being rotated is between the function and the x axis, but the axis of rotation is now the y axis.

Therefore, we will need to think about this in a different way.

Notice that, if you take a sliver of the graph below a particular point in the line at a particular x value, that little sliver will revolve all the way around the y axis. We can think of this little sliver as being a really, really thin strip of paper. If we cut the piece of paper, it will unfold into an extremely thin rectangular box.

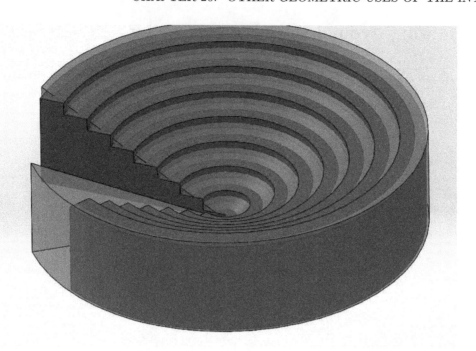

A rectangular box is extremely easy to calculate the volume for. It is simply:

$$\text{volume} = \text{length} \cdot \text{height} \cdot \text{thickness}$$

So, what do each of these refer to in our thin strip? Well, the strip is extremely thin. In fact, it is infinitely thin. It is only dx thick.

The height is straightforward. The height is merely the y value. Therefore, so far we have:

$$\text{volume} = \text{length} \cdot y \cdot dx$$

So what is the length?

Since the strip was rotated *around* the y axis, the length of the strip will be the *circumference* of the circle made by doing this rotation. The circumference of a circle is given by $2\pi r$, where r is the radius. What is the radius in this case?

Since we are rotating around the y axis, the y axis will be the center of the circle. The distance of a point from the y axis will be the radius. The distance of a point from the y axis is just the x value! Therefore, the radius is just x.

This means that the length of the strip will be $2\pi x$. Therefore, the final volume equation for an individual strip will be:

$$\text{volume} = 2\pi x y \, dx$$

Since the total volume is just the volume of each of these strips added together, all we have to do is take the infinite sum (i.e., the integral) of all of the infinitely small strips. The results in the following equation:

$$\text{volume} = \int_{x=\text{start}}^{x=\text{finish}} 2\pi x y \, dx \tag{20.3}$$

So, let's say we wanted to find the volume of $y = \frac{x}{2}$ revolved around the y axis from $x = 0$ to $x = 3$?

To do that, we just apply Equation 20.3:

$$\text{volume} = \int_{x=\text{start}}^{x=\text{finish}} 2\pi x y \, dx \qquad \text{the basic equation}$$

$$= \int_{x=0}^{x=3} 2\pi x \frac{x}{2} \, dx \qquad \text{substitute in our values}$$

$$= \int_{x=0}^{x=3} \pi x^2 \, dx \qquad \text{simplify}$$

$$= \int \pi x^2 \, dx \Big|_0^3 \qquad \text{convert to evaluation bar}$$

$$= \pi \frac{x^3}{3} \Big|_0^3 \qquad \text{perform indefinite integral}$$

$$= \pi \frac{(3)^3}{3} - \pi \frac{(0)^3}{3} \qquad \text{apply evaluation bar}$$

$$= 9\pi - 0 \qquad \text{simplify}$$

$$= 9\pi$$

$$\approx 28.2743$$

Example 20.2

Find the volume of the equation $y = \sin(x^2)$ rotated around the y axis from $x = 0$ to $x = 1.5$.

To find this, we simply apply Equation 20.3:

$$\text{volume} = \int_{x=\text{start}}^{x=\text{finish}} 2\pi x y \, dx \qquad \text{the basic equation}$$

$$= \int_{x=0}^{x=1.5} 2\pi x \sin(x^2) \, dx \qquad \text{substitute in our values}$$

$$= \int 2\pi x \sin(x^2) \, dx \Big|_0^{1.5} \qquad \text{convert to indefinite integral}$$

At this point, you should notice that we have an x^2 inside the sine function, and a $2x$ outside the sine function. This is perfect for a u substitution. If we set $u = x^2$ then $du = 2x \, dx$. Therefore, we can continue solving:

$$\text{volume} = \int 2\pi x \sin(x^2)\,\mathrm{d}x\,\Big|_{x=0}^{x=1.5}$$

$$= \int \pi \sin(u)\,\mathrm{d}u\,\Big|_{x=0}^{x=1.5} \qquad \text{perform } u\text{-substitution}$$

$$= \pi \int \sin(u)\,\mathrm{d}u\,\Big|_{x=0}^{x=1.5} \qquad \text{move constant out}$$

$$= -\pi \cos(u)\,\Big|_{x=0}^{x=1.5} \qquad \text{perform indefinite integration}$$

$$= -\pi \cos(x^2)\,\Big|_{x=0}^{x=1.5} \qquad \text{back-substitute for } u$$

$$= -\pi \cos((1.5)^2) - -\pi \cos(0^2) \qquad \text{apply evaluation bar}$$

$$\approx 1.9735 + 3.1416 \qquad \text{simplify}$$

$$\approx 5.1151$$

The volume is approximately 5.1151 cubic units.

20.3   Finding the Length of a Curve

Another usage of the integral is to find the *length* of a curve. That is, if we were to take a piece of string and lay the string over a segment of the curve, how long of a piece of string would be needed? That is what I mean by the length of the curve.

Let's say we had the following curve:

$$y = x^{\frac{3}{2}}$$

The graph of this curve looks like this:

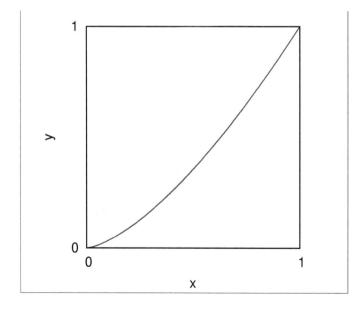

What is the length of this curve from $x = 0$ to $x = 1$? In other words, if we wanted to cover the curve from $x = 0$ to $x = 1$, how much string would we need?

This question may sound daunting, but we can use the same tools developed for finding areas under curves and volumes of revolution to figure out the process.

In the beginning of the chapter we laid out the criteria for applying an integral to a problem. The first question was whether we could break up a problem into an arbitrary number of pieces. Can we break up the length of a line into pieces? Sure we can! A line can be broken up into any number of smaller lines.

The second question was whether there was a way to *estimate* the value of a single piece of the problem. So how would you approximate the length of a curve? The best way to approximate it is simply with a straight line. We can find the distance of a straight line using the distance formula:

$$\text{length} = \sqrt{(\Delta x)^2 + (\Delta y)^2}$$

In this formula, Δx and Δy are the total change in x and y value for the piece of the curve we are looking at.

The third criteria is that the estimation improves as the pieces get smaller. I think we can tell that, if we break up the curve into smaller and smaller lines, this will give us increasingly accurate estimates of the total curve length.

To see that this is the case, let's look at that original curve again, but with straight lines superimposed over it spaced out every 0.5 units:

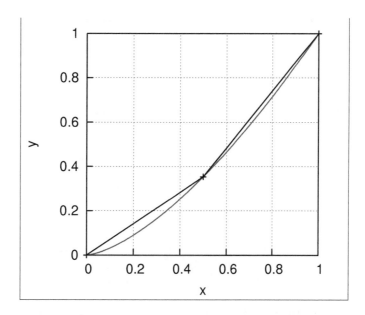

Since the lines are straight, we can use the pythagorean theorem to estimate their length. The first line goes from $(0,0)$ to approximately $(0.5, 0.35)$, and so its length is $\sqrt{0.5^2 + 0.35^2} \approx 0.61$. The second line goes from $(0.5, 0.35)$ to $(1, 1)$, and so its length is $\sqrt{0.5^2 + 0.65^2} \approx 0.82$. Therefore, the estimated total length of the curve is 1.43 units.

However, we can see that we will get a better approximation by drawing more lines. Below is the same graph but with the lines spaced out for ever 0.25 change in x:

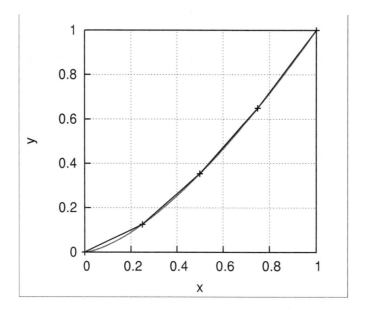

The original graph is almost completely matched by the superimposed lines. By calculating the length of these lines, we get a closer representation of the true length. We can continue to get a better approximation by decreasing the length we are using for each line (and thus increasing the number of lines we are using).

Now, to get an exact length, we iterate this process down to the infinitesimal case, and then add the lengths using an integral.

The formula we are using for length is $\sqrt{(\text{change in } x)^2 + (\text{change in } y)^2}$. Lets say that we kept reducing the length of x until it was down to an infinitely small change in x. What would we call that sort of change in x?

Hopefully by now you recognize that an infinitely small change in x calls for the differential $\mathrm{d}x$. Then, for the given change in x, we need the corresponding change in y, which is known as $\mathrm{d}y$. Therefore, we can calculate the length of each infinitely small line segment ($\mathrm{d}s$) as being:

$$\mathrm{d}s = \sqrt{\mathrm{d}x^2 + \mathrm{d}y^2}$$

Since we want an infinite sum of these pieces, we can convert this into a definite integral:

$$\text{length} = \int_{x=\text{start}}^{x=\text{finish}} \sqrt{\mathrm{d}x^2 + \mathrm{d}y^2} \tag{20.4}$$

This is correct conceptually, but the right-hand side is not in a form that we can solve. We have $\mathrm{d}x$ and $\mathrm{d}y$ mixed together, which makes integrating difficult.

However, since we know the equation of the original function, we can use the differentials of that function to find an appropriate replacement for $\mathrm{d}y$

Since the original function is $y = x^{\frac{3}{2}}$, the differential of that function is $\mathrm{d}y = \frac{3}{2}x^{\frac{1}{2}}\mathrm{d}x$. Therefore, we can replace $\mathrm{d}y$ with $\frac{3}{2}x^{\frac{1}{2}}\mathrm{d}x$ in the equation, yielding:

$$\text{length} = \int_0^1 \sqrt{\mathrm{d}x^2 + (\frac{3}{2}x^{\frac{1}{2}}\mathrm{d}x)^2}$$

Distributing the square gives us:

$$\text{length} = \int_0^1 \sqrt{dx^2 + \frac{9}{4}x\,dx^2}$$

From here, we can factor out dx^2 like this:

$$\text{length} = \int_0^1 \sqrt{dx^2(1 + \frac{9}{4}x)}$$

Since dx^2 is a proper factor, we can pull it out of the square root like this:

$$\text{length} = \int_0^1 dx\sqrt{1 + \frac{9}{4}x}$$

Now with a simple *u*-substitution of $u = 1 + \frac{9}{4}x$, we can easily solve for dx as follows:

$$u = 1 + \frac{9}{4}x \qquad \text{setup the substitutions}$$

$$du = \frac{9}{4}dx \qquad \text{differentiate}$$

$$\frac{4}{9}du = dx \qquad \text{solve for } dx$$

Now we can use this information to solve the original integral.

$$\text{length} = \int_0^1 dx\sqrt{1 + \frac{9}{4}x} \qquad \text{the original integral}$$

$$= \int_0^1 \frac{4}{9}du\sqrt{u} \qquad u\text{-substitution}$$

$$= \int \frac{4}{9}du\sqrt{u} \Big|_0^1 \qquad \text{rewriting as an indefinite integral}$$

$$= \frac{4}{9} \int \sqrt{u}\,du \Big|_0^1 \qquad \text{moving the constant outside the integral}$$

$$= \frac{4}{9} \int u^{\frac{1}{2}}\,du \Big|_0^1 \qquad \text{rewriting as a fractional exponent}$$

$$= \frac{4}{9}\frac{2}{3}u^{\frac{3}{2}} \Big|_0^1 \qquad \text{perform indefinite integration}$$

$$= \frac{8}{27}u^{\frac{3}{2}} \Big|_0^1 \qquad \text{simplify}$$

$$= \frac{8}{27}\left(1 + \frac{9}{4}x\right)^{\frac{3}{2}} \Big|_0^1 \qquad \text{substituting back in}$$

$$= \frac{8}{27}\left(1 + \frac{9}{4}(1)\right)^{\frac{3}{2}} - \frac{8}{27}\left(1 + \frac{9}{4}(0)\right)^{\frac{3}{2}} \qquad \text{apply evaluation bar}$$

$$= \frac{8}{27}\left(\frac{13}{4}\right)^{\frac{3}{2}} - \frac{8}{27} \qquad \text{simplify and evaluate}$$

$$\approx 1.7360 - 0.2963$$

$$\approx 1.4397$$

So the length of the curve between $x = 0$ and $x = 1$ is about 1.4397 square units.

I should warn you, however, that this curve was specially chosen to be easy to integrate. If you try this with an arbitrary curve, you are likely to arrive at something that is either very difficult to integrate or even impossible to integrate. However, everything in the homework will be specially chosen to be integratable unless otherwise noted.

Equation 20.4 can be used as a starting point for any equation for the length of a curve. However, it requires that the curve not retrace any steps along the x axis (i.e., the curve must be a true function of x).

20.4   Other Variations

These techniques have a lot of variations, and most of them can be solved fairly simply by just looking at the geometry of the situation. For instance, let's say that we wanted to revolve a curve around the line $y = 1$ instead of around the x axis. How would you do that?

Well, the line $y = 1$ is parallel to the x axis, so the only thing that will happen is that our y values will be 1 shorter when they are computed. Therefore, the equation will become:

$$\int \pi (y - 1)^2 \, dx$$

Sometimes, the question will call for rotating the area enclosed by a boundary of two equations. For that, you simply have to figure out how this impacts the geometry. For rotating around the x axis, you subtract the volume created by rotating the lower curve from the volume created by rotating the upper curve. For rotating around the y axis, you subtract the volume created by rotating the more leftwards curve from the volume created by rotating the more rightwards curve. If the bounds of integration are not given, this is usually because they want you to calculate where the lines intersect, and use the intersection points as the bounds of integration.

Review

In this chapter, we learned:

1. Just like for finding the area under a curve, entire classes of problems can be converted into a sum of infinitely small pieces.

2. To use an integral to solve a problem in this way, a problem has to have an estimation technique, be able to be broken down into an arbitrary number of pieces, each piece has to have the same form, and the result has to get closer to the true value as the number of pieces increase.

3. Then, applying the integral is simply breaking the problem down into an infinite number of infinitely small cases, and then using the definite integral to solve.

4. The general equation for the volume of a solid generated by revolving a curve around the x axis is given by Equation 20.2:
$$\text{volume} = \int_{x=\text{start}}^{x=\text{finish}} \pi y^2 \, dx$$

5. The general equation for the volume of a solid generated by revolving a curve around the y axis (using the area between the curve and the x axis) is given by Equation 20.3:

$$\text{volume} = \int_{x=\text{start}}^{x=\text{finish}} 2\pi x y \, dx$$

6. The general equation for the length of a curve is given by Equation 20.4:

$$\text{length} = \int_{x=\text{start}}^{x=\text{finish}} \sqrt{dx^2 + dy^2}$$

7. In these equations y or dy must be given in terms of x and/or dx in order to be solved. As with most integral problems, even then results are not guaranteed.

8. Because this is a geometric operation, variations of these methods can be considered by simply considering how the variation affects the geometry of the final shape. How this impacts your equation can usually be discovered by basic geometric reasoning.

Exercises

1. Find the volume of the solid formed by rotating the curve $y = 4$ around the x axis from $x = 6$ to $x = 10$.

2. Find the volume of the solid formed by rotating the curve $y = x$ around the y axis from $x = 1$ to $x = 6$.

3. Find the volume of the solid formed by rotating the curve $5y = x$ around the x axis from $x = 2$ to $x = 5$.

4. Find the volume of the solid formed when the curve $y = \frac{1}{x}$ is rotated around the x axis from $x = 1$ to $x = 3$.

5. Find the length of the curve $y = \frac{x^3}{12} + \frac{1}{x}$ from $x = 1$ to $x = 2$.

6. Find the volume of the solid formed when the curve $y = e^x$ is rotated around the x axis from $x = 0$ to $x = 2$.

7. Find the volume of the solid formed when the curve $y = x^3$ is rotated around the y axis from $x = 0$ to $x = 3$.

8. Find the length of the curve $y = \sqrt{4 - x^2}$ from $x = 0$ to $x = 2$. This will require you to consult Appendix H.7 for integral tables. It will also require some creative manipulation to complete.

Chapter 21

Transforming Equations for Integration

Unfortunately, as we have noted, integration is not just a simple application of rules like we had for differentiation. Therefore, in integration, many different tricks have been developed to make integration of certain kinds of problems easier.

For any given expression, there are multiple ways of writing it. As an example, if you are given $\int \frac{1}{x^2}$, you can solve it easily by simply rewriting $\frac{1}{x^2}$ as x^{-2} and then using the power rule. Those two expressions, $\frac{1}{x^2}$ and x^{-2}, are equivalent, but the latter is much easier to integrate. Many times, being able to integrate an equation is simply finding a way to rewrite the given expression in an equivalent but different-looking way. Finding the right transformation is large part of the technique of integration. This chapter will focus on a few transformations that seem to be helpful across a wide variety of circumstances.

Keep in mind that, in addition to general tricks that you will learn here, entire books containing specific integral forms have been published. Knowing these tricks to integration is important because they do occur often, but, ultimately, there really are too many to learn them all. The most important thing is to know that there are often things available that can be done to make integration possible even if the integral looks really ugly.

21.1 Integration Using Partial Fraction Decomposition

Let's say that we wanted to evaluate the following integral:

$$\int \frac{6x + 13}{x^2 + 5x + 6} \mathrm{d}x$$

This is rather difficult to do using our current set of techniques. It doesn't really match any given pattern that we've studied. The fraction is too complex for u-substitution, with the top version not really being a derivative of the bottom.

However, we can *rewrite* the integral in a way that is easier to solve. To do this, we will use **partial fraction decomposition**. The idea behind partial fraction decomposition is to take a complicated polynomial fraction and reduce it to simpler fractional terms which can be more easily integrated. In this book, we will focus on cases where the denominator can be factored into linear factors (i.e., factors where x is only of degree 1).[1]

---

[1]In theory, partial fraction decomposition is supposed to be taught in Algebra 2, but I have rarely found an Algebra 2 student who remembered how to do this.

So, let's look again at the expression we are going to integrate: $\frac{6x+13}{x^2+5x+6}\,\mathrm{d}x$. Can the denominator be factored into linear factors? Yes, it can—we can factor it into $(x + 3)$ and $(x + 2)$. So, we can rewrite the expression as follows:

$$\frac{6x + 13}{(x + 3)(x + 2)}$$

Now, the goal for partial fraction decomposition is to rewrite the expression where we only have constants in the numerator. In other words, we want to rewrite the fraction above in such a way as to give us something like

$$\frac{A}{x + 3} + \frac{B}{x + 2}$$

where A and B are simple numeric constants. If we can do this, each term is actually easily integratable with u-substitution.

In order to perform a partial fraction decomposition, all you have to do is to *assume* that this can be done, and then solve for A and B.[2]

If you actualy added together $\frac{A}{x+3} + \frac{B}{x+2}$ you would have to find a common denominator for the addition. Therefore, you would need to cross multiply before adding. The steps for adding these two together would be as follows:

$$\frac{A}{x + 3} + \frac{B}{x + 2} \qquad \text{the original expression}$$

$$\frac{A(x + 2)}{(x + 3)(x + 2)} + \frac{B(x + 3)}{(x + 2)(x + 3)} \qquad \text{cross multiply to get a common denominator}$$

$$\frac{A(x + 2) + B(x + 3)}{(x + 3)(x + 2)} \qquad \text{combine the fractions}$$

$$\frac{Ax + 2A + Bx + 3B}{x^2 + 5x + 6} \qquad \text{distribute and expand}$$

Remember, in all of these steps we never changed the value of the expression. Additionally, we are assuming that $\frac{A}{x+3} + \frac{B}{x+2}$ is equal to our original expression, $\frac{6x+13}{x^2+5x+6}$. If you look on the last line, however, you will notice that we have the following expression in the numerator:

$$Ax + 2A + Bx + 3B$$

However, in the original equation, we are just given the following in the numerator:

$$6x + 13$$

That must mean that these expressions are equal. In other words:

$$Ax + 2A + Bx + 3B = 6x + 13$$

Additionally, notice how we have some terms of x and some terms with just plain units. Because we are assuming that A and B are just numbers (and not an expression in terms of x), this means that we can

---

[2]The reason why you can make this assumption is a little complicated. Nonetheless, this decomposition is always possible when you can factor the denominator into linear factors.

actually break this apart into two different equations:

$$Ax + Bx = 6x$$

$$2A + 3B = 13$$

The reason that you can do this is because the final value for the numerator is in terms of both xs and numbers. Since A and B are not themselves in terms of x, we can assume that only when A and B are explicitly multiplied by x to they yield an x value. This is what allows us to break up the single equation into two separate equations.

Also, since we have two equations and two variables, we can solve for the variables! We can take the first equation and solve for A:

$$Ax + Bx = 6x \qquad \text{original equation}$$
$$A + B = 6 \qquad \text{divide by } x$$
$$A = 6 - B$$

Now, solved for A, we can solve for B in the second equation:

$$2A + 3B = 13 \qquad \text{original equation}$$
$$2(6 - B) + 3B = 13 \qquad \text{substitute for } A$$
$$12 - 2B + 3B = 13 \qquad \text{simplifying}$$
$$12 + B = 13$$
$$B = 1 \qquad \text{solved}$$

Since $B = 1$ that means that $A = 6 - 1 = 5$. Therefore, we now have both A and B and can substitute it back in into our integral:

$$\int \frac{5}{x+3} \, dx + \frac{1}{x+2} \, dx$$

Using u-substitution for the bottom of each fraction, we can easily solve the integral:

$$\int \frac{5}{x+3} \, dx + \frac{1}{x+2} \, dx \qquad \text{the original integral}$$
$$= \int \frac{5}{u} \, du + \frac{1}{v} \, dv \qquad u\text{-substitution}$$
$$= 5 \ln |u| + \ln |v| + C \qquad \text{perform integration}$$
$$= 5 \ln |x+3| + \ln |x+2| + C \qquad \text{back-substitute for } u$$

— Example 21.1

Perform the integral $\int \frac{9}{x^2+5x-14}$.

In this case, we have a complicated polynomial fraction which can't be solved directly with u-substitution. However, the denominator is factorable into linear factors, $(x-2)$ and $(x+7)$. Therefore, we will assume that this can be rewritten as a sum of two fractions with these as denominators, and will solve for the numerator of those fractions.

$$\frac{9}{x^2 + 5x - 14} = \frac{9}{(x-2)(x+7)}$$

$$= \frac{A}{x-2} + \frac{B}{x+7}$$

$$= \frac{Ax + 7A}{(x-2)(x+7)} + \frac{Bx - 2B}{(x-2)(x+7)}$$

$$= \frac{Ax + 7A + Bx - 2B}{x^2 + 5x - 14}$$

So, we now have a numerator that is equivalent to our original numerator, which was 9. Therefore, we can say,

$$Ax + 7A + Bx - 2B = 9$$

We can also split this out like the following:

$$Ax + Bx = 0x$$

$$7A - 2B = 9$$

Using the first equation, we can see that $A = -B$. Substituting into the second equation, we get:

$$7A - 2B = 9$$

$$7(-B) - 2B = 9$$

$$-7B - 2B = 9$$

$$-9B = 9$$

$$B = -1$$

$$A = 1$$

Therefore, the fraction can be rewritten as:

$$\frac{1}{x-2} + \frac{-1}{x+7}$$

When put back into our integral, this can be easily solved using u-substitution (the actual u-substitution step is left out because it is really basic):

$$\int \frac{1}{x-2} dx + \frac{-1}{x+7} dx$$

$$= \ln|x-2| + -\ln|x+7| + C$$

— **Example 21.2**

Find the integral $\int \frac{2x^2+3x+5}{x^3-19x-30} dx$ (hint: the denominator factors into $(x-5)(x+3)(x+2)$).

This is exactly like before, but, since denominator is a cube, the numerator can include a square. This will give us *three* values—A, B, and C.

The problem told us in the hint what the denominator factors to. Therefore, the result will look like this:

$$\frac{A}{x-5} + \frac{B}{x+3} + \frac{C}{x+2}$$

To recombine them, we just need to cross-multiply to put them back over the same denominator:

$$\frac{A(x+3)(x+2)}{(x-5)(x+3)(x+2)} + \frac{B(x-5)(x+2)}{(x-5)(x+3)(x+2)} + \frac{C(x-5)(x+3)}{(x-5)(x+3)(x+2)}$$

Multiplying all of these through leaves us with:

$$\frac{Ax^2 + 5Ax + 6A}{x^3 - 19x - 30} + \frac{Bx^2 - 3Bx - 10B}{x^3 - 19x - 30} + \frac{Cx^2 - 2Cx - 15C}{x^3 - 19x - 30}$$

Combining these gives us:

$$\frac{Ax^2 + 5Ax + 6A + Bx^2 - 3Bx - 10B + Cx^2 - 2Cx - 15C}{x^3 - 19x - 30}$$

Since this is still equal to our original fraction, and both fractions have the same denominator, that means that the numerators are equal. So we can say:

$$Ax^2 + 5Ax + 6A + Bx^2 - 3Bx - 10B + Cx^2 - 2Cx - 15C = 2x^2 + 3x + 5$$

Because A, B, and C are simple numbers, with no x in them, we can split this out into three equations:

$$Ax^2 + Bx^2 + Cx^2 = 2x^2$$

$$5Ax + -3Bx + -2Cx = 3x$$

$$6A + -10B + -15C = 5$$

This can be solved however you like to solve systems of equations. For this example, I am going to solve for A in the first equation, giving us:

$$Ax^2 + Bx^2 + Cx^2 = 2x^2$$

$$A + B + C = 2 \qquad\qquad \text{divide by } x^2$$

$$A = 2 - B - C$$

Now, in the second equation, I will replace A with $2 - B - C$ and then solve for B:

$$5Ax + -3Bx + -2Cx = 3x$$

$$5A + -3B + -2C = 3 \qquad\qquad \text{divide by } x$$

$$5(2 - B - C) + -3B + -2C = 3 \qquad\qquad \text{replace } A$$

$$10 - 5B - 5C + -3B + -2C = 3 \qquad\qquad \text{simplify and solve}$$

$$-8B + -7C = -7$$

$$-8B = -7 + 7C$$

$$B = \frac{7}{8} - \frac{7}{8}C$$

Now we can solve for C with the third equation:

$$6A + -10B + -15C = 5$$

$$6(2 - B - C) + -10B + -15C = 5 \qquad \text{substitute for } A$$

$$6(2 - (\frac{7}{8} - \frac{7}{8}C) - C) + -10(\frac{7}{8} - \frac{7}{8}C) + -15C = 5 \qquad \text{subsitute for } B$$

$$12 - \frac{42}{8} + \frac{42}{8}C - 6C + \frac{-70}{8} - \frac{-70}{8}C + -15C = 5 \qquad \text{simplify and solve}$$

$$\frac{42}{8}C - 6C + \frac{70}{8}C + -15C = 5 + -12 + \frac{42}{8} + \frac{70}{8}$$

$$42C - 48C + 70C + -120C = 40 + -96 + 42 + 70$$

$$-56C = 56$$

$$C = -1$$

Now we can solve for B:

$$B = \frac{7}{8} - \frac{7}{8}C$$

$$B = \frac{7}{8} - \frac{-7}{8}$$

$$B = \frac{14}{8}$$

$$B = \frac{7}{4}$$

Now we can solve for A:

$$A = 2 - B - C$$

$$A = 2 - \frac{7}{4} - -1$$

$$A = \frac{8}{4} - \frac{7}{4} + \frac{4}{4}$$

$$A = \frac{5}{4}$$

Now that we have the decomposition, we can easily rewrite the integral in a way that is easy to solve:

$$\int \frac{A}{x-5}dx + \frac{B}{x+3}dx + \frac{C}{x+2}dx$$

$$\int \frac{\frac{5}{4}}{x-5}dx + \frac{\frac{7}{4}}{x+3}dx + \frac{-1}{x+2}dx$$

$$\frac{5}{4}\ln|x-5| + \frac{7}{4}\ln|x+3| + -\ln|x+2| + C$$

As you can see, as you expand the degree of the denominator, the problem becomes more and more complicated. It is still the same basic process, assuming that the denominator can still be factored into linear factors.

There are some additional considerations for partial fraction decomposition. We aren't terribly concerned with them in this book, but I thought I'd mention them for completeness:

1. If the numerator is an equal or higher degree than the denominator, performing polynomial division first will convert the problem into a solvable form.

2. If the denominator has a square factor, then the decomposition must include both a term for the factor itself as well as for its square. That is, if the denominator is $(x + 1)^2$ then I need to decompose that into $\frac{A}{x+1} + \frac{B}{(x+1)^2}$.

3. If the denominator has factors which are not reducible to linear factors, the process is much more complicated, and is not guaranteed to give you a result.

21.2   Integration Using Trigonometric Substitutions

Overall, I've tried to rely very minimally on trigonometry throughout the book. Many calculus courses place undue emphasis on the calculus of trigonometry functions, which I think is counter-productive to learning what calculus is and why it is important. However, if you look at the table of trigonometric identities in Appendix H.5, you will notice that there are many interesting substitutions that can be done with trigonometry. These identities are excellent fodder for aiding in the solution of strange integrals, because you can transform them into something else.

If you ever have a strange square root with squares inside, trig identities can often help you out.

For instance, take the integral:

$$\int \sqrt{1 - x^2}\,\mathrm{d}x$$

The answer to this is difficult to come up with (even with the tricks here!). u-substitution as we have normally practiced it doesn't get you anywhere. If we set $u = 1 - x^2$, then $\mathrm{d}u = -2x\,\mathrm{d}x$, and we aren't any further than where we started.

However, if you look at the Pythagorean identities in Appendix H.5, you will see the identity: $\sin^2(u) + \cos^2(u) = 1$. If we rearrange this, we get $\cos^2(u) = 1 - \sin^2(u)$. This almost matches what is in our square root!

We can then make a u-substitution. However, normally, when we do u substitutions, we have been setting u to some value that we see (or nearly see) in the equation. In this case, we will actually be doing something different. Instead of setting u to be some function of x, we will be setting x to be some function of u.

In this case, we will say that $x = \sin(u)$. This also means that $\mathrm{d}x = \cos(u)\,\mathrm{d}u$. That means that we will replace x with $\sin(u)$ and $\mathrm{d}x$ with $\cos(u)\,\mathrm{d}u$ This transforms our equation to the following:

$$\int \sqrt{1 - \sin^2(u)}\,\cos(u)\,\mathrm{d}u$$

Now, we can use our trig identity $\cos^2(u) = 1 - \sin^2(u)$ and replace the interior of the square root as follows:

$$\int \sqrt{cos^2(u)}\,\cos(u)\,\mathrm{d}u$$

Which then simplifies to:

$$\int \cos(u)\,\cos(u)\,du$$

This can be rewritten as

$$\int \cos^2(u)\,du$$

We're getting closer! However, $\cos^2(u)\,du$ is also hard to integrate. However, if you look into Appendix H.5, you will see a section titled "Power-Reducing Identities." These are trig identities that will rewrite a trig function into an equivalent form, but with a lower exponent. From this list, we see that $\cos^2(u) = \frac{1+\cos(2u)}{2}$. Therefore, we can rewrite our integral as follows:

$$\int \frac{1 + \cos(2u)}{2}\,du$$

This is finally in a solvable form! We can solve it like this:

$$= \int \frac{1 + \cos(2u)}{2}\,du \qquad\qquad \text{power-reducing trig identity}$$

$$= \int \frac{1}{2}\,du + \int \frac{1}{2}\cos(2u)\,du \qquad\qquad \text{separating terms}$$

$$= \int \frac{1}{2}\,du + \frac{1}{2}\int \cos(2u)\,du \qquad\qquad \text{simplify}$$

$$= \frac{1}{2}u + \frac{1}{2}\frac{1}{2}\sin(2u) + C \qquad\qquad \text{integrate}$$

$$= \frac{1}{2}u + \frac{1}{4}\sin(2u) + C \qquad\qquad \text{simplify}$$

Now, this is great, and it is correct as far as it goes. However, we are going to want to back-substitute for u to get it in terms of x. However, before we do that, notice that we have a $2u$ inside of the sin. That can be broken out using the rules under the "Angle Addition and Subtraction Identities" because u is the same as $u + u$. Therefore, we can rewrite this result as:

$$\frac{1}{2}u + \frac{1}{4}(\sin(u)\cos(u) + \sin(u)\cos(u)) + C$$

This further reduces to:

$$\frac{1}{2}u + \frac{1}{4}(2\sin(u)\cos(u)) + C$$

And again:

$$\frac{1}{2}u + \frac{1}{2}(\sin(u)\cos(u)) + C$$

Now the problem is that we have the answer in terms of u, while the problem is in terms of x. Therefore, we need to back-substitute for u. To do this, we just need to find the inverse of the function that originally gave us u:

$$x = \sin(u)$$

$$\arcsin(x) = \arcsin(\sin(u))$$

$$\arcsin(x) = u$$

Substituting yields:

$$\frac{1}{2}\arcsin(x) + \frac{1}{2}(\sin(\arcsin(x))\cos(\arcsin(x))) + C$$

This becomes:

$$\frac{1}{2}\arcsin(x) + \frac{1}{2}(x\cos(\arcsin(x)) + C$$

Since we have cosine and arcsine, it would be better to just have sine (since arcsine is its inverse). We can convert cosine to sine by noting that since $\cos^2(u) = 1 - \sin^2(u)$ then we can square root both sides and get $\cos(u) = \sqrt{1 - \sin^2(u)}$. Substituting for that gives us:

$$\frac{1}{2}\arcsin(x) + \frac{1}{2}(x\sqrt{1 - \sin^2(\arcsin(x))}) + C$$

Since arcsine is just the inverse of sine, that reduces to:

$$\frac{1}{2}\arcsin(x) + \frac{1}{2}(x\sqrt{1 - x^2}) + C$$

And this is the final answer.

One thing to notice is that, when you do trig substitutions, you often don't stop with a single substitution. You often have to roll back-and-forth along a series of them. Also note that trig substitutions are not the only types of functions available for substitutions, but they are the most commonly used, and they are the ones we will focus on in this book.

Now, you may be mystified as to when to use a particular substitution. Here are some common substitutions and when to use them. In these examples, A represents some constant:

1. For $\sqrt{A^2 - x^2}$ try $x = A\sin(u)$

2. For $\sqrt{x^2 - A^2}$ try $x = A\sec(u)$

3. For $\sqrt{A^2 + x^2}$ try $x = A\tan(u)$

However, even in the sample problems, there are all sorts of possibilities to try. Sometimes you need u-substitution, sometimes you just need to do a basic trig substitution. You might just take some time looking at Appendix H.5 to get a feel for possible substitutions and manipulations you might try.

— Example 21.3

Perform the following integral: $\int \sin^3(x)\,\mathrm{d}x$

To perform this problem, recognize that we can break out $\sin^3$ into $\sin^2(x) \cdot \sin(x)$ $\sin^2(x)$ can be transformed into $1 - \cos^2(x)$. Therefore, this becomes:

$$\int (1 - \cos^2(x))\sin(x)\,\mathrm{d}x$$

We can expand this out into:

$$\int \sin(x)\,\mathrm{d}x - \cos^2(x)\sin(x)\,\mathrm{d}x$$

The first part of this is immediately integratable, so that it becomes:

$$-\cos(x) - \int \cos^2(x)\sin(x)\,\mathrm{d}x$$

Then, we can do a u-substitution for $u = \cos(x)$, so that $du = -\sin(x)\,dx$. Therefore, this becomes:

$$-\cos(x) + \int u^2\,du$$

This is a straightforward power rule integral, which yields:

$$-\cos(x) + \frac{u^3}{3} + C$$

Because $u = \cos(x)$ this becomes:

$$-\cos(x) + \frac{1}{3}\cos^3(x) + C$$

Review

In this chapter, we learned:

1. For difficult integrals that don't appear to be directly amenable to u-substitution, applying a transformation to the expression can help you to solve the integral.

2. Partial fraction decomposition works well for polynomial fractions where the numerator is of a lower degree than the denominator, and the denominator can be factored entirely into linear factors.

3. Trigonomic substitution works best for getting combinations of powers and constants out from under a radical.

4. When doing trigonometric (and other) substitutions, don't forget to also differentiate the substitution formula so that you can substitute for the differential as well.

5. Trigonometric substitution problems often require continual reworking using different trig substitutions.

6. When the problem is solved, *don't forget to back out your substitution to get the original variable!*

7. There are no definitive rules—the rule is to play with the equation until it is recognizable as something that you can integrate.

8. These techniques are mostly important to let you know that they exist. Even though there are impossible integrals, just because something *looks* impossible doesn't mean that it is.

Exercises

Integrate the following using partial fraction decomposition:

1. $\int \frac{2x+3}{x^2-x-2}\,dx$

2. $\int \frac{x-5}{x^2-x)}\,dx$

3. $\int \frac{x+4}{x^2+10x+25}\,dx$

4. $\int \frac{x-12}{x^2-2x-35}\,dx$

Integrate the following using trigonometric substitutions. Note that these problems may take a lot more creativity than previous homework assignments.

5. $\int \frac{1}{\sqrt{1-x^2}} dx$

6. $\int \frac{\cos^2(x)}{1+\sin(x)} dx$

7. $\int \frac{1}{4+x^2} dx$

8. $\int \frac{1}{x^2 \sqrt{16-x^2}} dx$

Chapter 22

Integration by Parts

As we have noted, integration is unfortunately full of tricks rather than rules. However, one trick in integration is used nearly everywhere—integration by parts. In addition to being a great tool, the ideas behind it give insight into how mathematicians think about formulas.

However, before we talk about integration by parts, we need to remember back to the Product Rule from differentiation.

22.1 The Product Rule

Let's remember back to the product rule that we learned way back in Chapter 12. The product rule states that if we have two variables, u and v multiplied together, then their differential is given by the following rule:

$$\mathrm{d}(u\,v) = u\,\mathrm{d}v + v\,\mathrm{d}u$$

If we have the function $x^2 \sin(x)$, we can find the differential with the product rule. We can set $u = x^2$ and $v = \sin(x)$, and then the product states that the differential will be:

$$x^2 \cos(x)\,\mathrm{d}x + \sin(x)\,2x\,\mathrm{d}x$$

Now, imagine that you are given the following integral:

$$\int x^2 \cos(x)\,\mathrm{d}x + \sin(x)\,2x\,\mathrm{d}x$$

As you can see, this is just the integral of our differential. And, because integration is merely the reverse of differentiation, that means that the integral will just be our original equation (with a $+C$ added). In other words, we can see that:

$$\int x^2 \cos(x)\,\mathrm{d}x + \sin(x)\,2x\,\mathrm{d}x = x^2 \sin(x) + C$$

But how would you have known that if we had not just now taken the differential? In order to take the integral of this differential, you have to be able to "see" that this expression is the result of the product rule. You have to be able to see that $2x\,\mathrm{d}x$ is the differential of x^2 and that $\cos(x)\,\mathrm{d}x$ is the differential of $\sin(x)$. Then, you have to see that the specific arrangement is similar to what you would see with the product rule.

Without thinking about products, we might be tempted to try to use the addition rule and separate this out into $\int x^2 \cos(x)\,\mathrm{d}x + \int \sin(x)2x\,\mathrm{d}x$. However, we will quickly recognize that this doesn't fit any rule that we know. Because neither part is a differential of the other part, $x^2\cos(x)\,\mathrm{d}x$ cannot be rewritten as a basic rule!

—   Example 22.1

Find $\int(\ln(x)\cos(x)\,\mathrm{d}x + \sin(x)\frac{1}{x}\,\mathrm{d}x)$.

If you break this up into terms, on the left-hand side we have $\ln(x)$, $\cos(x)$, and $\mathrm{d}x$. On the right-hand side we have $\frac{1}{x}$, $\sin(x)$, and $\mathrm{d}x$.

Notice that, on the right side, if we put the $\frac{1}{x}$ and the $\mathrm{d}x$ together into a single term, $\frac{\mathrm{d}x}{x}$, this is the differential of $\ln(x)$ on the left-hand side. Likewise, $\cos(x)\,\mathrm{d}x$ on the left-hand side is the differential of $\sin(x)$ on the right side.

Therefore, we can set $u = \ln(x)$ and $v = \sin(x)$, and that will mean that $\mathrm{d}u = \frac{\mathrm{d}x}{x}$ and $\mathrm{d}v = \cos(x)\,\mathrm{d}x$. Therefore, our problem becomes:

$$\int (u\,\mathrm{d}v + v\,\mathrm{d}u)$$

Which is a perfect match for the product rule. Therefore:

$$\int (u\mathrm{d}v + v\mathrm{d}u) = u \cdot v + C \qquad \text{product rule}$$

$$= \ln(x)\sin(x) + C \qquad \text{substituting and constant of integration}$$

Again, integration requires being able to easily identify differentials on sight, and then piece back together the equations that they arose from. Practice is the best tool for learning to identify differentials, and it will become easier with practice.

22.2   Integration by Parts

One thing you may have noticed is that the product rule, while it only has one multiplication term on the left-hand side, has *two* multiplication terms on the right-hand side. Therefore, it doesn't help us much with standalone products when integrating. In other words, if I were to just have the integral $\int x\cos(x)\,\mathrm{d}x$, the product rule does not help me here.

In order to apply the product rule in reverse, the integral would have to be the sum of *two* products, and that would only work *if* they matched the rule exactly!

Unfortunately, there is no general multiplication rule for integration. However, there is a rule, based on the product rule, that helps us to *transform* an integral with products in it into a different form which *might* be easier to integrate. This is known as **integration by parts**.

Integration by parts is not a way to directly perform an integral of two functions multiplied by each other. Instead, it is a way to *reformulate* an existing integral into one that *might* be easier to solve.

To understand integration by parts, first we need to revisit the product rule again. For differentials, the product rule states:

$$d(u\,v) = u\,dv + v\,du$$

Therefore, as we saw earlier, the product rule for integrals is the opposite:

$$\int (u\,dv + v\,du) = u\,v$$

We are leaving out the constant of integration for ease of description.

The rule is correct as far as it goes—the problem is that integrals rarely take this form. The goal of integration by parts is to *reformulate* an integral so that it becomes something we *might* be able to integrate easily. We can do this by rearranging the product rule around a little bit.

First, we can use the addition rule to break this up into separate integrals:

$$\int u\,dv + \int v\,du = u \cdot v$$

Now, if we subtract $\int v\,du$ from both sides, this becomes:

$$\int u\,dv = u\,v - \int v\,du \qquad (22.1)$$

This is our *transformation* rule, known as the **integration by parts** rule. What this says is that if, when doing an integral, we have a product of two functions, we are allowed to rewrite it as a slightly different integral and see if that new integral can be integrated easier. So, if the integral looks like the left side, we can rewrite it to become the right side. This still leaves an integral in the equation, but there is a chance that this integral will be easier to solve than our original integral.

In order to apply this rule you have to think about your integral in a funny way. Take the two things being multiplied together, and choose one of them as the u and one of them as the dv. Then, you take the *integral* of the one you assigned as dv and the *differential* of the one you assigned as u to get v and du. You can then rewrite the integral according to Equation 22.1.

Note that your new equation *still* has an integral associated with it that must be solved, it just *might* be easier to solve than the original integral.

That probably sounds confusing. I'm sorry, it kind of is. However, I think an example will help you.

Let's say we wanted to evaluate the following integral:

$$\int x\,\cos(x)\,dx$$

In this example, $x\,dx$ is not the differential of $\cos(x)$, nor is $\cos(x)dx$ the differential of x. This means that we cannot perform a simple integration using basic rules or u-substitution. However, we can rewrite the integral using integration by parts to see if we can get an easier integral to solve.

The integration by parts equation is:

$$\int u\,dv = uv - \int v\,du$$

Therefore, we must decide which part of this integral is u and which part is dv. Let's say that we choose x to be u and $\cos(x)\,dx$ to be dv.

You may be wondering why I made that decision. We will get to that eventually. For now, just know that I chose this way because I know that this will work out better in the end. Soon, you will be able to make this sort of judgement also.

Therefore, to rewrite the problem, we need to differentiate u to find du and integrate dv to find v. The differential of $u = x$ is $du = dx$. The integral of $dv = \cos(x)\,dx$ is $v = \sin(x)$.

Therefore, our rule states that we can rewrite our equation like this:

$$\int u \qquad dv \quad = u \quad v \quad - \int \quad v \quad du$$
$$\downarrow \qquad \downarrow \qquad \downarrow \quad \downarrow \qquad\qquad \downarrow \quad \downarrow$$
$$\int \boxed{x}\boxed{\cos(x)\,dx} = \boxed{x}\boxed{\sin(x)} - \int \boxed{\sin(x)}\boxed{dx}$$

This is actually much easier to integrate because the part that has to be integrated is just $\int \sin(x)\,dx$, which integrates to $-\cos(x)$. Therefore, the full solution becomes the following (note that the double-negative becomes a positive):

$$\int x\,\cos(x)\,dx = x\,\sin(x) + \cos(x) + C$$

— Example 22.2

Find $\int x\,e^x\,dx$

You might have wondered how to choose which terms to use for u and which terms to use for dv. The answer, unfortunately, is that you again have to have some intuition about which ones are likely to work out. In this example, we will start by seeing what happens when the <u>wrong</u> terms are chosen for u and dv.

Let's choose $x\,dx$ for dv and e^x for u. Therefore, we need to find du and v:

$$u = e^x$$

$$\mathrm{d}u = e^x \mathrm{d}x$$

$$\mathrm{d}v = x \, \mathrm{d}x$$

$$\int \mathrm{d}v = \int x \, \mathrm{d}x$$

$$v = \frac{x^2}{2}$$

Therefore, with integration by parts, we can rewrite the integral like this:

$$\int x \, e^x \mathrm{d}x = \int u \mathrm{d}v$$

$$\int u \, \mathrm{d}v = u \, v - \int v \, \mathrm{d}u \qquad \text{integration by parts}$$

$$= e^x \frac{x^2}{2} - \int \frac{x^2}{2} e^x \, \mathrm{d}x \qquad \text{substituting}$$

This definitely gives us a new integral, but not one that is easier to solve. When this happens, simply go back and pick different values for u and $\mathrm{d}v$.

For our next try, we will use $u = x$ and $\mathrm{d}v = e^x \mathrm{d}x$. This will give us $v = e^x$ and $\mathrm{d}u = \mathrm{d}x$. Therefore, the equation will be rewritten as:

$$\int u \, \mathrm{d}v = u \, v - \int v \, \mathrm{d}u \qquad \text{integration by parts formula}$$

$$\int x \, e^x \, \mathrm{d}x = x \, e^x - \int e^x \, \mathrm{d}x \qquad \text{substituting our improved substitution choices}$$

$$= x \, e^x - e^x + C \qquad \text{exponential rule with constant of integration}$$

22.3 Using Integration by Parts More Than Once

Sometimes, the result of integration by parts does not give you an integral that can be solved, but instead gives you an integral that can be solved *if you do the integration by parts procedure again.*

This can become difficult to keep track of. However, just like the chain rule for differentials, as long as you go a step at a time and don't skip any steps, the process works out just like normal. The biggest problem is knowing *when* integration by parts is likely to work on repeated application, even if it doesn't work at first.

—   Example 22.3

Find $\int x^2 \sin(x)\,dx$.

Because this is a long problem to begin with, I won't lead you to any dead ends. However, you should recognize that it is certainly possible to find them.

To solve this problem, we will set $u = x^2$ and $dv = \sin(x)\,dx$. This means that $du = 2x\,dx$ and $v = -\cos(x)\,dx$ Using integration by parts, we can then rewrite the problem like this:

$$\int u\,dv = u \cdot v - \int v\,du \qquad\qquad \text{integration by parts}$$

$$\int x^2 \sin(x)\,dx = -x^2\cos(x) - \int(-\cos(x)\,2x\,dx) \qquad\qquad \text{substituting back in}$$

$$= -x^2\cos(x) + 2\int x\,\cos(x)\,dx \qquad\qquad \text{rearranging}$$

This result is much simpler, but still not directly integratable. However, based on our experience so far, we should recognize it as being able to be integrated by parts.

Now, let's separate out the new integral. We will have to insert it back into the expression above later, but for now we will just consider the integral itself: $\int x\,\cos(x)\,dx$.

For integration by parts, we will make the substitutions $u = x$ and $dv = \cos(x)dx$. That means that $du = dx$ and $v = \sin(x)$. This will give us:

$$\int u\,dv = u \cdot v - \int v\,du \qquad\qquad \text{integration by parts}$$

$$\int x\,\cos(x)\,dx = x\,\sin(x) - \int \sin(x)\,dx \qquad\qquad \text{substituting back in}$$

$$= x\,\sin(x) - (-\cos(x)) \qquad\qquad \text{simple integration}$$

$$= x\,\sin(x) + \cos(x) \qquad\qquad \text{simplifying}$$

Now we need to put this result back into our original integration by parts solution:

$$\int x^2 \sin(x)\,dx = -x^2 \cos(x) + 2 \int x \cos(x)\,dx \qquad \text{result of the first integration by parts}$$

$$\int x \cos(x)\,dx = x \sin(x) + \cos(x) \qquad \text{result of the second integration by parts}$$

$$\int x^2 \sin(x)\,dx = -x^2 \cos(x) + 2(x \sin(x) + \cos(x)) \qquad \text{substituting the second result into the first}$$

$$= -x^2 \cos(x) + 2x \sin(x) + 2 \cos(x) \qquad \text{simplifying}$$

$$\int x^2 \sin(x)\,dx = -x^2 \cos(x) + 2x \sin(x) + 2 \cos(x) + C \qquad \text{final result with constant of integration}$$

22.4   Choosing u and dv

While there is no hard and fast rule about which term to use for u and which term to use for dv, one commonality you might have picked up is that if one of your multipliers is x or x raised to some positive integer power (i.e., x^n), you are *usually* better off to pick that part of the product for u and the other part of the product for dv.

The reason for this is simple. Whatever value you choose for u on the left-hand side will become du in the new integral on the right-hand side. That means that on the right-hand side, x will be raised to a lower power(i.e., x^{n-1}). Eventually, after n iterations of integration by parts, all that is left will simply be dx. This means that the other half of the function will simply undergo a simple integration at this point.

However, in order for this to work, whatever is chosen for dv has to integrate, and it has to follow a simple integration pathway. For instance, take $\sin(x)$. The integral of $\sin(x)\,dx$ is $-\cos(x)$, and the integral of $-\cos(x)\,dx$ is $-\sin(x)$. This integral will keep shifting back and forth between $\sin(x)$ and $\cos(x)$ forever. Likewise for e^x. Choosing $e^x\,dx$ for dv is simple, because it will simply integrate back to e^x.

Note that this idea does not cover all possible integration by parts problems, but it does cover a very large number of them. Again, to apply the rule, look for an integral of the form:

$$\int x^n f(x)\,dx$$

Where $f(x)\,dx$ will integrate cleanly repeatedly at least n times. Then, set $u = x^n$ and $dv = f(x)\,dx$ and perform integration by parts.

—   **Example 22.4**

Find $\int e^x x^3\,dx$

Notice that in this problem, we have x^n where n is a positive integer (x^3 in this case) and e^x which is a function that will integrate cleanly every single time. Therefore, we will use $u = x^3$ and $dv = e^x dx$.

Then, the solution is as follows:

$$\int e^x x^3 \mathrm{d}x = \int u \mathrm{d}v$$

$$\int u \mathrm{d}v = uv - \int v \mathrm{d}u$$

$$= e^x x^3 - \int e^x 3x^2 \mathrm{d}x$$

$$= e^x x^3 - 3 \int e^x x^2 \mathrm{d}x$$

Then, to solve for $\int e^x x^2 \mathrm{d}x$, do:

$$\int e^x x^2 \mathrm{d}x = \int u \mathrm{d}v$$

$$\int u \mathrm{d}v = uv - \int v \mathrm{d}u$$

$$= x^2 e^x - \int e^x 2x \, \mathrm{d}x$$

$$= x^2 e^x - 2 \int e^x x \, \mathrm{d}x$$

Then, to solve for $\int e^x x \, \mathrm{d}x$, do:

$$\int e^x x \, \mathrm{d}x = \int u \mathrm{d}v$$

$$\int u \mathrm{d}v = uv - \int v \mathrm{d}u$$

$$= e^x x - \int e^x \mathrm{d}x$$

$$= e^x x - e^x$$

Now we can combine these back together to get our final answer:

$$\int e^x x^3 \mathrm{d}x = e^x x^3 - 3(x^2 e^x - 2(e^x x - e^x)) \qquad \text{substituting}$$

$$= e^x x^3 - 3x^2 e^x + 6e^x x - 6e^x \qquad \text{simplifying}$$

$$= e^x x^3 - 3x^2 e^x + 6e^x x - 6e^x + C \qquad \text{constant of integration}$$

22.5   Integration by Parts in a Circle

Another thing that can happen when doing integration by parts is that you may wind up in a loop. As we have shown, sometimes integration by parts requires multiple applications of the procedure. In a small number of cases, after you have applied the procedure a few times, you might wind up in a loop, where the result of an application of the integration by parts procedure gives you the result you obtained in a previous application of the procedure on the same equation. This is not necessarily cause for alarm, as it can in some cases more easily show you the answer.

To show how this works, consider the following integral:

$$\int e^x \sin(x)\,\mathrm{d}x$$

To start with, we are going to set $u = \sin(x)$ and $\mathrm{d}v = e^x \mathrm{d}x$, which will make $\mathrm{d}u = \cos(x)\mathrm{d}x$ and $v = e^x$. Using integration by parts, this will allow us to rewrite the equation as:

$$\int e^x \sin(x)\,\mathrm{d}x = e^x \sin(x) - \int e^x \cos(x)\,\mathrm{d}x$$

Now, let's take a look at our new integral, $\int e^x \cos(x)\,\mathrm{d}x$. This is very similar to our original integral, but not quite. Let's do a similar substitution to what we did before. We'll set $u = \cos(x)$ and $\mathrm{d}v = e^x\,\mathrm{d}x$, which will mean that $\mathrm{d}u = -\sin(x)\,\mathrm{d}x$ and $v = e^x$. Let's take a look at what happens when we transform the new integral using integration by parts:

$$\int e^x \cos(x)\,\mathrm{d}x = \cos(x)\,e^x - \int e^x(-\sin(x)\,\mathrm{d}x)$$

$$= \cos(x)\,e^x + \int e^x \sin(x)\,\mathrm{d}x$$

Notice that $\int e^x \sin(x)\,\mathrm{d}x$ is actually identical to the original problem. This allows us to do a neat trick. If we substitute this integration by parts back into the original equation, we get:

$$\int e^x \sin(x)\,\mathrm{d}x = e^x \sin(x) - \left(\cos(x)\,e^x + \int e^x \sin(x)\,\mathrm{d}x\right)$$

If we apply the negative sign through the expression, we get:

$$\int e^x \sin(x)\,\mathrm{d}x = e^x \sin(x) - \cos(x)\,e^x - \int e^x \sin(x)\,\mathrm{d}x)$$

Now, let's add $\int e^x \sin(x)\,\mathrm{d}x$ to both sides:

$$2\int e^x \sin(x)\,\mathrm{d}x = e^x \sin(x) - \cos(x)\,e^x$$

Now, divide both sides by two:

$$\int e^x \sin(x)\, \mathrm{d}x = \frac{e^x \sin(x) - \cos(x)\, e^x}{2}$$

Now we have a solution to our original equation! We only need to add in the constant of integration to be finished:

$$\int e^x \sin(x)\, \mathrm{d}x = \frac{e^x \sin(x) - \cos(x)\, e^x}{2} + C$$

In short, if you are integrating by parts, if you hit an integral that is identical to a previous integral, you may be able to algebraically manipulate the equation to stop your integration by parts.

This works best for equations where the derivatives are circular. For example, the derivative of e^x *is* e^x, and the derivatives of $\sin(x)$ go in the circle: $\cos(x)$, $-\sin(x)$, $-\cos(x)$, $\sin(x)$. In such a case, when integration by parts is performed, you are likely to wind up with an integral on the right-hand side which matches a previous integral or the integral on the left-hand side, and therefore it can be algebraically manipulated away.

22.6   Other "Integration by Parts" Formulas

I should note that this section is mostly brain candy, and it is not generally helpful in solving practical integrals. If you are having difficulty with the concept of integration by parts, you should probably skip this section and focus on the other sections in this chapter.

While the term "Integration by Parts" usually refers to Equation 22.1, it is actually possible to formulate other, similar formulas using differential rules. Any differential rule that involves a function of more than one variable can be restated as an integration by parts rule.

For example, take the generalized power rule:

$$\mathrm{d}(u^v) = vu^{v-1}\, \mathrm{d}u + \ln(u)\, u^v\, \mathrm{d}v$$

Using the same techniques that we used for the product rule, we can rearrange this into an integral rewriting equation:

$\mathrm{d}(u^v) = vu^{v-1}\, \mathrm{d}u + \ln(u)\, u^v\, \mathrm{d}v$	the generalized power rule
$\int \mathrm{d}(u^v) = \int vu^{v-1}\mathrm{d}u + \int \ln(u)\, u^v\, \mathrm{d}v$	integrate both sides
$u^v = \int vu^{v-1}\, \mathrm{d}u + \int \ln(u)\, u^v\, \mathrm{d}v$	this leaves u^v on the left-hand side
$\int vu^{v-1}\, \mathrm{d}u = u^v - \int \ln(u)\, u^v\, \mathrm{d}v$	solved for one of the integrals
$\int vu^{v-1}\, \mathrm{d}u = u^v - \int \ln(u)\, u^v\, \mathrm{d}v + C$	(22.2)

We can also solve for the other term as well, yielding:

$$\int \ln(u)\, u^v\, \mathrm{d}v = u^v - \int vu^{v-1}\, \mathrm{d}u + C \qquad (22.3)$$

These are not as useful in practice as the product rule (I can hardly think of even one equation where this would be helpful), but I wanted to show you that this was indeed possible. For *any* composite function which has a known differential, an "integration by parts" rule can be established.

22.7   Other Notes on Integration by Parts

While this chapter has shown many different examples of integration by parts working, there are many instances where it simply does not work. In these cases, it is really hard to tell the difference between a problem that you are having trouble with and need to work harder on, and a problem for which there is no solution.

Unfortunately, there is no single way to determine whether there is no solution. However, take heart! All of the integrals in the exercises for this book have solutions.

One final note is that the integrals of several standard functions with known differentials can be proved using integration by parts, where dv is simply equated to dx. For examples of how this is done, see Appendix F.10.

Review

In this chapter, we learned:

1. Solving an integral that is a product of two functions is often a difficult task, and integration by parts can help you solve such integrals.

2. The product rule for differentials, $d(u\,v) = u\,dv + v\,du$ is at the heart of integration by parts.

3. It is hard to use the product rule directly for integrals, as it requires an integral of a precise form to work. The integration by parts transformation is a much more general tool.

4. Integration by parts *does not* provide solutions to integrals directly. Instead, integration by parts is a tool that can be used to *rewrite* an integral into *a different integral* that will hopefully be easier to solve.

5. The integration by parts transformation is $\int u\,dv = u\,v - \int v\,du$.

6. To do the transformation, choose part of the integral you are wanting to solve to be dv (this *must* contain the differential) and the rest will be u. Then find v and du from those terms. Finally, rewrite the integral on the left using the given formula for the right with u, du, v, and dv all appropriately substituted.

7. After the transformation, see if your integral is easier to solve or not. You may have to adjust which terms get included in u and dv in order to solve the integral, or it may not be solvable using this method.

8. Integration by parts may have to be repeated multiple times to work.

9. This method works best with an integral in which one term is progressing towards dx with more and more derivatives (i.e., a polynomial) and the other term has a cyclical derivative (i.e., sin, cos, e). u should contain the term progressing towards dx and dv should contain the rest.

10. Sometimes, integrals of simple functions can be deduced by simply using integration by parts and setting dv to dx.

11. Other "integration by parts" rules can be established for any function of multiple variables with a known differential. However, the main rule (Equation 22.1) is the one you shown to be most useful in practice.

Exercises

Integral the following:

1. $\int x \sin(x) dx$

2. $\int x e^x dx$

3. $\int x^2 3^x dx$

4. $\int 2x^2 \cos(x) dx$

5. $\int x \ln(x) dx$

6. $\int 3x \, 5^{2x} dx$

Integrate the following without using the table of integrals in Appendix H.7. You *may* use the table of differentials in Appendix H.6. Also note that these may require more than one technique to perform.

7. $\int \ln(x) dx$

8. $\int \arcsin(x) dx$

Solve the following:

9. Find the volume of the solid formed when the curve $y = e^x$ is rotated around the y axis from $x = 0$ to $x = 2$.

10. Create an "integration by parts" rule using the quotient rule (i.e., $d(\frac{u}{v})$). Note that you will need to split the fraction to create the rule.

Chapter 23

Problem-Solving Using the Integral

The uses that have been found for the integral have been almost unlimited. The ability to take relative changes in quantities (i.e., dx and dy) and use those to come up with formulas for the absolute quantities themselves (i.e., x and y) through integration revolutionized several fields of inquiry. The revolution began in physics, but the use of integration to find governing equations for various phenomena extended through to biology, economics, probability, and beyond. The goal of this chapter is to provide some context about different ways that an integral can be utilized.

So far in this book, the usage of the integral has been geometric—finding totals, areas, volumes, and lengths. A wide variety of problems from different fields can, in fact, be converted to problems of totals, areas, volumes, and lengths. So, in a sense, very little in this chapter is really all that new. Nonetheless, this chapter will provide some additional, hopefully helpful, ways of looking at the practical application of integration.

The main modes of application of integration covered in this chapter are:

1. Total accumulation problems

2. Average value of continuous function problems

3. Converting dynamic relationships into static relationships

In reality, while we have broken this up into separate "modes of application," many of these modes can be interconverted with each other. Nonetheless, I think that separating them out in this way will help you recognize more places where you can apply the integral.

23.1   Total Accumulation

Because an integral is merely an infinite sum, many applications of integration are about total accumulation. Total accumulation can be broken down into three main subsets—basic accumulation, compounded accumulation, and probabilistic accumulation.

In basic accumulation, the value being accumulated doesn't have any real impact on the equation itself. For instance, if a vehicle is moving, the total accumulated distance that the vehicle travels doesn't affect its speed—its speed is independent of the accumulated distance.

In compounded accumulation, the value being accumulated *does* have an impact on the equation itself. For instance, if you have money in a bank account earning interest, the amount of interest you receive gets added back into the bank account, so that future interest payments will be based not only on the amount of money you started with, but also on the accumulated money that has gone into your bank account because of previous interest payments.

In probabilistic accumulation, the value being accumulated is a probability. That may sound strange, but, actually, it is a very standard usage of calculus. Essentially, given a distribution function $f(x)$ for a variable x, the accumulated values of $f(x)\,dx$ over a specific range of x represent the probability of that value of x occurring.

The following subsections will illustrate how each of these are dealt with using integration.

23.1.1   Basic Accumulation

One of the first ways that integration was applied was in physics. Think about an object moving along a line, like a car moving down a road. It is *accumulating* changes in position as it goes on.

What determines the amount of accumulation that takes place over a given amount of time? Well, the car's *velocity* is merely the rate of accumulation. Therefore, the accumulation of changes in position is merely the summation of all of the infinitely small changes given by the car's velocity.

We noted in Chapter 15 that velocity is the derivative of position. That means that $v = \frac{dp}{dt}$. Therefore, let's say that you are traveling at a constant velocity of $5\frac{\text{mi}}{\text{hour}}$. If we assume that the units of position are miles and the units of time are hours, we can write this out as:

$$\frac{dp}{dt} = 5$$

To find the actual position at time t, we just multiply both sides by dt and integrate:

$$\frac{dp}{dt} = 5 \qquad\qquad \text{equation for velocity}$$

$$dp = 5\,dt \qquad\qquad \text{multiply by } dt$$

$$\int dp = \int 5\,dt \qquad\qquad \text{integrate both sides}$$

$$p = 5t + C \qquad\qquad \text{perform integration}$$

This means that, to find p at time t, all you have to do is multiply t time 5. But what about the constant of integration? If we set $t = 0$, then $p = C$. This means that the constant of integration is merely the *starting position*, which, in physics, is often referred to as p_0.

We can do the same thing with velocity. Instead of a constant velocity, we will accelerate. We noted in Chapter 15 that acceleration is the derivative of velocity. In other words, $a = \frac{dv}{dt}$.

Let's say that we have a constant acceleration of $3\frac{\text{mi}}{\text{hour}^2}$ (miles per hour per hour).[1] Therefore, we can find

---

[1] Acceleration is miles per hour per hour because it is the rate at which we are accumulating velocity.

out an equation for our velocity just like before:

$$\frac{\mathrm{d}v}{\mathrm{d}t} = 3 \qquad\qquad \text{starting equation}$$

$$\mathrm{d}v = 3\,\mathrm{d}t \qquad\qquad \text{multiply by } \mathrm{d}t$$

$$\int \mathrm{d}v = \int 3\,\mathrm{d}t \qquad\qquad \text{integrate both sides}$$

$$v = 3t + C \qquad\qquad \text{perform integration}$$

So what is C? Well, when $t = 0$, then $v = C$. Therefore, C is our *starting velocity*, which is often referred to as v_0. Therefore, the equation for the velocity will be:

$$v = 3t + v_0$$

So, if our starting velocity is 1 and $t = 2$, then the velocity at t will be $3(2) + 1 = 7$.

However, we can go even further. If we wanted to *generate* an equation that works for *any* constant acceleration, we can just use a as a constant. Therefore, we can rewrite the equation as:

$$v = at + v_0 \tag{23.1}$$

Now, if we remember that v (velocity) is the derivative of position, we can find the equation for the position at time t by just integrating. First, we will convert v into derivative form, $\frac{\mathrm{d}p}{\mathrm{d}t}$ (a and v_0 will stay as they are, since they represent constants). This gives us:

$$\frac{\mathrm{d}p}{\mathrm{d}t} = at + v_0$$

We will solve it like this:

$$\frac{\mathrm{d}p}{\mathrm{d}t} = at + v_0 \qquad\qquad \text{the original equation}$$

$$\mathrm{d}p = at\,\mathrm{d}t + v_0\,\mathrm{d}t \qquad\qquad \text{multiply by } \mathrm{d}t$$

$$\int \mathrm{d}p = \int at\,\mathrm{d}t + v_0\,\mathrm{d}t \qquad\qquad \text{integrate both sides}$$

$$p = \frac{1}{2}at^2 + v_0 t + C \qquad\qquad \text{perform integration remembering } a \text{ and } v_0 \text{ are constant}$$

Again, to find out what C represents, if we set $t = 0$ we get $p = C$. Therefore, C is our starting position, which we will represent by p_0. The equation then becomes:

$$p = \frac{1}{2}at^2 + v_0 t + p_0 \tag{23.2}$$

If you have taken a physics course, this equation is easily recognizable. Equations 23.1 and 23.2 are known as the kinematic equations.[2] These equations describe the velocities and positions of objects given a constant acceleration. This is very useful because, in physics, the acceleration due to gravity *is* constant.

So, in this section, we looked at how position is the accumulation driven by velocity, and velocity is the accumulation driven by acceleration. Using just these facts, we deduced equations for velocity and position assuming some constant acceleration. We wound up discovering the standard kinematic equations from physics, without actually having to do any experiments!

---

[2]Sometimes, Equation 23.2 is written without p_0 and is solved for *displacement* rather than position. This is reasonable, because displacement is just the change in position. In other words, it is just what the position would be if we assumed the starting position was 0.

23.1.2   Compounded Accumulation

A total accumulation problem is one where you know the *rate* (really, the *instantaneous rate*) of something being added, but you want to know the total accumulation of that something after a given amount of time.

Let's take, for instance, the nominal annual percentage rate (also known as APR) of interest for a loan. Even though it is called an "annual percentage rate," that does not mean that this is how much interest will accrue over a year. The "annual" means that this is merely the unit of measurement. In other words, if you have an APR of 5%, this means that your interest rate at any given time is $\frac{5\%}{\text{year}}$. The total amount you owe will be more than that because, as you accumulate more debt through the interest, you have to pay money on the accumulated interest as well.

This is known as **compounded accumulation**, and it applies not only to money but to all sorts of things such as:

1. Interest rate paid back to you on savings accounts (the more money you receive in interest continues to gain interest going forward)

2. Biological reproduction (a population which has more babies then has more creatures available to make babies)

3. Viral adoption of products and technology (the more people who use the product generates more people who will tell others about it)

Any time that *the thing that is growing* is the *same thing that is causing the growth*, you will usually have compound accumulation. In order to apply calculus to solve this, the accumulation must be continuous or approximately continuous.

Biological reproduction, for instance, is not continuous. There are a discrete number of organisms. Each organism can only carry a discrete number of organisms at a time, and it takes a fixed period of time for this to happen. Nonetheless, with enough organisms present, the population can act as if it were continuous.

The same is true of money. To use calculus, we must assume that interest is being compounded *continuously*. This is a good approximation if interest is being compounded often (say, daily), but it gets off if interest is only being compounded monthly or yearly.

For the purposes of this chapter, we will always assume that the functions can be continuously modeled.

So, how does this modeling work?

For the basic case, let's say that m represents the amount of money that we have on hand, in dollars. Now, let's say that our interest rate is $\frac{5\%}{\text{year}}$. The interest rate is a rate of change, but not quite in the calculus sense. To use calculus, we need the rate of change in the same units as our variable. Since m is in dollars, we need the rate of change in dollars as well.

In other words, we need to find $\frac{\mathrm{d}m}{\mathrm{d}t}$.

The rate of money in dollar terms that we will get is based on the amount of money we have. So, if m is the amount of money, then the rate is $5\% \cdot m$, or $0.05m$. We can write this as:

$$\frac{\mathrm{d}m}{\mathrm{d}t} = 0.05m$$

Since we want to know what the *total accumulation* is, we want to find out what the total value of m is based on the value of t. Therefore, we will need to find a way to integrate this problem so that we wind up with only m and t and not their differentials.

This equation can be rearranged so that is it easier to integrate. Multiplying by dt and dividing by m yield the following equation:

$$\frac{dm}{m} = 0.05dt$$

Integrating both sides gives us:

$$\ln(m) = 0.05t + C$$

Closer, but now we only have the equation for the logarithm of m. So, to get rid of the logarithm, we will exponentiate both sides and simplify:

$$\ln(m) = 0.05t + C \qquad \text{the original equation}$$
$$e^{\ln(m)} = e^{0.05t+C} \qquad \text{exponentiate both sides}$$
$$m = e^{0.05t+C} \qquad \text{simplify the left-hand side}$$
$$m = e^C \cdot e^{0.05t} \qquad \text{exponent rules}$$
$$m = C \cdot e^{0.05t}$$

The last step, where we converted e^C into C requires a little explanation. Since C is a constant we don't know, then e^C will also be a constant we don't know. Therefore, we might as well just write it as C, since we know that it is still a constant, and we haven't figured out what it is yet.

Now, to solve for C, we have to think about the problem. At time $t = 0$, $e^{0.05t}$ will simplify to e^0 which is 1. Therefore, at time $t = 0$, $m = C$. That means that C is the starting amount of money in our account.

This type of equation is known as the exponential growth equation. For simple exponential growth, you can simply use the equation as-is. The most general form of the equation is:

$$v = C \cdot e^{\frac{r}{100}t} \qquad (23.3)$$

In this equation, v is your value at time t, t is the time (using whatever units you wish), and r is your percentage growth rate (expressed in the same units as t).

Now, there are more complicated forms of this equation as well. These occur when the growth rate itself is not fixed. In those cases, you have to go back to the original differential and re-solve for the total accumulated value.

23.1.3 Accumulation and Areas

In systems of two variables, accumulation is geometrically identical to the area under the curve.[3] With two variables, areas and accumulations are just two different ways of thinking about the same thing. For visual people, sometimes thinking about areas under a curve is more intuitive than thinking about total accumulation. However, if you tend to like equations better, accumulation tends to be the more natural intuition.

---

[3]This is the reason why integration is often mistaken for finding the area under a curve. It is an *application* of integration, not integration itself. However, it is so close to the actual operation that they are often confused.

In any case, the relationship between area and accumulation breaks down when multiple variables are introduced.

23.1.4   Probabilities as Areas

One interesting application of thinking about accumulation and the area under a curve is probabilities. A **probability curve** is a curve representing possible outcomes of an event on the x axis, and the relative density of that outcome happening on the y axis. So, for instance, x may represent the size of an animal, the scores on a test, etc. The height of the curve is the relative frequency of that size, score, or whatever occurring. The area under the curve over a particular range of x values is the probability that some value within that range will occur.

A standard "normal" probability distribution of a random continuous variable is given below:

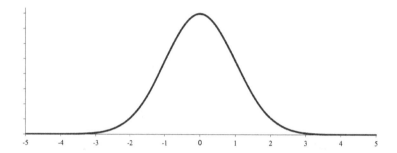

On a true "normal" probability distribution curve, the edges actually extend out forever in both directions. However, the area under the curve for any given stretch of the graph is the probability that the variable will wind up at one of those x values.[4] In other words, the total accumulation of $f(x)\,dx$ over a range of x values is equivalent to the probability of any of those x values occurring.

What is the probability that it will wind up *anywhere* on the graph? Think about what that means graphically. As we have said, the area under the curve for a given x range represents the probability of the event having one of those x values. That means that the chance of an event having any value at all is the total area under the entire curve.[5] Well, every organism has a height. Therefore, the chances of an organism having a height of any value is 100%, or, represented as a decimal, 1.

In other words, when all probabilities within any distribution are added up together, they equal 1. Therefore, the total area under the curve of *any* probability distribution is 1.

You can write this as an integral, assuming that $p(x)$ represents your probability distribution function:

$$\int_{-\infty}^{+\infty} p(x)\,dx = 1 \tag{23.4}$$

That equation is the foundation of much thinking about probability. We won't get into this deeply enough to ask you detailed questions, but I did want you to know about this very important application/overlap of integrals to probability.

---

[4]Probability in this case is given as a value between 0 and 1. So, 0.5 represents a 50% probability, and 0.134 represents a 13.4% probability.

[5]So, instead of asking, for instance, what the probability that a given organism has a particular range of heights, we are saying that the total area under the curve is like asking about what is the change that a given organism has any height at all.

For a probability distribution function, the area under the curve in a region is the probability that the variable will land in that space, and the total area under the curve should total up to one.[6]

23.2 Finding the Average Value

Another common usage of the integral (but one that will require a new technique!) is finding the average value of a continuous function.

Imagine the curve $y = x^2$. Let's say that we wanted to know the average (i.e., the mean) y value over the interval $x = 2$ to $x = 4$. In the graph of $y = x^2$, the values get higher as we move down the x axis, so the average will not be in the center, but rather weighted towards the right.

So how do we calculate the average exactly?

The average value of a function (also known as the *mean value*) can also be found using the integral. The first step in understanding how to do this is to understand how to find the *average slope* of a given function. You might not see how the average slope of a function relates to its average value, but we will get to that shortly.

Back in Section 17.1 we talked about the old joke about going uphill both ways. Remember that if a function is continuous, no matter how tumultuous it gets, the total changes between two points is the sum of all of the ups and downs of the function. In a like manner, the *slope* between two points is the average of all of the slopes travelled between those two points.

We can see the basic idea in the graph below:

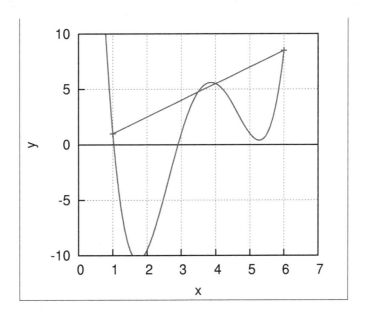

The direct slope from the first point to the second point is the *exact same* as the average slope of all of the points on the curve. For every time it has a slope that goes down, it requires a steeper slope to bring it back up. Therefore, the average slope from the first point to the second point is the same as the direct line from the first point to the second point. In such a case, you can use the point-slope formula (Equation 3.2) to to find the average slope.

---

[6]Technically, the probability distribution can be less than one if there is a possibility that the variable won't have a value, but that is a rarely considered case.

Now remember, what is the tool we use to find the slope of a function? It is the derivative! Therefore, when we draw the line between these two points, what we are finding is the average slope, which means it is the average value of the *derivative* across that range.

If the average *slope* between two points can be found between two points on a graph can be found using the direct slope between the two points, how does that help us find the average *value* of a graph?

Sometimes in order to find something out, you have to look at it from a different direction. In this case, it is fairly obvious how to see that the slope between two points is the average of the derivative. But remember—*any* function is the derivative of some other function! So, if instead of wanting to find the average slope, I wanted to find the average *value*, I would find the function *for which my function is the slope—the derivative.*

In other words, to find the average value of a function over a range, we need to find the integral. Then, once we have the integral, we compute the slope between two points on the range, which will yield the average value of its derivative (i.e., the average value of the function we started with).

So, let's say that $f(x)$ is our starting function, and $F(x)$ represents the integral of $f(x)\mathrm{d}x$. Therefore, the point-slope formula is:

$$\text{average of } f(x) \text{ from } a \text{ to } b = \frac{y_1 - y_0}{x_1 - x_0}$$
$$= \frac{F(b) - F(a)}{b - a}$$

Now, you may have noticed that $F(b) - F(a)$ is the same result as the definite integral of $f(x)\mathrm{d}x$ from b to a. Therefore, this can be replaced by simply saying:

$$\text{average of } f(x) \text{ from } a \text{ to } b = \frac{\int_a^b f(x)\,\mathrm{d}x}{b - a} \qquad (23.5)$$

Let's look at an example.

— Example 23.1

Find the average value of x^2 from $x = 1$ to $x = 5$.

So, to find the average value of the function, the first thing we need to do is find the integral. Therefore, using the power rule, if $y = x^2$ then area under the curve will be $\frac{x^3}{3} + C$.

Now we can use the point-slope formula to find the slope between two points in our new function:

$$m = \frac{y_1 - y_0}{x_1 - x_0}$$

$$= \frac{\frac{5^3}{3} - \frac{1^3}{3}}{5 - 1}$$

$$= \frac{\frac{75}{3} - \frac{1}{3}}{4}$$

$$= \frac{\frac{74}{3}}{4}$$

$$= \frac{37}{6}$$

Therefore, the average value of x^2 from $x = 1$ to $x = 5$ is $\frac{37}{6}$.

23.3 Converting a Dynamic Problem into a Static One

Many relationships between entities are easier to establish by considering differentials and derivatives than by considering the values themselves. Many measured values are really *rates*, and, as we saw in Chapter 14, a rate is merely a derivative with the bottom differential being the differential of time, dt. As we mentioned in Chapter 14, equations involving differentials are considered *dynamic* relationships, and equations without them are considered *static* relationships.

In Chapter 14, we focused on converting static relationships into dynamic ones by differentiating. However, when discovering new relationships, we often have to go the other way. That is, we may learn a new dynamic relationship among rates, and then we will want to convert that relationship into a static one by integrating it.

For instance, **Newton's Law of Cooling** states that if an object is hotter than the ambient temperature, then the rate of cooling of the object is proportional to the temperature difference. If we use y as the temperature of the object, A as the ambient temperature (which will not change), and t as the time, and a constant of proportionality k, Newton's Law of Cooling can be expressed as:

$$\frac{dy}{dt} = -k(y - A) \tag{23.6}$$

Here you have a very simple relationship, but it is a relationship based on a rate—a differential. We can solve it by rearranging it a bit as follows (and remember that k and A are constants):

$$\frac{dy}{dt} = -k(y - A)$$ the original equation

$$u = y - A$$ u-substitution since A is a constant

$$du = dy$$

$$\frac{du}{dt} = -ku$$ using our u-substitution

$$\frac{du}{u} = -k\,dt$$ rearranging for integration

$$\ln(u) = -kt + C$$ performing integration

$$e^{\ln(u)} = e^{-kt+C}$$ getting rid of the ln

$$u = e^{-kt+C}$$

$$u = e^{C}e^{-kt}$$ power rule

$$u = Ce^{-kt}$$ e^{c} is just as arbitrary as C

$$y - A = Ce^{-kt}$$ back-substituting for u

$$y = Ce^{-kt} + A$$ solved for y

So, by using integration, we converted our dynamic relationship into a static one.

We can even solve for C. Remember, that, at the start of this, the time is zero. Therefore, at time zero, $e^{-kt} = 1$, making this equation reduce to:

$$y = C + A$$

Therefore, C must be $y - A$, where y is the starting temperature (i.e., the temperature at time zero), which we can denote as y_0.

So, the final equation becomes:

$$y = (y_0 - A)e^{-kt} + A$$

Remember that k is an unknown constant.

This is a simple example of a type of problem known as a **differential equation**. A differential equation is an equation involving differentials and derivatives, where the goal is to solve for the static formula.

There are entire courses on how to solve equations like this. However, even though there are many cases like the one described here which are solvable, in many cases, the general formula cannot be solved. However, even in the unsolvable cases, being able to formulate the question correctly allows its behavior to be more accurately described, reasoned about, and even approximated (see Chapter 24 for information about how to approximate integrals).

—   Example 23.2

In Section 15.6 we discussed a mixing problem in engineering. At the time, we used our knowledge of derivatives to find the rate at which we had to add water in order to maintain a steady-state of 4 pounds of dirt in the mixing tank. In this example, we are going to show how to convert the dynamic relationship (i.e., the relationship among differentials) that we found into a static relationship (i.e., a relationship without differentials).

It would be best to go back and read Section 15.6. However, in short, we came up with a formula that said that the rate of change in the number of pounds of dirt in the tank ($\frac{dp}{dt}$) can be given by the following equation, where w is a constant telling you the amount of water in the tank, p is a variable representing the total amount of dirt present in the tank at any given time, k is the rate (a constant) at which water is being removed/added, and q is the rate (also a constant) that dirt is coming into the tank:

$$\frac{dp}{dt} = q + k \cdot \frac{p}{w}$$

So, to convert that equation into a static relationship between p and t, we have to find a way to make this equation integrable. What makes this difficult is that if we multiply both sides by dt to separate the differentials, that will give us on the right hand side an integral of the form $\int p \, dt$. Since the variables are different, we can't perform that integration.

In many of these types of equations, the way to solve them is to try to get them into a form similar to $\frac{du}{u}$ so they integrate to $\ln(u)$. The right-hand side of this equation can actually be collapsed into a u. We can say:

$$u = q + k \cdot \frac{p}{w}$$

Because q, k, and w are all constants, the differential is simply:

$$du = \frac{k}{w} \, dp$$

We can solve for dp by multiplying both sides by $\frac{w}{k}$:

$$dp = \frac{w}{k} \, du$$

Therefore, the differential simplifies to:

$$\frac{w}{k} \frac{u}{dt} = u$$

We can solve this as follows:

$$\frac{w}{k} \frac{du}{dt} = u \qquad \text{starting equation}$$

$$\frac{w}{k} \frac{du}{u} = dt \qquad \text{multiply by } \frac{dt}{u}$$

$$\frac{du}{u} = \frac{k}{w} \, dt \qquad \text{multiply by } \frac{k}{w}$$

$$\int \frac{du}{u} = \int \frac{k}{w} \, dt \qquad \text{integrate both sides}$$

$$\ln(u) = \frac{kt}{w} + C \qquad \text{perform integration}$$

$$e^{\ln(u)} = e^{\frac{kt}{w} + C} \qquad \text{exponentiate both sides}$$

$$u = e^{C} e^{\frac{kt}{w}} \qquad \text{simplify both sides}$$

$$u = C e^{\frac{kt}{w}} \qquad e^{C} \text{ and } C \text{ are both equally arbitrary}$$

Now we have solved this in terms of u. Now we need to back out the u substitution and solve for p:

$$u = Ce^{\frac{kt}{w}}$$ starting point

$$q + k \cdot \frac{p}{w} = Ce^{\frac{kt}{w}}$$ back out the u substitution

$$k \cdot \frac{p}{w} = Ce^{\frac{kt}{w}} - q$$ solve for p

$$p = \frac{w}{k}Ce^{\frac{kt}{w}} - \frac{qw}{k}$$

$$p = Ce^{\frac{kt}{w}} - \frac{qw}{k}$$ $\frac{w}{k}C$ is just as arbitrary as C

Now we need to solve for what C is. The original problem statement from Section 15.6 says that the tank starts with no dirt in it. That means that at $t = 0$, p will also be zero. That means that:

$$p = Ce^{\frac{kt}{w}} - \frac{qw}{k}$$

$$0 = Ce^{\frac{k \cdot 0}{w}} - \frac{qw}{k}$$

$$0 = Ce^{0} - \frac{qw}{k}$$

$$0 = C - \frac{qw}{k}$$

$$\frac{qw}{k} = C$$

Therefore, the final equation is:

$$p = \frac{qw}{k}e^{\frac{kt}{w}} - \frac{qw}{k}$$

Or, we can simplify this into:

$$p = \frac{qw}{k}(e^{\frac{kt}{w}} - 1)$$

Then, you can substitute for any q, w, and k to find the particular equation you are looking for.

Review

In this chapter, we learned:

1. Several types of problems that can be solved using integrals include (a) value accumulation problems (of various sorts), (b) average value problems for continuous functions, and (c) problems where dynamic relationships need to be converted to static relationships.

2. Basic total accumulation problems reflect the fact that the integral is merely an infinite sum (i.e., an accumulation) of infinitely small values. To solve these problems, you must identify the infinitely small value (in terms of differentials) that are being added together, and use an integral to solve.

3. In a compounding total accumulation problem, the thing being accumulated affects the amount of accumulation going forward, such as with compound interest or biological reproduction.

4. The area under a curve is another way of looking at a total accumulation problem (the area under the curve being the thing that is accumulating). However, some problems are easier to think about geometrically, and thus as areas under a curve.

5. In probability distributions for the variable x, the accumulated area under the distribution curve represents for a given range of x values represents the probability of an x value in that range occurring.

6. In probability distributions, the total area for all possible values of x is 1 (i.e., 100%).

7. Many problems require the average values of continuous functions over a given range from $x = a$ to $x = b$. Such averages can be found using Equation 23.5.

8. Other types of problems involve the general problem of converting dynamic relationships (i.e., equations involving rates) into static relationships (i.e., equations without differentials). These are known as differential equations.

9. When doing post-integration manipulations of equations, any arithmetic involving any set of constants and an unknown constant (i.e, C) yields a resulting constant that is just as arbitrary (and just as constant) as C, so the arithmetic can be simplified to just C.

10. After doing integration, the constants of integration can often be shown to be some interesting value of a function, such as its starting value.

11. If y represents the value of a function at any given time t, y_0 is usually used for the constant value that represents the starting point where $t = 0$. It is often the case that the constant of integration can be found in terms of y_0 or some similar variable.

Exercises

1. The acceleration due to gravity is $-9.8067 \frac{m}{sec^2}$ (meters per second squared). The acceleration is negative because acceleration brings you back to earth rather than up, up, and away. Derive an equation for position given the acceleration due to gravity. The initial velocity is given as v_0 and the initial position is given as p_0.

2. Using the previous equation, if I dropped a ball from a tower 100 m tall, how long would it take to hit the ground? We will use the top of the tower as position 100 m, and the ground as position 0 m.

3. Instead of a *constant* acceleration, let's say the equation for the acceleration of a vehicle at a given time is given by the formula $a = 3\sqrt{t}$. Assuming that position and velocity are zero when the time begins, at what position is the vehicle when $t = 5$.

4. If you deposit your money in a bank that has an interest rate of 4% per year, work out an equation, starting with differentials, of how much money (m) you will have after t years, if you start out with m_0 dollars. Use standard assumptions of calculus to find the equation.

5. Find the average (mean) value of the function $\sin(x)$ from $x = 1$ to $x = 1.5$ (use radians for $\sin(x)$).

6. Bacterial populations can undergo rapid growth given the right conditions. The size of the population is represented by the variable p. The instantaneous growth rate of a population of E. coli bacteria is found to be 150% per hour. Using the general assumptions of calculus, find out an equation for the number of bacterial cells at any given time t where t is measured in hours. Use p_0 to represent the starting population at time $t = 0$.

7. Using the equation generated in the previous question, find out how long it would take for 100 cells to grow into 1,000,000 cells.

8. Find the average value of the function $x^3 + 12x^2 - 5$ from $x = 6$ to $x = 8$.

9. In a probability distribution, what is the *total* area under the entire probability distribution?

10. If someone told you the following probabilities (given as a decimal) for the heights of a type of organism, what would you think was wrong with those probabilities?

- < 30cm: 0.4
- 30cm $- -60$cm: 0.5
- > 60cm: 0.3

11. Radium-226 decays at an instantaneous rate of $\frac{0.0436\%}{\text{year}}$. Using the variable r for the amount of Radium-226 in grams, find the equation to represent the amount of Radium-226 left after time t, where t is in years, and r_0 is the starting amount of Radium-226.

12. A pot of soup on the stove starts at 370K (Kelvin), and the ambient temperature of the room is 300K. Say that the cooling constant is $\frac{0.001}{\text{sec}}$. Begin with Newton's Law of Cooling, and build an equation which tells you the temperature of the pot at time t (where t is in seconds).

13. Given the equation from the previous question, what is the temperature of the pot after 500 seconds?

Chapter 24

Numeric Integration Techniques

Many integrals are difficult or impossible to do symbolically. That is, there is no way to write the integral in terms of standard functions. The integral $\int \cos(x^2)\,dx$, for instance, is a very short, easy-to-write integral, but it has no symbolic solution in terms of standard functions. Pretty much every differential of standard functions can be written in terms of standard functions, but that is not true of integrals.

Therefore, even though *indefinite* integrals might not be available, you can often still estimate *definite* integrals using techniques known collectively as **numeric integration techniques**. They are called numeric techniques because we completely skip the process of symbolic integration, and we merely attempt to estimate the final result of definite integration. Numeric techniques for integration allow us to approximate the answer to a definite integral even if we can't solve for it exactly, or don't want to for some reason.

A good practitioner of calculus can recognize a problem to be an integral, while at the same time realizing that *actually solving* the symbolic integral is beside the point. Many times, you don't need the equation for the symbolic solution, you just need a number, and it doesn't need to be exact. Just as a point of terminology, the equation that solves an integral is known as the **symbolic solution** while the number that represents the answer you are looking for is the **numeric solution**. When doing definite integration, we have so far done both—we solved the integral symbolically, and then evaluated the new equation at the limits of integration using the evaluation bar.

Numeric techniques allow you to skip the process of finding the symbolic solution, and go straight to the process of finding a "close enough" approximate numeric answer. This is perfect because there are many integrals for which symbolic solutions simply don't exist.

24.1   Riemann Sums

We have already looked at numeric integral techniques when we were developing the integral formalism, though we didn't study it in depth.

In Chapter 18 we looked at the connection between the integral and the area under a particular curve.

We introduced this picture of the integral of $y = x^2$:

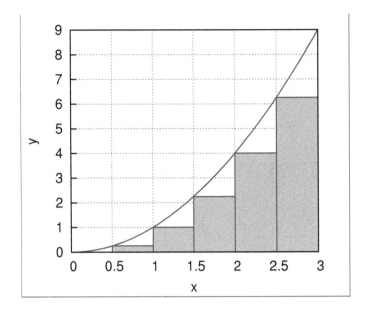

In this picture, the integral is approximated by finding rectangles that are 0.5 units wide where the upper-left-corner of each rectangle touched the line. The integral is then measured by counting up the areas of all the rectangles and adding them together. This is known as a **Riemann Sum**.

That's all there is to it! Well, almost, but not quite. As with everything, there are a lot of additional possibilities, but that is the core idea. The goal of this chapter is to develop a slightly more formalized understanding of this, so it can be more rigorously applied when needed.

The basic process is as follows:

1. Start with an equation, and the starting and ending points for where you want to find the area under the curve.

2. Break up the curve into sections of equal width. We will call this width Δx.

3. Create rectangles that are the width of the section, and where the the recangle touches the curve on the top left corner.

4. Calculate the area of each rectangle (because finding the area of a rectangle is easy). It is simply the y value multiplied by Δx.

5. Add up all the areas of the rectangles for the region you are looking at.

The interesting thing to note about this: if you choose smaller and smaller widths to break up the equation, you get a closer and closer approximation to the "true" value of the integral.

Now, if I told you to take a graph and mark it at regular intervals, then draw rectangles where the top-left corner touches the line, and then add up the area of those rectangles, you could probably do it on your own. You don't need an equation to tell you what to do.

However, in math, we almost always prefer equations because they are both precise (there is no ambiguity about how the instructions are to be interpreted) and succinct (you can write a whole lot in a small space). Additionally, because equations have a logical structure, they can be manipulated easier than sentences and paragraphs. Finally, equations are very well-suited for translation into a computer program, which is what winds up happening with a lot of numeric integration problems. Therefore, we are going to deduce an equation to tell us how to perform these area calculations.

We can generate a mathematical representation of the Riemann Sum as follows:

1. Start with a function $f(x)$ for which we want to find the area under this function from $x = a$ to $x = b$. In other words, we are looking for an approximation of $\int_a^b f(x)\,dx$.

2. Decide how many partitions do divide this into. This is an arbitrary decision based on how precise you need your results to be. We will use n to represent the total number of subdivisions.

3. Assuming the subdivisions are equally wide, we can represent the size of each subdivision with Δx, and calculate it with the following equation:

$$\Delta x = \frac{b - a}{n} \tag{24.1}$$

4. The current x value under consideration will be notated as x_k. The first x_k value will start at a, and then we will add Δx units to it every time through.

5. The y value (i.e., the height of the rectangle) is given by $f(x)$ at the current value of x, which is x_k. Therefore, the height will be $f(x_k)$.

6. Each individual rectangle will be calculated by multiplying the value of the function at the current point (the height of the rectangle) by Δx (the subdivision width). In other words, $\text{area}_k = f(x_k)\,\Delta x$.

7. The total area can be found by a summation of all of the areas from $k = 1$ to $k = n$.

The equation that this generates is as follows:

$$\int_a^b f(x)\,dx \approx \sum_{k=1}^{n} f(x_k)\,\Delta x \tag{24.2}$$

Notice how closely the discrete finite summation on the right aligns with our continuous infinite summation on the left. They are exactly equivalent when $n = \infty$.

Now, the equation, as written, doesn't tell us how to find x_k or Δx. The kth x value can be found by starting at $x = a$ and then adding Δx units to it each time through. We can represent that with the following equation:

$$x_k = a + (k - 1)\,\Delta x \tag{24.3}$$

This works because we start at a—that's our first x value. Each time through, we increase by Δx. Therefore, at the kth Δx, we will have moved $k - 1$ times (we subtract one since we don't move the first time through), moving Δx each time.

Now, we can substitute Equation 24.3 back in to Equation 24.2 like this:

$$\int_a^b f(x)\,dx \approx \sum_{k=1}^{n} f(a + (k - 1)\,\Delta x)\,\Delta x \tag{24.4}$$

This is a little messier, but it more explicitly tells us how the problem should be solved.[1] We don't have to look somewhere else to find out what x_k should be.

---

[1]You can actually simplify this a bit further, but it makes it less clear where the terms come from. Since Δx is a constant throughout the sum, and is multiplied by every term, you can actually move Δx out in front as a constant multiplier for the whole sum. This saves a step in each run through the equation, at the cost of clarity as to where your numbers are coming from. This equation looks like this:

$$\int_a^b f(x)\,dx \approx \Delta x \left(\sum_{k=1}^{n} f(a + (k - 1)\,\Delta x) \right) \tag{24.5}$$

We can also get rid of Δx in a similar way, since Equation 24.1 gives us a formula that we can replace Δx with. However, this equation is more messy with less benefit, since Δx can be replaced with a constant at the beginning of the process once we know a, b, and n.

If we did replace Δx it would look like this:

$$\int_a^b f(x)\,\mathrm{d}x \approx \sum_{k=0}^n f\left(a + (k-1)\frac{(b-a)}{n}\right)\left(\frac{b-a}{n}\right) \tag{24.6}$$

This equation has all of the redundancies removed, but it is a lot less clear. Therefore, we will prefer to use Equation 24.4.[2]

— Example 24.1

Use a Riemann Sum to find an approximation of the integral of $\int_2^3 x^3\,\mathrm{d}x$ using 6 subdivisions.

We can use Equation 24.4 to solve this. However, to use the equation, we must first solve for Δx using Equation 24.1. This gives us:

$$\Delta x = \frac{b-a}{n}$$
$$= \frac{5-2}{6}$$
$$= 0.5$$

Now, we can substitute these values into Equation 24.2:

$$\int_3^5 f(x)\,\mathrm{d}x \approx \sum_{k=1}^6 f(3 + (k-1)\cdot 0.5)\cdot 0.5$$

The summation operator ($\sum$) says that we have to perform the operation to its right once for every value from $k = 1$ to $k = 6$, and then add up all of the results that we get.

Therefore, we will put this information in a table, consisting of each value of k, the value of Δx (it will always be the same, but is included for reference), each x_k, each value for $f(x_k)$ (where $f(x_k) = (x_k)^3$), and the area of the rectangle ($f(x)$ times Δx). The table is below:

k	Δx	x_k	$f(x_k)$	area
1	0.5	2	8	4
2	0.5	2.5	15.625	8.3125
3	0.5	3	27	13.5
4	0.5	3.5	42.875	21.4375
5	0.5	4	64	32
6	0.5	4.5	91.125	45.5625

---

[2]In the examples described, we have focused figuring out Δx based on the number of subdivisions we want to make (i.e., n). Alternatively, if we already knew the Δx we wanted to use, we could then calculate n based on that: $n = \frac{b-a}{\Delta x}$. However, since we are doing a discrete summation process, n would have to either result in an integer, or we would have to round it up or down, losing more accuracy in the process. In any case, if we wanted to proceed this way, we could rewrite the sum as:

$$\int_a^b f(x)\,\mathrm{d}x \approx \sum_{k=1}^{\frac{b-a}{\Delta x}} f(a + (k-1)\Delta x)\Delta x$$

The total area will be found by summing up all the values in the rightmost column:

$$4 + 8.3125 + 13.5 + 21.4375 + 32 + 45.5625 = 124.8125$$

Therefore, the total area under the curve $y = x^3$ from $x = 2$ to $x = 5$ can be estimated as 124.8125 square units.

Since this is a simple integral, we can check this with our normal definite integral techniques:

$$\int_2^5 x^3 = \int x^3 \Big|_3^5 = \frac{x^4}{4} \Big|_3^5 = \frac{(5)^4}{4} - \frac{(2)^4}{4} = 152.25$$

You might not think that 124.8125 is very close to 152.25, but actually, given the steepness of the curve and how few subdivisions of the curve we actually performed, the result is pretty accurate. If we doubled the number of partitions ($n = 12$), the result would be 137.953125. You get pretty close to the real answer with 100 partitions, but it takes more than 700 partitions to get it within 0.25 of the true value. When doing real projects in math and science, sometimes many thousands of subdivisions (or even more!) are used to get precise answers.

24.2   Other Riemann Sums

The technique described in the previous section is known specifically as a *Left* Riemann Sum because the top of the rectangles touch the line on their left side. It is equally valid to draw the rectangles so that the rectangle touches the line on the top right corner. This is known as a *Right* Riemann Sum.

The only difference in the equations is that the Right Riemann Sum uses k instead of $k - 1$, because it uses the x value that occurs *after* advancing Δx (rather than *before* advancing, like the Left Riemann Sum does). The equation is below:

$$\int_a^b f(x)\,\mathrm{d}x \approx \sum_{k=1}^{n} f(a + k\,\Delta x)\,\Delta x \tag{24.7}$$

These methods are actually equivalent in the long run (though the differences may be important in the short run). You can tell that because as the width of the rectangles gets smaller and smaller, so does the difference between the left and right sums, because the left and right side of the rectangle are getting closer and closer together!

There are other ways to calculate the Riemann sum as well. The Midpoint Rule, for instance, is made by having the *center* top of the rectangle touch the curve. For this, we just adjust the x_k value accordingly to be $a + k\,\Delta x - \frac{\Delta x}{2}$:

$$\int_a^b f(x)\,\mathrm{d}x \approx \sum_{k=1}^{n} f\left(a + k\,\Delta x - \frac{\Delta x}{2}\right)\Delta x \tag{24.8}$$

We can also break the problem up into rectangles of non-uniform width. If you know that a problem is very flat in one area and very bumpy in another, you can use larger rectangles for the flatter area, and a lot of smaller rectangles for the bumpier area. The problem here is that it depends on *you* to figure out the best way to break this up.

24.3   Non-Rectangular Riemann Sums

We don't even have to use rectangles. As long as we have a rectangular base, pretty much any shape on top will work for a Riemann sum. Remember, as long as our accuracy is increasing when we make our subdivisions smaller, then it will work as an estimating technique. As our subdivisions get smaller, the way that the top of the shape looks becomes less and less relevant.

However, for estimating, if we want to use *fewer* subdivisions, the top of our shape matters more and more. The closer it becomes to the actual shape of the graph, the more accurate it will be.

The simplest non-rectangular shape is to use trapezoids. The Trapezoid Rule tells us how to do this. The area of a trapezoid is the the distance between two sides multiplied by the average size of the two sides. In this case, the two sides are the $f(x_k)$ and $f(x_k + \Delta x)$, and the distance between them is Δx. The Riemann sum for these is:

$$\int_a^b f(x)\, dx \approx \sum_{k=1}^n \frac{f(a + k\,\Delta x) + f(a + (k-1)\,\Delta x)}{2}\, \Delta x \tag{24.9}$$

There are even more complex shapes we could do, though. Simpson's Rule is based on estimating the shape as a quadratic curve. Even though it usually provides more accurate estimates, I find Simpson's Rule (and similar methods) are unnecessarily complicated for introductory calculus. It is good to know that such techniques are available if you ever need to look them up, but not important enough to actually put here.

24.4   Choosing a Method

Really, the choice of method is kind of irrelevant. You are approximating, right? If you want to approximate better, use a smaller width for your x values! But, there are times when the method is important.

Essentially, the method you choose is a combination of the following considerations:

1. Whether you want to spend more time setting up the problem or more time calculating the problem.

2. Whether you prefer overestimates or underestimates.

If you want to spend more time setting up the problem and less time calculating it, Simpson's Rule is a great way to do this. You can get more accuracy with fewer subdivided units with Simpson's Rule. If you want to spend very little time setting up the problem but don't mind spending more time calculating it, then a simple Left Riemann Sum is a great way to do this. In the age of computers, this is often what is done—you can let the computer do your calculations for you, and it doesn't mind repeating them more often!

Even with computers, though, if you are using billions of subdivisions for a really difficult problem, taking more care with setting up the problem may save you thousands or even millions of dollars in hardware, because you drastically decreased the number of subdivisions needed for an operation.

Then there is the question of overestimation and underestimation. If a curve is increasing, a Left Riemann Sum will underestimate the value, and a Right Riemann Sum will overestimate the value. It is the reverse for a decreasing curve.

24.5 Why Integrate Symbolically?

You may be wondering, if we can skip the process of symbolic integration, why do we bother with it in the first place? There are several reasons:

1. When finding a symbolic solution, the solution is not only "close enough," it is *exact*.

2. Symbolic solutions *teach* us about the nature of the problem, rather than just provide us with answers. That is, we can look at the solution, and *understand* how the bits work together and why, rather than just asking our calculators to do the work.

3. Symbolic solutions allow us to *build* on our knowledge. Just knowing the specific answer to a specific problem cuts us off from being able to build on that knowledge. The symbolic solution gives us an equation, which is itself a brand new idea. This new idea can then be applied to other situations. It may even wind up as a piece of another problem that needs to be integrated!

4. If a symbolic solution can be found, its solution can sometimes (though definitely not always) be very simpler, making numeric solutions the harder approach.

Imagine what would happen if nobody did performed symbolic integration, and everybody just used numeric techniques.[3] For instance, in Chapter 20, we show how to use symbolic integration techniques to find the volume of a cone. The result of this was a simple equation that you probably learned in geometry class: $v = \frac{1}{3}\pi r^2 h$. Now, imagine that nobody bothered with symbolic integration, and everybody just said, "you don't need symbolic integration—you can just do everything numerically!" Then, instead of having a formula for the volume of a cone, anytime we wanted the volume of a cone, we would have to break the cone up into segments, calculate the volume of each of these segments, and then add it up. That would be a lot of work for a simple volume of a cone! Then, if you needed a *really* accurate volume for a cone, you would have to break the cone up into innumerable segments in order to get your answer. Then, imagine that you need the volume of several more cones—even more work!

However, since someone bothered to actually compute the volume of a cone symbolically, we now have a nice little formula that even elementary school students can use to get exact answers.

The way to think about it is this—when you calculate an answer numerically, you are finding an answer for yourself. When you calculate an answer symbolically, you are extending knowledge—both for yourself and for society.

Review

In this chapter, we learned:

1. If an integral cannot be solved symbolically, it can usually still be at least approximated numerically.

2. Because the integral can be thought of as the area under the curve, the general method of numeric integration is to break a curve up into subdivisions, and then use a simplistic method for calculating the area of the subdivision (such as treating the subdivision as a rectangle), then adding up the areas of all of the subdivisions for the final result.

---

[3]As a side note, one approach to evaluate policies—whether personal policies, business policies, public policies, educational policies, etc., is to ask yourself, "what would happen if *everybody* followed the policy, and what would happen if *nobody* followed the policy?" Oftentimes, if you can see that everyone following the policy will be beneficial, it lends credence to the policy. If you can see that everyone ignoring the policy will be harmful, it also lends credence to the policy. So, even if you only used numeric techniques yourself (which is not an uncommon occurrence), having the *policy* of teaching symbolic techniques makes sure that these consequences don't happen.

3. The different numerical methods for integrals are based on different ways of calculating the area of the subdivision.

4. The choice of numerical method is based on a number of factors, such as how accurate you want to be, how complicated the problem is to setup, how complicated the problem is to calculate, and the nature of the resulting error.

5. Even though it is often less thinking to come up with a numeric solution to a definite integral, finding a symbolic solution is generally preferable because it simplifies future problem-solving and allows more knowledge-building both for yourself and society.

Exercises

Find the following definite integrals using a Left Riemann Sum:

1. Find $\int_1^2 x^2 \, dx$ using $n = 4$ partitions.

2. Find $\int_0^3 e^x \, dx$ using $n = 3$ partitions.

3. Find $\int_0^2 \sin(x^2) \, dx$ using $n = 4$ partitions.

Find the following numeric integrals using a Right Riemann Sum:

4. Find $\int_2^3 \ln(x) \, dx$ using $n = 3$ partitions.

5. Find $\int_5^7 x \cos(x) \, dx$ using $n = 4$ partitions.

Part IV

Manipulating Infinity

One of the many benefits of calculus is that it provides a means of manipulating infinity. What is a derivative but a slope between two points infinitely close to each other? What is an integral but an infinite sum of infinitely small pieces? The goal of this part of the book is to expand upon our abilities in manipulating infinities, and think more closely about the infinite and what it means.

Chapter 25

Modeling Functions with Polynomial Series

In this chapter we will look at ways of modeling special functions using polynomials with an infinite sequence of terms. We will also discuss a general approach for solving impossible problems.

25.1 Modeling Complicated Functions with Simple Tools

When you first learn polynomials, you get used to being able to express curves in terms of taking a variable and then manipulating it through squaring, cubing, and so forth. When you first start doing this, it seems that the entire universe of functions can be modeled in this way. Part of that is because, in fact, these tools are very powerful, but part of it is a selection effect—your teachers were only giving you problems in which these were the proper tools.

Therefore, when you began to learn about sine and cosine, you may have been surprised to learn that these curves cannot be modeled through a polynomial. It takes an entirely new type of function to model these curves!

As it turns out, there is a huge variety of different types of functions that cover different types of curves. There are trigonometric functions, exponential functions, hyperbolic functions, and all sorts of other types of functions. We get even more classes of functions if we don't limit ourselves to curves, if we add in dimensions, etc.

However, as we have learned in calculus, it is often beneficial to model complicated things with simple tools. When applying the integral geometrically, for instance, we just used basic formulas of simple shapes to help us figure out the formulas for more complicated shapes. The area of a rectangle, the volume of a box, and the volume of a cylinder were all we needed to know in order to find areas and volumes of all sorts of complex shapes. Using simple tools make complicated things much easier to analyze.

In Chapters 18 and 20, we figured out that starting off with a simple and straightforward estimation procedure that can be improved is oftentimes the first step to getting an exact answer. In this chapter, we are going to focus on approximating functions like $\sin(x)$, $\cos(x)$, and e^x. You might be used to just plugging in numbers into a calculator to get the answers to these functions, but what procedure does the calculator use?

It turns our that the calculator can only approximate the values for these types of functions, but, it is "close enough" that you would never notice with the number of digits that the calculator displays.

Now, we can approximate functions using just about anything. If we wanted to, we could approximate a function with a straight line. It will be wrong more than it is right, but we can make an approximation that works for a certain set of points.

Here is $\sin(x)$ is approximated using a straight line:

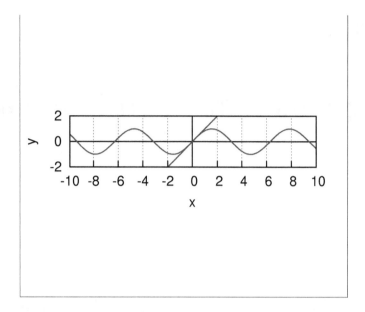

As you can see, the line actually approximates the graph pretty well from about -0.5 to 0.5.

Now, if we take that approximation and increase the number of lines, our approximation of the function becomes closer and closer to reality. That is, we can make closer approximations of functions using two lines rather than with one. As we add more lines, we can get our approximation closer and closer to the "true" function.

Here is $\sin(x)$ approximated using multiple lines:

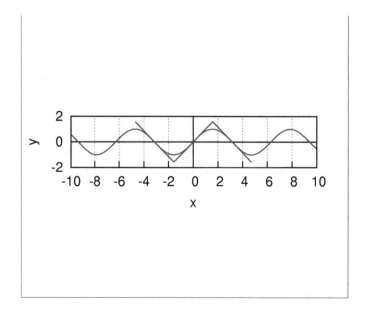

we can add more lines in-between and get a better and better approximation. However, the problem with lines is that lines are not smooth. In calculus, we like smooth functions because you can analyze the slope easier.

Therefore, instead of using straight lines to model function behavior, we can use polynomials. Here is $\sin(x)$ modeled with a cubic equation (the equation, for reasons you will see later, is $y = x - \frac{1}{6}x^3$):

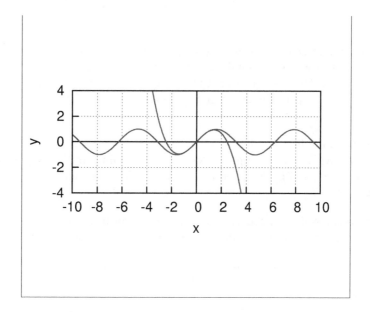

As you can see, the model works pretty well from about -1.5 to 1.5. The model becomes even closer as we add more terms. This next equation is $y = x - \frac{1}{6}x^3 + \frac{1}{120}x^5 - \frac{1}{5040}x^7$, and it works well from about -2.5 to 2.5:

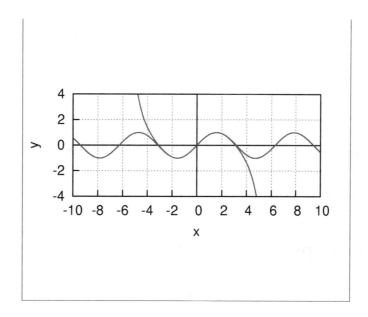

As we add terms to our polynomial, the domain for which it serves as a valid approximation of $\sin(x)$ increases.

25.2   Polynomials, Their Importance, and Their Limitations

So why do we want to limit ourselves to a polynomial model of a function like $\sin(x)$?

Well, in modern life, we want to do everything with computers. Computers, however, do not intrinsically understand functions like sine and cosine. You may have a cosine button on your calculator, but your calculator doesn't *actually* know how to calculate the cosine of a number. It only knows how to *approximate* the cosine of a number.

Calculators are computers, and computers are pretty limited in the type of mathematical operations they can perform. They fool us all the time through clever programming, but at the end of the day, the core set of features of computers are pretty much restricted to adding, subtracting, multiplying, dividing, comparing, branching (choosing to do some operation or set of operations based on a previous comparison), and moving numbers around.

Modern processors might throw in a few more operations, but they are pretty tied down to operations on this level. Every other operation that a computer does, it has to reduce to these operations. Exponentiation to an integer power can be achieved by repeated multiplication (and, in fact, even multiplication is achieved by mere repeated addition!).

Thus, in actuality, since computers can only add, subtract, multiply, divide, and do integer exponents, computers can *only* actually process polynomials. They can't do anything else *at all*.

Therefore, if we want to model various different kinds of functions in a computer (trig functions, hyperbolic functions, exponentials, etc.), then we have to be able to approximate these functions with polynomials.

Now, one of the interesting features of modeling functions with polynomials is that if you restrict the domain (i.e., the allowable x-coordinates) that you are looking at, you can make a polynomial closer and closer to the target function by adding more and more terms to the polynomial. We saw this in the previous section with our approximations of the $\sin(x)$ function.

Depending on the function you are trying to model, your polynomial might wind up with too many or too few humps *elsewhere* (i.e., outside of your restricted domain), but within that restricted domain you can get closer and closer to the "real" function by adding terms to polynomials, and the domain for which your polynomial serves as an accurate measurement will increase as well.

Note that, in addition to modeling known functions (like $\sin(x)$ and e^x), polynomial modeling is also used a lot in engineering when we want to model functions where the actual physical relationships are not known, but we have a graph that we want to match up with. We can simply create a polynomial that gives us the right shape within a certain boundary, and then only use the polynomial equation within that boundary. This provides a smooth curve that can be used for approximating the "true" underlying function, whatever it actually is.

Unfortunately, it is impossible to model the complete $\sin(x)$ function exactly using polynomials.

25.3   Doing the Impossible

Of course, just because something is impossible doesn't mean we aren't going to do it anyway! After all, this is calculus class!

So, how might you model a non-polynomial *perfectly* using polynomials? How do you do the impossible?

It turns out that when anybody tells you that something is *impossible*, what they usually mean is "given a set of assumptions that I may not even realize I am making, this is impossible." The key to solving impossible situations is to learn to identify the unstated assumptions. Once you realize the sorts of things that people are unknowingly assuming, whole worlds open up for you. You find out that many times people may be correct in what they are saying, but they presume a whole set of assumptions that their listeners might not hold to.[1]

In philosophy, these unstated assumptions are known as *ceteris paribus* clauses, which means "all else being equal" in Latin. The goal is to find out what in this universe of assumptions is causing problems, and then try to imagine the world without those assumptions. Doing so will help you figure out which assumptions are needed, and, more importantly, *when* are they needed.

I've often seen people argue about things, where the arguers on both sides were technically correct in their statements, but the statements only applied within certain sets of assumptions. Where they actually differed was not on their statements, but on what sets of assumptions (i.e., what *ceteris paribus* clauses) made their statements true. A better discussion would have been had if the arguers would have instead talked about which sets of underlying assumptions better represented reality, or more specifically the situation which they were discussing.

In this chapter, we are focusing on doing the impossible. To do the impossible, you first have to identify the set of statements that make something impossible. Once you do that, you find out which of the assumed statements can be removed to make the impossible possible.

When we say that "it is not possible to model a cosine function with a polynomial," what we are actually saying is "it is not possible to model a cosine function with a polynomial *using a finite number of terms*." We just assume, quite reasonably, that since we generally have to write down our equations, any equation we come up with will have to have a finite number of terms because we couldn't possibly write down an infinite number of them. However, if we allow ourselves an *infinite* number of terms, then all of a sudden it becomes possible to model additional classes of functions with only polynomials.

25.4 Modeling with an Infinite Number of Terms

If we have a polynomial with an infinite number of terms, we first have to stop and think of what that will look like. We are going to take several stabs at writing this down, as the first one will not be the best way to do so.

---

[1]Arthur C. Clarke formulated several adages known as Clarke's Three Laws. The first one is relevant here—"When a distinguished but elderly scientist states that something is possible, they are almost certainly right. When they state that something is impossible, they are very probably wrong." While I am a big proponent of doing impossible things (and one of my goals this chapter is to make sure you know how to do them!), I find this formulation unhelpful.

I have seen experts be equally wrong on both sides of the table. Sometimes they say that something is possible, but they are wrong. Sometimes they say that something is impossible, but they are wrong. I think what Clarke was getting at is that an expert probably knows where the current trends in his own field will lead, but the expert does not have the same insight about new trends that are just being explored. Experts will have a tendency to regard the trends that they have dealt with their whole lives as being the "real" trend. They will then discount the new trends as being just a bunch of kids who don't know what they are doing. I think that is a true statement of human nature, but I think it gives us no benefit to knowing who is correct. Young upstarts can be just as correct or incorrect as old fogeys.

I think the key is simply being philosophical enough to recognize the assumptions that different people are making, where those assumptions lead, and then, in the last place, to determine which assumptions are true. I think we make a mistake to presume that the new assumptions are better or worse than the old ones. What we must do, is to examine everything with great care, and hold on to the good stuff (1 Thess 5:21). We shouldn't dismiss things because they are new, and we shouldn't consider anything to be outmoded just because it is old. That, fortunately or unfortunately, means that each one of us is responsible for a whole lot of philosophical legwork. However, as I pointed out in Chapter 2, for the mathematician, the first step of mathematics is philosophy. So learning to think clearly is something you already need to be learning to do!

So, how do we write down a polynomial generally? Usually, we write something down like:

$$y = ax^2 + bx + c$$

In this equation, a, b, and c are the *coefficients*. We can expand this idea to a higher-order polynomial by doing:

$$y = ax^5 + bx^4 + cx^3 + dx^2 + ex + f$$

We can keep expanding this out, but soon we will run out of letters. So, instead of using different letters for coefficients, we will simply number them. Since they are constant, we will represent them with a C, and so the first coefficient will be C_0, the next C_1, etc. However, since this is an infinite-term polynomial, since we normally write the highest power x on the left, that will be x^∞.

Therefore, the first way we will try to write the general form of the polynomial will look something like the equation below, with C_n representing a particular constant:

$$\cos(x) = C_0 x^\infty + C_1 x^{\infty-1} + C_2 x^{\infty-2} + C_2 x^{\infty-3} \ldots C_{\infty-2} x^2 + C_{\infty-1} x + C_\infty \qquad (25.1)$$

So, we can define our function as an infinite set of constants attached to a polynomial. However, the way that it is written gets in the way of really manipulating it. Because you have the constants starting at subscript zero, but the powers start at infinity. Since the subscripts of the constants are arbitrary, we can actually rewrite this with the subscripts starting at infinity and moving down, just like the powers. That looks like this:

$$\cos(x) = C_\infty x^\infty + C_{\infty-1} x^{\infty-1} + C_{\infty-2} x^{\infty-2} + C_{\infty-3} x^{\infty-3} \ldots C_2 x^2 + C_1 x + C_0 \qquad (25.2)$$

Here, the subscripts match the powers. This doesn't do a whole lot, but it certainly helps us think about the series easier. It is very clear that C_{200} goes with the x^{200} power, and so forth. Even C_0 follows this rule, since x^0 is just one. We just don't bother to write x^0 since it doesn't matter.

The problem, though, is that the sequence, as written, has two ends. It has a beginning, at infinity (which is certainly hard to conceive of, and doesn't really exist in the way that the other numbers do), and then has an ending at C_0. Can you think of another way to write this that might be even easier to manage?

Think of it this way—while we normally write polynomials with the highest power first (as it is in the attempts above), we will wind up being able to do interesting things if we turn it around and write the highest power last, like this:

$$\cos(x) = C_0 + C_1 x + C_2 x^2 + C_3 x^3 + C_4 x^4 + \ldots + C_\infty x^\infty \qquad (25.3)$$

In this form, the subscripts of the constants match the power of x as before. But, since we started at the low powers, the only ones we have to write down are the finite powers. The "infinity" is implied by the "..." at the end. It just goes and goes, and we don't even have to name infinity explicitly.

This is known as a **polynomial expansion** of the cosine function.

Because the subscripts and the powers line up so nicely, it allows us to write this expansion in a really compact with with a summation notation, like this:

$$\cos(x) = \sum_{k=0}^{\infty} C_k x^k \qquad (25.4)$$

The next trick is to find out what the particular values of the coefficients are. We have a nice notation that tells us what an infinite polynomial will look like. However, the right-hand side could be *any* function. The (infinite) list of coefficients will convert that polynomial into the specific one for the cosine function.

Notice that, so far, we haven't actually done anything to *solve* the problem of finding the polynomial expansion yet, but we have now started thinking about the problem in different ways and writing it down in different ways, which is usually the first step to solving difficult problems.

Next, we need to find a way to figure out what each coefficient is. You might be thinking, "there's an infinite number of them, that will take forever! Literally!" However, sometimes, if you are willing to *begin* an impossible journey, you will find that it isn't as impossible as it seems.

25.5   Finding C_0

Now, before we dive headfirst into finding an entire infinite list of coefficients for our infinite polynomial, let's see if we can find a way to determine a *single* coefficient. Just one.

Let's take a look at our polynomial from Equation 25.3:

$$\cos(x) = C_0 + C_1 x + C_2 x^2 + C_3 x^3 + C_4 x^4 + \ldots + C_\infty x^\infty$$

Do you notice anything different about that first term? Technically, it is $C_0 x^0$, but, since x^0 reduces to 1, C_0 does not get multiplied by x or any version of x at all. In fact, it is the *only* coefficient in the *entire* polynomial that doesn't get multiplied by x. Can you think of an x value we could try to use which would allow us to ignore all of the other polynomial coefficients?

What would happen if we tried to find the value of the series at $x = 0$? In that case, any term involving x would be set to zero, would it not? Therefore, it would reduce the formula to the following:

$$\cos(x) = C_0 + C_1 x + C_2 x^2 + C_3 x^3 + C_4 x^4 + \ldots + C_\infty x^\infty$$
$$\cos(0) = C_0 + C_1 \cdot 0 + C_2 \cdot 0^2 + C_3 \cdot 0^3 + C_4 \cdot 0^4 + \ldots + C_\infty \cdot 0^\infty$$
$$\cos(0) = C_0 + 0 + 0 + 0 + 0 + \ldots + 0$$
$$\cos(0) = C_0$$

So, by setting $x = 0$, the entire polynomial drops off except the first coefficient! Now, if you remember your trigonometry, you should have memorized that the cosine of 0 is 1. Therefore, we can then say:

$$\cos(0) = C_0 = 1$$

This gives us the first coefficient for our polynomial!

We still have an infinite number of them left to do, but at least we have a start. By checking the value of the function at $x = 0$ we have determined what the coefficient C_0 is in the polynomial expansion.

We can do this for any function for which we know its value at $x = 0$. For instance, take the polynomial expansion of the function $\sin(x)$. We can find its first coefficient in the same way:

$$\sin(x) = C_0 + C_1 x + C_2 x^2 + C_3 x^3 + C_4 x^4 + \ldots + C_\infty x^\infty$$

$$\sin(0) = C_0 + C_1 \cdot 0 + C_2 \cdot 0^2 + C_3 \cdot 0^3 + C_4 \cdot 0^4 + \ldots + C_\infty \cdot 0^\infty$$

$$\sin(0) = C_0 + 0 + 0 + 0 + 0 + \ldots + 0$$

$$\sin(0) = C_0$$

$$\sin(0) = 0$$

$$C_0 = 0$$

Now, we don't have to write all of that out every time, we can just remember the fact that the value of the function at $x = 0$ will be the value of the first coefficient. So, for instance, if we have the function e^x, we can just substitute in a zero for x to get the first coefficient of its expansion. Since $e^0 = 1$, for the polynomial expansion of e^x, C_0 is 1.

25.6 Finding the Next Values

Okay, bravo. We found the first term of the expansion of $\cos(x)$. What about the rest? There's only infinitely many of them left to go.

Well, let's take a look at that expansion again:

$$\cos(x) = C_0 + C_1 x + C_2 x^2 + C_3 x^3 + C_4 x^4 + \ldots + C_\infty x^\infty$$

Remember that, in an equation, we can do anything we want to the equation, as long as we do the same thing to both sides. So, let's take the derivative of both sides, shall we?

On the left side, we have $\cos(x)$. The derivative of $\cos(x)$ is $-\sin(x)$. On the right-hand side, C_0 drops off, because it is just a constant. Then, on the next term, the derivative of $C_1 x$ is just C_1, giving us another equation with a single constant term! So, we can determine that:

$$\cos(x) = C_0 + C_1 x + C_2 x^2 + C_3 x^3 + C_4 x^4 + \ldots$$

$$D_x(\cos(x)) = D_x(C_0 + C_1 x + C_2 x^2 + C_3 x^3 + C_4 x^4 + \ldots)$$

$$-\sin(x) = 0 + C_1 + 2C_2 x + 3C_3 x^2 + 4C_4 x^3 + \ldots$$

Now, if we want to know the value of C_1, we can just substitute 0 in for x on our new function, $-\sin(x)$:

$$-\sin(x) = 0 + C_1 + 2C_2 x + 3C_3 x^2 + 4C_4 x^3 + \ldots$$

$$-\sin(0) = 0 + C_1 + 0 + 0 + 0 + \ldots$$

$$-\sin(0) = C_1$$

$$-\sin(0) = 0$$

$$C_1 = 0$$

Now we know two coefficients! C_0 is 1 and C_1 is 0.

Notice that, since we are dealing with a polynomial, each time we take a derivative, it reduces the power of the x value for the coefficient by 1. Therefore, we should be able to find the nth coefficient using the nth derivative. Below is the continuation of this process through C_4, where we get the next derivative, and then find the value of that function at zero.

$$\cos(x) = C_0 + C_1 x + C_2 x^2 + C_3 x^3 + C_4 x^4 + \dots$$

$$\cos(0) = C_0 \qquad\qquad = 1$$

$$D(\cos(x)) = D(C_0 + C_1 x + C_2 x^2 + C_3 x^3 + C_4 x^4 + \dots)$$

$$-\sin(x) = 0 + C_1 + 2C_2 x + 3C_3 x^2 + 4C_4 x^3 + \dots$$

$$-\sin(0) = C_1 \qquad\qquad = 0$$

$$D(-\sin(x)) = D(0 + C_1 + 2C_2 x + 3C_3 x^2 + 4C_4 x^3 + \dots)$$

$$-\cos(x) = 0 + 0 + 2C_2 + 6C_3 x + 12C_4 x^2 + \dots$$

$$-\cos(0) = 2C_2 \qquad\qquad = -1$$

$$D(-\cos(x)) = D(0 + 0 + 2C_2 + 6C_3 x + 12C_4 x^2 + \dots)$$

$$\sin(x) = 0 + 0 + 0 + 3C_3 + 24C_4 x + \dots$$

$$\sin(0) = 3C_3 \qquad\qquad = 0$$

$$D(\sin(x)) = D(0 + 0 + 0 + 3C_3 + 24C_4 x + \dots)$$

$$\cos(x) = 0 + 0 + 0 + 0 + 24C_4 + \dots$$

$$\cos(0) = 24C_4 \qquad\qquad = 1$$

Now, if you paid attention, something interesting started happening with coefficient C_2. Notice that we did not find the value of C_2, but rather $2C_2$. $2C_2$ is -1, so that means that C_2 by itself is $-\frac{1}{2}$.

Why do the coefficients starting with C_2 and going further all have factors in front of them, and is there a pattern to them? The reason they have factors in front of them is that they all started out with powers higher than one. When a derivative happened to the term, the power *came out in front*, and then the term dropped to the next power. This continued on until the power reaches zero.

This means that the coefficient will wind up being multiplied by *every number from the power of x it started with down to one*. Another name for this is the factorial! In other words, the multiplier in front of the coefficient will by $n!$, where n is the nth derivative we have taken (the function itself is counted as the 0th derivative, and the factorial of 0 is 1).

The next thing to notice is that the derivatives are going in a circle. cos goes to *sin* goes to $-$ cos goes to sin which goes back to cos and the process repeats. Forever.

Therefore, the result of each step (the nth derivative applied to an x value of zero) is cycling between 1, 0, -1, 0, over and over again. That means that we can write out the polynomial for the cosine function as:

$$\cos(x) = \frac{1}{0!} + \frac{0}{1!}x + \frac{-1}{2!}x^2 + \frac{0}{3!}x^3 + \frac{1}{4!}x^4 + \frac{0}{5!}x^5 + \frac{-1}{6!}x^6 + \frac{0}{7!}x^7 + \frac{1}{8!}x^8 + \dots \qquad (25.5)$$

All you have to do to write out the function is to keep cycling the numerator through the sequence 1, 0, -1,

0 and moving the denominator through the factorials, and finally keep the powers of x increasing.

If you do this forever, you will get the full series!

25.7   Using Our Series

Now, even though it takes an infinite number of terms to model the cosine function precisely, even with the few terms we have written out so far, it models it pretty well between -3 and 3:

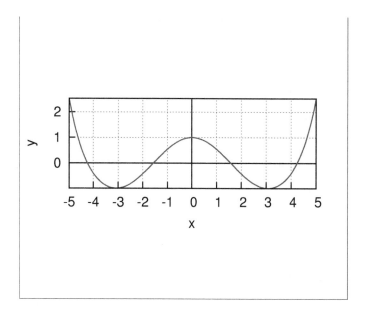

When it is near 0, the graph really looks and behaves a lot like the cosine function. Tricks like this allow us to write computer programs that get very close to the true values of functions like sine and cosine even though they aren't really native to computers. The programmer can use methods like this to build a program that he can implement on the computer to make up for the fact that there is no real cosine function available.

Let's calculate an example value and see how close we come. The cosine of $\frac{\pi}{4}$ is known to be $\frac{\sqrt{2}}{2}$, which is about 0.707. Let's see how close our first few coefficients get us to. In order to use them, we'll need to expand π out to a number, so we will use 3.14159. Since we are trying to find the cosine of $\frac{\pi}{4}$, we will use a close numeric approximation: $\frac{3.14159}{4} \approx 0.7853975$. So we will be looking for $\cos(0.7853975)$. Substituting it into our polynomial expansion, we find:

$$\cos(x) \approx \frac{1}{0!} + \frac{0}{1!}x + \frac{-1}{2!}x^2 + \frac{0}{3!}x^3 + \frac{1}{4!}x^4 + \frac{0}{5!}x^5 + \frac{-1}{6!}x^6 + \frac{0}{7!}x^7 + \frac{1}{8!}x^8$$

$$\cos(0.7853975) \approx \frac{1}{0!} + 0 + \frac{-1}{2!}0.7853975^2 + 0 + \frac{1}{4!}0.7853975^4 + 0 + \frac{-1}{6!}0.7853975^6 + 0 + \frac{1}{8!}0.7853975^8$$

$$\approx 0.70710727 \qquad\qquad\qquad\qquad\qquad\qquad\qquad\qquad\qquad \approx 0.707$$

The actual answer has a very large number of decimal points, but we can see that our polynomial is approximately correct for known values of the cosine function.

25.8 Making a General Formula

So, while we have an idea for a formula for the cosine function *in our minds*, we haven't quite yet gotten to the place where we can write it down. Before we get to the precise formula for the cosine function, let's think about a general formula for doing what we have done in this chapter.

We took an arbitrary function, which we can call $f(x)$, and we turned it into a polynomial. Something like this:

$$f(x) = C_0 x^0 + C_1 x^1 + C_2 x^2 + C_3 x^3 + C_4 x^4 + \ldots + C_\infty x^\infty \tag{25.6}$$

Now, I put in x^0 and x^1 explicitly in this formula, because it will make the next step more understandable. Notice that the entirety of the formula is simply a sum. Well, we have a notation for summation, namely $\sum$. Likewise, each of the terms in our equation follows a very precise formula, so we can rewrite our general formula as:

$$f(x) = \sum_{n=0}^{\infty} C_n x^n \tag{25.7}$$

This sort of a formula takes a lot of the guesswork out of things, because we don't have those little dots ($\ldots$) which force people to use their imaginations to tell what the next thing is. With this notation, the notation actually tells you how the series progresses.

However, we have also figured out in previous sections what the formula is for C_n. It is the nth derivative of the function evaluated at 0, divided by $n!$. So, we can use that information as follows:

$$f(x) = \sum_{n=0}^{\infty} \frac{f^{(n)}(0)}{n!} x^n \tag{25.8}$$

In this formula, $f^{(n)}(0)$ refers to the nth derivative of f evaluated at 0 (*not* $f(0)$ raised to the nth power), where the 0th derivative of f is the function f itself. Putting parentheses around the superscript n is often used as a marker to indicate the nth derivative.

This formula makes what is called a Maclaurin series. It works for a large variety of functions—namely smooth, differentiable functions where every derivative is defined (and calculatable!) at zero.

25.9 Finding a Specific Formula

Now, the situation is sometimes more complicated if you want to find a specific summation formula for a specific function. For instance, we *can* write our cosine function with the following formula:

$$\cos(x) = \sum_{n=0}^{\infty} \frac{\cos^{(n)}(0)}{n!} x^n$$

Again, $\cos^{(n)}(0)$ refers *not* to $\cos(0)$ raised to a power, but to the nth derivative of cos evaluated at zero. Now, we know from experimenting with this in previous sections that this cycles through 1, 0, −1, 0 over and over again. However, it would be nice if we could write this fact into our formula.

When things cycle, I like to use -1 raised to a power to provide cycling. -1^1 is -1, -1^2 is 1, then -1^3 is -1 again. So we can use -1 to provide the ability to cycle.

Now, interestingly, our function has *two* cycles. The first cycle is back-and-forth to zero each time, and the second cycle is going from positive to negative and back. Therefore, we need to develop a formula as a function of n to reflect what any particular coefficient of our function will be.

So, to cycle back-and-forth between zero, we can use the formula $\frac{1+(-1)^n}{2}$. When $n = 0$, this will be $\frac{1+(-1)^0}{2} = \frac{1+1}{2} = 1$. When $n = 1$, this will be $\frac{1+(-1)^1}{2} = \frac{1-1}{2} = 0$. When $n = 3$, this will be $\frac{1+(-1)^2}{2} = \frac{1+1}{2} = 1$. It will continue to cycle back and forth, giving us a multiplier that will zero out the even terms.

The second cycle is back and forth between positive and negative. If we were to cycle *every* time, we would just raise -1 to the nth power. However, because the odd terms will be zeroed out, we need to raise it to the $\frac{n}{2}$ power like this: $-1^{\frac{n}{2}}$. Therefore,

- When $n = 0$, this will be $-1^0 = 1$.

- When $n = 1$, the value will be ignored because the other term will be zero.

- When $n = 2$, this will be $-1^1 = -1$.

So, putting these together, you can get the following formula:

$$\cos(x) = \sum_{n=0}^{\infty} \left((-1)^{\frac{n}{2}} \right) \left(\frac{\frac{1+(-1)^n}{2}}{n!} \right) x^n \qquad (25.9)$$

This allows us to specify any arbitrary term and to get the coefficient at that term.

Now, what I like about Equation 25.9 is that it tracks very closely with the Maclaurin expansion we have worked on in this chapter. It is a bit convoluted, but we have made the direct connection between each part of the formula and where we obtained it from.

However, there is a much more popular version of this which has the same result, but it looks a bit cleaner.

$$\cos(x) = \sum_{n=0}^{\infty} \left((-1)^n \right) \left(\frac{1}{2n!} \right) x^{2n} \qquad (25.10)$$

The problem with this formulation is that it is harder to see the direct connection between each piece of the formula and the general formula for a Maclaurin series (i.e., Equation 25.8). What this formula does is that, rather than including the terms that go to zero, it simply rewrites the formula so that it only produces nonzero terms. That is why the factorial is for $2n$—it is *only* doing the even ns from the previous formula ($2n$ will always yield an even result).

25.10   Applying the Maclaurin Series

Now that we have learned the basics of how to make a Maclaurin series using the cosine function, let's apply it to a different function—e^x. What we want is a polynomial expansion of e^x.

Using Equation 25.8, we can start by writing this as:

$$f(x) = \sum_{n=0}^{\infty} \frac{f^{(n)}(0)}{n!} x^n$$

where $f(x)$ is e^x, and $f^{(n)}(0)$ is the nth derivative of e^x at zero. But wait—*all* derivatives of e^x are just e^x. And, e^x *at zero* will just be e^0. Anything raised to the 0th power is just 1. Therefore, we can just replace $f^{(n)}(0)$ with 1. This gives us the equation:

$$e^x = \sum_{n=0}^{\infty} \frac{1}{n!} x^n \qquad (25.11)$$

Interestingly, this also gives us an easy way to calculate e itself. Since e is just e^1, we can substitute 1 in for x in this equation, which will give us:

$$e = \sum_{n=0}^{\infty} \frac{1}{n!} 1^n = \sum_{n=0}^{\infty} \frac{1}{n!}$$

We can estimate e to any degree of precision we want by simply taking a certain number of terms from this expansion. If we want five terms of this expansion, we will get:

$$1 + 1 + \frac{1}{2} + \frac{1}{6} + \frac{1}{24} = \frac{65}{24} \approx 2.708$$

We can get closer by doing seven terms:

$$1 + 1 + \frac{1}{2} + \frac{1}{6} + \frac{1}{24} + \frac{1}{120} + \frac{1}{720} = \frac{1957}{720} \approx 2.718$$

The more terms we add, the closer and closer to the true value for e that we will get.

25.11   Another Way of Looking at the Maclaurin Series

While the Maclaurin series is a nice trick, some people have trouble wrapping their minds around what is really happening here.

Let's say that we go outside and look at the thermometer. The thermometer say it is 67°F outside. Now, it's good to know what the temperature is *now*, but what is the likely temperature in two hours? Let's create a function called *temp*(x) that returns the temperature x hours from now. So, the current temperature is *temp*(0) = 67.

Well, assuming that we don't know anything about how temperature works or what the weather is like in our area, the best estimate that we can make for the temperature in 2 hours is to simply say that it is going to be the same temperature as it is now.

Therefore, our first approximation for the full temperature function is going to just be *temp*(0). In other words, we will guess that:

$$temp(x) = 67$$

However, let's say that someone tells us that the temperature is *changing* 3 degrees per hour. That means that the *derivative* of the temperature right now is 3. In other words, *temp*'(0) = 3.

Therefore, we can create a line containing both pieces of information—the temperature that it is now and how it is changing. The resulting equation will be:

$$temp(x) = 67 + 3x$$

Now, let's say that the same person tells us that not only is the current rate of change of the temperature change 3 degrees per hour, but that rate itself is changing −1 degree per hour per hour. That means that $temp''(0) = -1$. Because it is "per hour per hour", that is the same as "per hour squared." Therefore, it will be multiplied by the square of the current time (x) to balance out units. However, its total impact will be less, because it takes a while for it to take effect, so we will divide this number by two.[2]

So, our new equation is:

$$temp(x) = 67 + 3x + \frac{-1x^2}{2}$$

As you can see, we can write this just like our Maclaurin series expansion:

$$temp(x) = \frac{temp(0)}{0!} + \frac{temp'(0)}{1!}x + \frac{temp''(0)}{2!}x^2$$

The more we know about how the temperature is changing through its various derivatives, the better we will be able to create an equation to model the temperature.

Each derivative will give us more information about how the temperature is changing, which we can continue to add into our model and expand. A perfect model of temperature change would likely include an infinite number of terms, but by adding more and more terms, we can get closer and closer to the true value of the function using a polynomial model.

25.12   A General Overview of Solving Impossible Problems

We spent a lot of time in the details of finding the polynomial expansion of functions. However, I want to take a moment and go back and review the general steps we took for finding the solution of an impossible problem.

1. We started by naming the problem. We established what the impossible problem was and what it was that made the problem impossible.

2. Next, we identified the assumptions that made the problem impossible.

3. Then, we removed the assumptions that made the problem impossible to see if the problem is now solvable.

Now, this didn't solve our problem. In fact, while it removed the "impossibility" part of the problem, it introduced a new set of problems. Many times, on the road to solving a problem, you may find yourself lost. If you look back to Equation 25.1, we were pretty lost ourselves. Here are some things that you can do to get yourself out of being lost:

1. Play with how the problem is written. In our case, we had to rewrite the problem numerous times before we had a version that we could easily work with.

---

[2]The technical reason you would divide by two is that the total impact of this derivative is obtained by integrating it twice. The first integral would be $-1x$, and the second integral is $\frac{-1x^2}{2}$. Each additional term would have to be integrated yet another time to reach its total impact. This is what causes the bottom term to be consecutive factorials—each time you integrate, you divide by the next number. By the time you get to the nth term, you have to integrate n times to find the total impact, which will cycle through dividing by all of the integers from 1 to n.

2. Identify what it is that is making the problem difficult. In our case, we identified two problems—that the subscripts were going to infinity from different directions, and that we were having to write out both the finite and infinite cases. These were both solved by rewriting the problem in a new way.

3. Find the solution to a subset of the problem. Our biggest breakthrough happened when we found C_0. The first key insight was that evaluating the function at $x = 0$ isolated C_0 among the infinite sea of coefficients. We would never have solved the problem by trying to solve the whole thing at once. By focusing on just one super-tiny subset of the problem, we were able to get started.

4. Find a mechanism to build success upon success. In our case, we figured out that taking the derivative of the polynomial caused the next coefficient in line to reduce its power to zero so it could be isolated. This allows us to find the "next" thing in line.

5. Identify patterns in the result. Building success upon success enough times allowed us to identify the pattern which was emerging. Once we could see the pattern clearly, we didn't need to solve for all infinity terms. We could write a formula to do it for us!

Anytime you are stuck in a mathematics (or other!) issue, I hope you come back here are remember that, even if the problem is indeed impossible, you have the tools to solve it.

Review

In this chapter, we learned:

- Polynomials can be used to approximate most other smooth functions given a sufficient (possibly inifinite) number of terms.

- Computers can compute approximate values of many smooth functions by using truncated versions of these infinite polynomials.

- For most smooth functions, increasing the number of terms in the polynomials yields better accuracy for the result.

- For infinite series of polynomial terms, it is usually beneficial to arrange them in order from the *lowest* power of x (starting with x^0, the constant) to the highest power of x (i.e., x^∞).

- The first (constant) term of the polynomial can be found by finding the value of the function at 0.

- Each term can be isolated by taking the nth derivative of the original function, finding the value at zero, and dividing by $n!$.

- The summation equation for this is given in Equation 25.8, and is known as the Maclaurin series for a function.

- When writing formulas for the Maclaurin series of a function, finding a formula for the constant is sometimes difficult.

- When writing formulas for the Maclaurin series of a function, creating cycles for the constant can often be done by raising -1 to a power related to n.

- When someone says something is "impossible," sometimes even if they are right, it is often only impossible because of certain assumptions they have made. There may be other assumptions that cause different conclusions.

- The best way to solve an "unsolvable" problem is to find the assumptions that people might not even recognizing that they are making.

- Removing assumptions can make impossible things possible.

Exercises

1. Use the process in the book in Sections 25.5 and 25.6 to find the first six terms for the polynomial expansion of $\sin(x)$.

2. Use the process in the book in Sections 25.5 and 25.6 to find the first six terms for the polynomial expansion of 2^x.

3. Using the previous two problems, find an approximate value for $\sin(1.1)$ and $2^{1.1}$. Compare these answers to what your calculator yields (don't forget to use radians!).

4. Try to come up with a formula for $\sin(x)$ that is similar in style to Equation 25.9.

5. Estimate the value of e using the first ten terms of the expansion of e^x. Round off to eight decimal places. Look up the value of e in a book or on the web. How many decimal places were you accurate to?

6. Use Equation 25.8 to find the $n = 8$ term for the expansion of e^x.

7. Using Equation 25.8, find the first four terms of a polynomial representation of $x\, e^x$.

8. Use the previous question to write a formula for every term of the expansion of $x\, e^x$.

9. Write out the expansion of $\cos(x)$ to ten terms (including the zeroed out terms) using Equation 25.9.

10. What is the term for $n = 513$ (i.e., the 514th term) of the expansion of $\cos(x)$ according to Equation 25.9? If there are any factorials in the result, leave them as factorials.

11. What is the term for $n = 8214$ (i.e., the 8215th term) of the expansion of $\cos(x)$ according to Equation 25.9? If there are any factorials in the result, leave them as factorials.

Chapter 26

Advanced Topics in Polynomial Series

In Chapter 25 we discussed how to convert a function whose derivatives we know into an infinite series of polynomials. This is especially useful for the transcendental functions—functions that cannot be expressed in simple terms of algebra (addition, subtraction, multiplication, and division), as it gives us a way to calculate them using those tools. Especially since the introduction of computers, converting transcendental functions into a series of algebraic terms has become increasingly important, since those are the only operations that come built-in on computers.[1]

In this chapter, we will extend our knowledge of series and how they can be used.

26.1   The Taylor Series

The Maclaurin series representation that we established in Chapter 25 isn't the only type of series available. The choice of series representation depends on what you intend on doing with the series.

For instance, the Maclaurin series depends on finding the value of the function (and its derivatives) at zero. What if the function you need a series for isn't defined at zero? What if one of its derivatives isn't defined at zero? If either of these are the case, then the Maclaurin series can't work because some terms will be undefined.

Another problem with the Maclaurin series is that it focuses around the value of the function *at* zero. In other words, the further away from zero you get, the more terms you need to use to model the function with equivalent accuracy. For sine and cosine near zero, you only need a small number of terms to get the correct result with a Maclaurin series. However, as you expand outward towards positive or negative infinity, the Maclaurin series needs more and more terms to be anywhere near correct.

This isn't so much of a problem for sine and cosine in particular (since we know that it repeats, we actually only need values from $x = 0$ to $x = 2\pi$). However, there may be situations where we need the function that we are modeling with polynomials to be accurate near some other value. Now, keep in mind, the Maclaurin expansion is actually 100% accurate if you include all infinity of the terms. However, we are often using such expansions to give us an approximation, so we usually just use the first few terms ("few" in this case can mean hundreds or thousands, but that is still "few" compared to the infinite number of terms available). Therefore, it may matter where the function is represented most accurately with a fixed number of terms from its series expansion.

---

[1]Technically, multiplication and division can be built out of addition and subtraction, so those aren't even required in computing. However, most modern computing systems go beyond what is strictly necessary.

The easiest solution to these issues is to use a Taylor Series. A Taylor Series is very similar to a Maclaurin series, but it uses a value *other than zero* to center the expansion around. With the Maclaurin Series, we were doing $f(0)$, $f'(0)$, $f''(0)$, $f'''(0)$, etc. But some functions such as the natural log do not work at zero. $f(0)$ is undefined, as is $f'(0)$ and all the rest.

The problem, though, is that the Maclaurin series expansion is based on using zeroes. Remember, the way that the Maclaurin series works is that, when x is zero, then all terms that include x drop out of the picture. So, if the polynomial series is

$C_0 + C_1 x^1 + C_2 x^2 + C_3 x^3 + \ldots$

then $f(0)$ causes all terms with x in them to drop out (i.e., go to zero), leaving us with just C_0. Then, for each successive derivative, the previous constant coefficient drops out, and the next coefficient in line drops its x value, so that, for example, $f'(0)$ tells us about C_1 by itself. But, if we were looking at *any other x* value, this wouldn't work. For instance, $f'(1)$ makes use of every term in the series, so doing $f'(1)$ doesn't allow us to isolate a particular value in the series.

To solve this, let's look at the natural log function in particular: $\ln(x)$. As mentioned, $\ln(0)$ is undefined (essentially negative infinity). The derivative at zero is also undefined at zero—it is $\frac{1}{x}$, and at zero that goes towards infinity.

To figure this out, let's just say that we wanted to use 1 as the point for expansion. This is actually a nice point for a natural log, because, although $\ln(x)$ often produces odd values, $\ln(1)$ is 0, and its derivatives ($\frac{1}{x}$, $\frac{-1}{x^2}$, $\frac{2}{x^3}$, etc.) are all nice fractions at $x = 1$. So, how do we transform this into a polynomial series where we can find individual coefficients?

To do this, let's imagine a new function. We will call it $Z(x)$. The function $Z(x)$ behaves *exactly* like $\ln(x)$ with one exception. $Z(x) = \ln(x + 1)$. In other words, if we are looking for $Z(52)$, then that will give us the exact same answer as looking for $\ln(53)$.

The nice thing about $Z(x)$ is that, instead of being undefined at zero, it is undefined at negative one! At zero, it is perfectly well-defined. It is the same answer as $\ln(1)$.

Therefore, although we can't directly find a series expansion for $\ln(x)$, we *can* find a series expansion for $Z(x)$, which is *almost* the same thing. In fact, their derivatives will also be identical, except that x will be replaced by $(x + 1)$ in all of the derivatives.

So, to find a series we will start by doing a series expansion of $Z(x)$, and then we will figure out how to get it back into a form that works for $\ln(x)$.

The formula for the Maclaurin series expansion of a polynomial is given by Equation 25.8 and is repeated below:

$$f(x) = \sum_{n=0}^{\infty} \frac{f^{(n)}(0)}{n!} x^n$$

Remember that $f^{(n)}(0)$ represents the nth derivative of the function.

The first few terms of the series expansion for $Z(x)$ are below:

n	nth derivative	$f^{(n)}(0)$	C_n (i.e., $\frac{f^{(n)}(0)}{n!}$)
0	$\ln(x+1)$	0	0
1	$\frac{1}{x+1}$	1	1
2	$\frac{1}{-(x+1)^2}$	-1	$-\frac{1}{2}$
3	$\frac{2}{(x+1)^3}$	2	$\frac{1}{3}$
4	$\frac{-6}{(x+1)^4}$	-6	$-\frac{1}{4}$
...	...	...	...

The series itself looks like this:

$$Z(x) = 0 + x + -\frac{1}{2}x^2 + \frac{1}{3}x^3 + -\frac{1}{4}x^4 + \dots$$

This can be converted to a summation like the following:

$$Z(x) = \sum_{n=1}^{\infty} (-1)^{n+1} \frac{1}{n} x^n$$

Note that on this series, we start at $n = 1$. The reason for this is because the first term is zero, and it is easier to simply leave it off than try to find a way for the first term to be zero in the summation.[2] The remaining terms are unproblematic.

So, now we have an expansion for $Z(x)$. How do we convert this expansion to one for $\ln(x)$? Well, since $Z(x) = \ln(x + 1)$, that means that $Z(x - 1) = \ln(x)$. Therefore, by replacing every instance of x with $(x - 1)$ in our series, this will become the series expansion for $\ln(x)$. This looks like the following:

$$\ln(x) = Z(x - 1) = \sum_{n=1}^{\infty} (-1)^{n+1} \frac{1}{n} (x - 1)^n \tag{26.1}$$

Now we have a series expansion for natural log!

So how do we generalize this? How do we arrive at an equation like Equation 25.8 for expansions that aren't at around zero?

Let's use a as the number that we want to use as the number to expand around. As we saw with using $Z(x)$ instead of the natural log, each coefficient will be based on the nth derivative of the function at a. Then, afterwards, we will replace all x values with $(x - a)$ in the expansion. This gives the following general equation:

$$f(x) = \sum_{n=0}^{\infty} \frac{f^{(n)}(a)}{n!} (x - a)^n \tag{26.2}$$

This is known as the Taylor series expansion. Notice that the Taylor series expansion (Equation 26.2) and the Maclaurin series expansion (Equation 25.8) are equivalent when $a = 0$.

When talking about a Taylor series, it is always important to specify which value of a you are using. This is usually expressed as a "Taylor series about (or around) a"

---

[2] This can actually be done using some tricks with the factorial function, depending on how factorial is extended to the negative numbers. In the Roman factorial, the factorial of -1 is 1, which is what we will use here:

$$Z(x) = \sum_{n=0}^{\infty} \left(\frac{n(n-1)!}{n!} \right) (-1)^{n+1} \frac{1}{n} x^n$$

However, rather than doing tricks with factorials, it was just easier to start at $n = 1$ instead of $n = 0$.

26.2   Requirements and Limitations of Polynomial Expansions

Not every function works with a series representation, and not every value of every function can work with a polynomial expansion. A full understanding of why this is the case is outside the scope of this book, but this section will introduce a few ideas to help you get a feel for what is going on.

When we did the expansion for e^x, the series of terms was:

$$1 + x + \frac{1}{2}x^2 + \frac{1}{6}x^3 + \frac{1}{24}x^4 + \frac{1}{120}x^5 + \ldots$$

Notice that as the series gets bigger, the amount that the remaining terms adds to the result gets smaller. For instance, if we set $x = 1$, the series gives us:

$$1 + 1 + \frac{1}{2} + \frac{1}{6} + \frac{1}{24} + \frac{1}{120} + \ldots$$

As you can see, the biggest effects are in the first few terms, but, as we get more and more terms, each term has less and less impact, because it is being divided by a bigger and bigger factorial.

This has the effect of forcing the sequence to *converge*. What this means is that there is a number to which the sequence is getting closer and closer to as we add more terms. This is known as a **convergent sequence**.

For e^x, no matter what x value we use, the sequence will start converging at some point. However, some other sequences are known as **divergent sequences**. This means that adding more and more terms will not get us closer and closer to some particular value, but will head us off towards positive or negative infinity, or keep on bouncing us around.

If the sequence of values that a polynomial expansion creates for a particular value of x is *divergent*, then that means that this sequence will not give us a valid value for the function. In the case of our expansion for $\ln(x)$, it turns out that this is actually divergent for most numbers! It is valid for values of x between 0 and 2.

To see why, let's see what happens when we plug $x = 3$ into Equation 26.1:

$$\ln(3) = \frac{1}{1}(3-1)^1 + \frac{1}{2}(3-1)^2 + \frac{1}{3}(3-1)^3 + \frac{1}{4}(3-1)^4 + \frac{1}{5}(3-1)^5 \ldots$$

$$= 2 + 2 + \frac{8}{3} + 4 + \frac{32}{5} \ldots$$

As you can see, the numbers are actually getting larger and larger—they aren't converging on any value. Therefore, the sequence is divergent.

You may be wondering how to tell for sure whether or not a series will be convergent or divergent. Appendix C has some of the details on this. However, a good rule of thumb is that, if there is some non-smooth or non-continuous part of the function, then the Taylor expansion will usually be convergent within the distance between where the expansion was taken and the location of the "problem" (discontinuity or non-smoothness).

So, for instance, $\ln(x)$ has a discontinuity at $x = 0$. In other words, $\ln(0)$ has no defined value. Our Taylor series for $\ln(x)$ (i.e, Equation 26.1) was taken about the point $x = 1$. The distance between $x = 1$ (where we took the Taylor series) and $x = 0$ (where the nearest problematic value happens) is 1. Therefore, the Taylor series is only valid within a radius of 1 unit of $x = 1$ *on any side*.

Even though the discontinuity is to the left of $x = 1$, the valid set of numbers for which this formula for $\ln(x)$ works is only within 1 unit on *any* side. This is known as the **radius of convergence**.

If we had taken the Taylor series about 10, then the radius of convergence would be $10 - 0$, or 10, so the series would be valid for $0 < x < 20$ only.[3]

Functions like $\sin(x)$, $\cos(x)$, and e^x are smooth and continuous for all real numbers, therefore their radius of convergence is infinite. In other words, no matter what real number we stick in for x, the series will converge.

26.3 Extending Functions into Complex Domains

This book has not done a lot of discussions of domains and ranges. Generally, since we are dealing with continuous functions, we have just assumed that the domain for all of our functions have been the real numbers (technically, since differentials can be considered smaller than any real number, we are actually dealing with the hyperreal numbers). Remember that the **domain** of a function is the possible (i.e., allowed) values that you can send to the function. The **range** of a function is the possible values that you can get back.

There are many situations in which we might want to take a function that we understand that has one domain of values and *extend* that function so that it covers a wider range of numbers. This can allow you to do calculate things that you previously thought were uncalculatable.

As an example, consider the following function of the integers:

$$f(x) = \begin{cases} 1, & x = 0 \\ f(x-1) + 2 & x > 0 \end{cases}$$

If you plot this function, you will get a series of values like this:

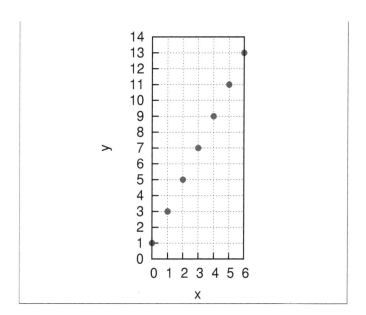

Now, we have defined this function on the positive integers. However, as you can see, the dots actually form a line.

---

[3]You may be wondering why we chose to do the Taylor series about 1 if it gives such a limited radius of convergence. The answer is simple—we don't even need a calculator to determine $\ln(1)$. Thus, we can build up the whole series without a calculator at all. Other values for a in the expansion would require the usage of a calculator, and, as such, we would be getting the answer from the calculator and not from first principles of understanding. That's not terrible, but I wanted you to see that you could generate a series for a strange function like $\ln(x)$ just from basic knowledge about its properties.

Therefore, we can *extend* this function into an equation for a line:

$$f(x) = 2x + 1$$

The resulting graph looks like this:

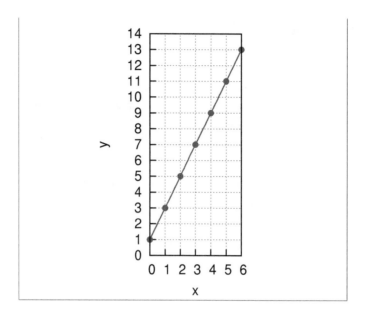

This is an *extension* of the function from the integers to the reals.

Likewise, we can take a function of the reals and convert it into complex numbers (i.e., numbers that include imaginary units). This is straightforward for simple functions like this (since the operations on reals is fairly well-defined), but is more difficult for complex numbers.

As an example, let's take a function like e^x and see how to get it to work with imaginary numbers—numbers that are multiplied by the imaginary unit i. It may seem odd to raise e to an imaginary power, but even though it is hard to *conceive* of, that doesn't mean it isn't possible.

To figure out how this is done, let's think about the series representation of e^x. In Chapter 25, we looked at a series representation of e^x:

$$e^x = \sum_{n=0}^{\infty} \frac{1}{n!} x^n$$

We can use this expansion to evaluate the result of using a complex value.

So, let's estimate e^x using the first four terms of the series:

$$e^x \approx 1 + x + \frac{1}{2}x^2 + \frac{1}{6}x^3$$

Now, since this is just a polynomial, we already know how to evaluate a complex value within a polynomial. Therefore, we can substitute a complex number into this polynomial in order to understand how e^x applies to complex numbers! Now, since this is a truncated version of the polynomial expansion, it will just be an estimate.

So, let's look at what the result will be of setting x to be the complex number $1 + 2i$. If we substitute this value into the formula as the value of x, we will get:

$$e^x \approx 1 + x + \frac{1}{2}x^2 + \frac{1}{6}x^3$$

$$e^{1+2i} \approx 1 + (1 + 2i) + \frac{1}{2}(1 + 2i)^2 + \frac{1}{6}(1 + 2i)^3$$

$$\approx 1 + (1 + 2i) + \frac{1}{2}(1 + 4i + -4) + \frac{1}{6}(1 + 6i - 12 - 8i)$$

$$\approx 1 + (1 + 2i) + \frac{1}{2}(-3 + 4i) + \frac{1}{6}(-11 - 2i)$$

$$\approx 2 + 2i + \frac{-3}{2} + 2i + \frac{-11}{6} + \frac{-1}{3}i$$

$$\approx -\frac{4}{3} + \frac{11}{3}i$$

This is not a great approximation because we used so few terms. But, as you can see, you can use polynomial series expansions to extend functions of real values to functions of complex values.

You can use any of the expansions we have developed so far to come up with complex expansions of functions that are normally used in the real domain.

For expansions that have a limited radius of convergence, you can find whether the expansion is valid for a particular complex number by measuring the distance between the location where the expansion occurred about and the complex number you are using for x. If the distance is greater than the radius of convergence, then the series will likely not converge.[4]

26.4 Other Types of Expansions

The extension of functions which are defined on the real domain to be also defined in the complex domain is fairly straightforward using the methodology presented in this chapter. However, other domain extensions are possible, though they are not as straightforward. For instance, there are systems which extend the domain of the factorial function beyond just the natural numbers. The Roman factorial function, for instance, extends the factorial function to negative integers. There are various other functions which extend the factorial function to the real numbers. In such extensions, the function has to cover the existing known values of the function exactly, as well as apply to the added numbers from the extended domain. Additionally, one has to identify which logical features of the function most need to be preserved in the extended domain.

These sorts of functions are outside the scope of this book, but they are extremely interesting.

26.5 Integrating Impossible Integrals

This part of the book has focused a lot on performing the impossible. I hope you can see how great mathematics (and specifically calculus) is because now you get to:

- find out non-existent values of functions (i.e., looking at limits with L'Hospital's Rule)

- find out what happens at the end of infinity (i.e., looking at limits at infinity)

---

[4]Complex arithmetic is outside the scope of this book. If you do not remember how to find the distance between two points on the complex plane, see Appendix H.2 or a book that covers complex numbers.

- solve impossible problems (representing functions as polynomials)

Here we will keep along the same lines to solve unsolvable integrals.

The following integral is unsolvable:

$$\int \cos(x^2) \, dx$$

It doesn't look ominous. The simplicity of the function may lead you to think that it must be solvable. But, sadly, it is not.

It's not just that no one has found the solution for the integral, but that there is provably no solution for the integral.

26.5.1 Checking Assumptions

Remember that in Chapter 25 we said that if someone says something is "impossible" that there is often some set of unstated assumptions that they are bringing in that makes the thing impossible. So, if we say that it is impossible to perform the operation $\int \cos(x^2) \, dx$, what are the assumptions that we are making?

Well, in general in this book, we have always assumed that functions are smooth and continuous. That is still the case here. It is also true that the function $\cos(x^2)$ generates a graph where we can quite easily see that there is in fact an area under the curve. The graph is below:

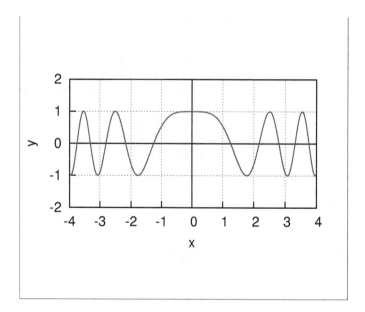

Therefore, we can't mean that there is no such thing as the area under the curve—the curve is just as drawable as any other function. So there must be *some* function that relates the region under consideration (i.e., the limits of integration) to the area under the curve.

There are two assumptions underlying the claim that $\int \cos(x^2) \, dx$ is impossible to solve, the disregarding of either one of which produces a perfectly coherent result. The assumptions are that the solution must be

1. in terms of a *finite number* of terms, and

2. those terms must be *elementary functions* (i.e., sine, cosine, exponentiation, etc.)

If you jettison either one of these assumptions, then you can suddenly solve the problem.

26.5.2 Non-Elementary Functions

The first possible mode of solution is that you can jettison the assumption that the solution has to be in terms of standard elementary functions. It sure is nice when a solution is in those terms, as we are all familiar with how those functions work. But reality might not be so nice, and we have to know when to jump ship and set off in new directions.

So, the easiest way to solve this integral is to simply *make up* a new function that represents the answer! So, we can just pull a letter from the alphabet to represent our new function (I personally like Q), and then create a new function that is merely *defined* to be the solution to the problem.

In other words, we will say that:

$$Q(x) = \int \cos(x^2)\,\mathrm{d}x$$

We should probably add in the constant of integration, so the actual result will be:

$$Q(x) + C = \int \cos(x^2)\,\mathrm{d}x \tag{26.3}$$

It may sound odd to say that we just named a function for something we didn't know how to perform, but this is often how mathematics works. Sometimes, rather than solving the problem in terms that we already know, the best solution is to simply *name* the problem. $Q(x)$ simply represents the solution to the problem, even though we don't really know anything about it. It's okay that we don't know anything about it. As long as we have named it and defined it, then the rest is just future work.

Sometimes the most important thing is to define a problem clearly and give it a name. This allows it to be examined by others in a clear, methodical way. Maybe someone else will find a solution in terms of elementary functions (they won't in this case), or, more likely, someone will recognize the connection between more than one problem of the same kind.

That is, if you came up with the function $Q(x)$ to represent a tough problem you couldn't solve, and someone down the street came up with the function $Z(x)$ to represent a problem they couldn't solve, then someone somewhere else may someday find connections between the way $Q(x)$ and $Z(x)$ work! This isn't possible unless the equations are carefully defined, which is what we did when we said that $Q(x) + C = \int \cos(x^2)\,\mathrm{d}x$.

In fact, this is precisely what happened with the equation inside mathematics. The Fresnel C integral is a function defined by Augustin-Jean Fresnel to perform this operation.[5] Just like we used $Q(x)$ above, Fresnel used $C(x)$ as his term of choice. There's nothing magic in the letter that you choose—as long as everyone is clear what you are talking about.

Anyway, I don't want to get too distracted talking about Fresnel integrals—they aren't really the point. The main point is that we can get around the fact that (a) we don't know how to perform an operation and (b) we don't know exactly what the result looks like by simply defining an operation and saving the rest of the work for later. Maybe we'll do the work ourselves at a later point. Maybe someone has already done the work, and we're just not aware of it. Maybe in two hundred years, someone will come along and finish the work.

---

[5]Note that different people define the Fresnel integrals different ways, so if you try to integrate $\cos(x^2)\,\mathrm{d}x$ on some computer algebra systems, you may get slightly different answers.

In any case, I just wanted to point out how powerful it is just to put a name on a particular problem. This is often true in life, too. Sometimes if we run into difficulties, just naming what it is that is happening will help us understand the issue in the future, and, eventually, we will figure out how to solve the problem.

26.5.3   Infinite Series Representation

The actual point of this chapter is to show how we can solve the integral by overcoming the other assumption—that we use only a finite number of terms. Just like in Chapters 25 and 26, we were able to convert a function that we couldn't express in terms of a finite number of polynomials into an infinite series of polynomials.

Why does that matter to us in trying to integrate $\cos(x)\,dx$?

Think about a polynomial. Each individual term in a polynomial is just a constant multiplier and a variable raised to a power. Nothing could be easier to solve for an integral! Also, the terms of a polynomial are all separated by addition. This means that there is nothing special about how they combine! If we can convert a function into an infinite series of polynomial terms (especially one that can be written using summation notation), then all we have to do to find the integral is to integrate the single term being summed![6] So, let's start by finding a Maclaurin series for $\cos(x^2)$. Equation 25.8 says that:

$$f(x) = \sum_{n=0}^{\infty} \frac{f^{(n)}(0)}{n!} x^n$$

Remember that in this formula, $f^{(n)}(0)$ refers to the nth derivative of f evaluated at 0. So, if we use a_n to refer to the coefficient of each term of the series, we can expand the series to say:

coefficient	$f^{(n)}(x)$	$f^{(n)}(0)$	$\frac{f^{(n)}(0)}{n!}$
a_0	$\cos(x^2)$	1	1
a_1	$-\sin(x^2)\,2x$	0	0
a_2	$-2\sin(x^2) - 4x^2\cos(x^2)$	0	0
a_3	$8x^3\sin(x^2) - 12x\cos(x^2)$	0	0
a_4	$48x^2\sin(x^2) - 12\cos(x^2) + 16x^4\cos(x^2)$	-12	$-\frac{1}{2}$
...			

This goes on quite a while. It is long and painful enough that we won't represent it here, but I did want to make sure you recognized that it could be done.

Eventually, you get to the point that you can see that the formula becomes:

$$\cos(x^2) = 1 + -\frac{x^4}{2} + \frac{x^8}{24} + -\frac{x^12}{720} + \frac{x^16}{40,320} + \ldots$$

This can be reduced to a summation notation, but it is somewhat complicated to generate that from the expansion above.

---

[6]One student, when hearing that infinity comes to the rescue for performing impossibly hard integrals, made the comment that this procedure reminds her of the verse in the Bible that says, "with man this is impossible, but with God all things are possible" (Matthew 19:26). I don't know if that exactly fits (an infinite sequence isn't God), but it does certainly resonate. The endless (i.e., infinite) unfailingness of God's nature is what allows us to surpass the limits of our finitude. If we put our trust in mathematics for generalizing the effectiveness of an infinite series to an infinite number of terms, how much more should we trust in God to add up our limited actions to serve in His infinite purposes? Thinking about infinity naturally leads to thinking about God, and, while we should be careful to not necessarily equate the properties of the two prematurely, I do think that practice in thinking about the infinite certainly helps us in thinking more clearly about God.

An even easier way to find an expansion is to take the series expansion given by the $\cos(x)$ formula, and then replace x with x^2 in the equation. We gave two formulas for a series expansion of $\cos(x)$, so for this problem we will use Equation 25.10 because it has a simpler form. So, using that equation, but replacing x with x^2 gives us:

$$\cos(x^2) = \sum_{n=0}^{\infty} ((-1)^n) \left(\frac{1}{2n!}\right) x^{4n} \tag{26.4}$$

This will be our starting point.

Remember that integration can be *split* at the point of addition into separate integrals using the addition rule.[7] Therefore, to integrate a summation series, we can just integrate each term individually. Even though the formula *seems* complicated, most of it is just the coefficient, which is just a constant term.

Therefore, to integrate this, we can just use the power rule:

$$\int \cos(x^2)\,dx = \int \sum_{n=0}^{\infty} ((-1)^n) \left(\frac{1}{2n!}\right) x^{4n}\,dx = \sum_{n=0}^{\infty} ((-1)^n) \left(\frac{1}{2n!}\right) \frac{x^{4n+1}}{4n+1} + C \tag{26.5}$$

This is the integral of our equation! So, even though it is physically impossible to get an integral in terms of a *finite number* of terms of elementary functions, we can get an integral in terms of an infinite number of terms.

Review

In this chapter, we learned:

1. The Taylor series extends the concepts of the Maclaurin series so that it can be centered around another number other than zero.

2. The general formula for the Taylor series is given by Equation 26.2:

$$f(x) = \sum_{n=0}^{\infty} \frac{f^{(n)}(a)}{n!} (x - a)^n$$

3. In order for a series representation to be well-behaved, the coefficients of the series must be convergent.

4. If a Taylor series representation is well-behaved, a subset of the coefficients can be used to approximate the behavior of the series.

5. A Taylor series representation about a number a is found for a function with a non-smooth or non-continuous portion, that series is only valid within the radius of convergence—the set of x values for which the Taylor expansion will give a convergent sequence.

6. The radius convergence for a Taylor series about a which has its nearest non-smooth or non-continuous point at b has a radius of convergence of $|a - b|$.

7. Series representations can be used to extend the domain of real-valued functions into the complex domain.

---

[7] As a reminder, the rule is $\int (f(x) + g(x))\,dx = \int f(x)\,dx + \int g(x)\,dx$.

8. Looking at the assumptions behind impossibility statements can help us see potential ways of doing impossible tasks and solving unsolvable problems.

9. Given an unsolvable integral (or any unsolvable problem), sometimes just naming the function that is generated can lead to long-term benefit, even if solutions cannot be found.

10. If an integral cannot be solved by a finite combination of elementary functions, it can often be solvable by transforming the function into a Maclaurin or Taylor series and then integrating the result. Series integration will be straightforward because the term is a simple polynomial term.

Exercises

1. Use the first four terms of the Taylor expansion of $\ln(x)$ given in Equation 26.1 (starting with $n = 1$) to approximate the value of $\ln(0.5)$. Use a calculator to check to see how close the approximation is. Note that you should keep it in fractional form until the very end to remove as much approximation error as possible.

2. Use the first four terms of the Taylor expansion of $\ln(x)$ given in Equation 26.1 (starting with $n = 1$) to approximate the value of $\ln(1.3)$. Use a calculator to check to see how close the approximation is.

3. Use the first four terms of the Taylor expansion of $\ln(x)$ given in Equation 26.1 (starting with $n = 1$) to approximate the value of $\ln(1 - \frac{i}{2})$, where i is the imaginary unit.   Find the first six terms for the Taylor expansion of $\sin(x)$ about π. Zero-terms can be included in your count, so do $n = 0$ to $n = 5$.

4. Find the first six terms for the Taylor expansion of $\cos(x)$ about π. Zero terms are included in the count, so perform the expansion from $n = 0$ to $n = 5$.

5. Use the Taylor expansion of $\cos(x)$ about π above to approximate the value of $\cos(4)$. Use 3.1416 for π.

6. Use the Taylor expansion of $\cos(x)$ about π above to approximate the value of $\cos(3 + 2i)$. Use 3.1416 as an approximation of π

7. Find the first four terms of the series expansion of $\log_{10}(x)$ (i.e., the base 10 logarithm of x) about 100. You will need to approximate decimals to eight places. Can you determine where this will be valid for?

8. Use the expansion of $\log_{10}(x)$ about 100 to estimate $\log_{10}(95)$.

   (a) What are the two main ways to integrate a non-integratable function?
   (b) Find the series representation for the solution of $\int \cos(x^3)\,dx$.
   (c) Find the series representation for the solution of $\int \cos(e^x)\,dx$.

Chapter 27

Thinking About Infinity

This part of the book has dealt with a lot of concepts dealing in the infinite, but we haven't bothered to stop and think about what this means in any sort of rigorous way. The concept of infinity has been elusive throughout all of mathematics. We won't get the idea perfect here, but ever since the work of Georg Cantor, ideas about infinity and how it can be properly thought about have been greatly improved.

27.1 The Human Vision of Infinity

Some people think that infinity is a far-off notion. They think that we should disregard infinity. They think that we should only include numbers that we can access. Since no one will ever count to infinity, we shouldn't use it as a substantial concept.

However, we actually utilize infinity all the time, even when we don't explicitly say so. When we first learn about the number line, we talk about numbers, and then the next number after that, and then the next number after that. Do you know what question I've never heard when discussing the number line? No person has ever asked me, "what is the last number on the number line?" Not a single person.

The idea that the numbers go on forever is essentially baked in to human thinking and rationality. I don't need to *tell* anyone that the number line never stops. This isn't a huge revelation. As soon as you describe how numbers work, people intuitively see that there is no ending for it![1]

In fact, infinity is a core constituent of rationality itself. There are two ways to define a term—by logic or by enumeration.[2]

Let's think of the word "nation." What does it mean? We could define the word nation in two ways:

1. We could make a list of all of the nations in the world. A "nation" is simply something on the list. This would be a definition by enumeration.

2. We could create a *logical definition* of what a nation *is*. A "nation" in this sense is *anything* that matches the definition. This is a definition by logic.

---

[1]There are, in fact, modifications to the number line which make it finite. Modular arithmetic, for instance, is based on a finite, circular number line, like a clock. For instance, if I add 24 hours to any clock hour, I get the same number back. However, this is a *later*, not an earlier, development of mathematics. The fundamental *starting* intuition that nearly every person gets is that the number line goes on forever.

[2]In the technical literature, a definition "by logic" is known as an *intensional* definitions and a definition "by enumeration" is known as an *extensional* definition. However, these terms are somewhat confusing to students, which is why I don't use them.

In the definition by enumeration, our definition applies to a fixed, finite number of things, because that's how the definition works. However, in the logical definition, there is no end to the number of things which, at least potentially, could apply to the definition. There may only be one nation, a hundred nations, or an infinite number of nations.

In other words, logical definitions, at least by default, implicitly allow for infinities.

What's even stranger are definitions where a finite number of things stand in for infinite numbers of things.[3] That is, if I tell you the sequence, "2, 4, 6, 8, 10, 12, 14, ...," then most people will pick up on the fact that I am listing the even numbers—which is an infinite sequence.

So, even though I only listed out seven numbers, you are (a) inferring a logical pattern, and then (b) inferring an infinity of numbers that follow that pattern!

As you can see, the infinite is baked right in to human rationality. Logical thought implies the ability to work with an manipulate infinities on some level.

That doesn't mean that we naturally manipulate infinity correctly every time it is applied. Just like children can naturally add (if you give them one object, and then two more objects, most children will recognize that they have three objects), this does not give them the automated ability to do addition of large numbers, or of decimals, or of algebraic terms. Likewise, we have some basic intuitions about dealing with infinite series, but that doesn't make all of our intuitions and assumptions correct.

In fact, there are some very odd features of infinity that we will explore in this chapter which took centuries to discover and figure out. There were paradoxes of infinity which caused many philosophers to say that infinities cannot exist, or can only exist in God.

Whether or not infinitely large or infinitely small things really exist in the physical world has not been demonstrated. That is surely an open question. However, infinity surely exists in our thoughts and in our minds. As we have shown, rationality implicitly assumes its existence.

Therefore, in order to take our rational processes forward to new levels, we must explore what infinity is and what infinity means. While our understanding of infinity has grown greatly over the years, I think there is much more hiding under the surface to learn as well.

27.2   An Introduction to the Infinite

What do we mean by the word infinity? An infinity of something is an unterminable number of them. Something for which there is no end. For something to count as an infinity, it cannot merely be big, it must be inexhaustible.

Infinity brings with it a number of paradoxes. These paradoxes arise because our normal intuitions and procedures are almost entirely based on finite mathematics. If these are unthinkingly applied to the infinite, we get bizarre results.

For instance, let's say that I have an infinite number of footballs. Now, let's say that you give me another football. Do I have more footballs than I did previously? Before you gave me the football, my supply of footballs was inexhaustible. It is still inexhaustible. Therefore, even though you gave me a football, I don't have more footballs than I did previously.

Likewise, if I give you a football, my supply is still inexhaustible. Therefore, I don't have any fewer footballs to give out. So, subtracting one from your infinite supply did not actually change the number of footballs

---

[3]These definitions are technically called *ostensive* definitions.

that you have. Likewise, if I double my supply of footballs, I *still* don't have any more!

This leads to another odd situation. Let's look at the set of all positive integers. It is infinite, right?

Now, let's look at the set of all even integers. That is infinite too, right?

Here we have two sets of numbers which are both the same size (i.e., infinite), but we encounter the even integers only half as often. It seems that there is a true way in which the set of even integers is the same size as the set of positive integers, but also a true way in which the set of even integers is half as big as the set of positive integers.

This gets even stranger with prime numbers. There are an infinite number of primes, but the frequency of their occurrence on the number line decreases as the number line progresses.

Now, although we are getting ahead of ourselves, I want to point out that all of the sets of infinity listed here are the same size, but that there are sets of infinity which are of a different size. We will get to those soon enough.

27.3 How to Tell if Two Infinities Have the Same Number of Elements

So, if I have two infinite sets, is it possible to tell whether or not they have the same number of elements? Let's say that Jim has a bag that has every positive integer in it—all infinity of them. Bob also has a bag of numbers, but Bob only has the even integers. Whose bag has more numbers in it?

One option might be to say that Jim and Bob both have an infinite set of numbers, so their bags are the same size. However, someone else might say that Bob only has half of the numbers that Jim does. So who is correct?

Sometimes, when faced with deep, philosophical problems, you have to back up a step. We have to both unlearn what we think we know and be able to look at things from more than one perspective. In this case, the problem is that our method for comparing sizes of things comes from the fact that we can usually count things. Generally, we can count how many things are there, and then we can just see which number is bigger. But, in this situation, the numbers are literally uncountable.[4]

To count the uncountable, the easiest way is to forget how to count. Imagine that Frank is a nomadic goat-herder that never learned to count. Now, imagine that Frank thinks that he has more goats than Charlie, who also doesn't know how to count. Take a minute to think about how they might resolve the question of who has more goats.

Did you think about it?

Don't look ahead until you've thought about it for a minute.

The best way for them to resolve the question is for Frand and Charlie to *match* their goats together. If they match each one of Frank's goats up with each of Charlie's goats, then whoever has goats that can't be matched must have more goats. In other words, if, for each of Frank's goats, Frank can match it with a goat of Charlie's, that means that Frank has the same or fewer goats than Charlie. If Frank has goats left over that can't be matched, then Frank has more goats than Charlie. The same is true if they match from Charlie's to Frank's. If every goat from Charlie's herd can be matched up with a single goat from Frank's herd, and every goat from Frank's herd can be matched up with a single goat from Charlie's herd, then they

---

[4]Just to be confusing, even though the numbers are uncountable, in mathematics, these particular infinities are known as countable infinities.

have the same number of goats.

All without counting them.

So, with infinite items, the goal is to come up with a *matching procedure*.

Let's say I have two sets, S_1 and S_2. If I can define a function, $f(x)$, such that each distinct member of S_1 is matched up with a distinct member of S_2, that means that S_1 is equal or smaller than S_2. If I can define a function, $g(x)$, such that each distinct member of S_2 is matched up with a distinct member of S_1, that means that S_2 is equal or smaller than S_1. If I can define both functions, then they are equal.

So, let's go back to the question of whether or not the set of *all* positive integers (we'll call this S_{all} is the same size as the set of *even* integers (which we will call S_{even}). Can we define a function $f(x)$ that will map each member of S_{all} to a distinct member of S_{even}?

Yes. As a matter of fact, if we say that $f(x) = 2x$, then any number we put into $f(x)$ will get turned out into a distinct even number, which will be a member of S_{even}. That means that the set of all integers is equal to or less than the set of even numbers.

What about the other way? Is there a $g(x)$ which goes from S_{even} to S_{all}? Yes—it is just $g(x) = \frac{x}{2}$. Therefore, we can say that S_{even} is equal to or smaller than S_{all}. Since both sets are equal to or smaller in size than each other, that means they must be equal in size to each other.

Thus, the set of all positive integers is equal in size to the set of even integers.

The reason why this is counter-intuitive is because we don't encounter the even integers as often in the number line as we do just general positive integers. For finite numbers, the total number of values present is usually related to the frequency with which we encounter them. Let's say I have a six-sided die. Bill chooses one number from it, and Sam chooses two numbers. Then, I am twice as likely to hit Sam's number when I roll the dice, because he has twice the coverage on the die. With infinite sets, the linkage between coverage and total quantity disappears.

In fact, what makes working with infinities difficult is that many features of numbers that we previously assumed were tied together wind up being and acting very differently.

27.4   Hilbert's Hotel

One of the classic discussions of the equivalence of infinite set sizes comes from an example known as "Hilbert's Hotel," a mythical hotel where there are no vacancies but there is plenty of room for everyone.

In Hilbert's Hotel, there are an infinite number of rooms, each with a room number, starting with the number 1. Every room in the hotel is occupied—there are no vacancies. However, along comes a weary traveler and asks the manager for a place to stay. Can the manager accommodate the traveler?

The manager is allowed to move people around—even an infinite number of them. What will happen is that, each guest will tell the manager their existing room number. The manager will then tell that guest the new room number based on their existing room number. Then, the manager will give room numbers to the arriving travelers. It is okay if there are empty rooms after everyone is accommodated.

The manager has pity on the traveler, and agrees to move people around to accommodate. What he does is to tell everyone that their new room number is their previous room number plus one. So, the formula f for your new room number based on your old room number (x) is $f(x) = x + 1$. So, everyone who used to have a room number gets a new number, and we have a formula which tells them what room they should go to when they ask. After everybody moves up one, the first room is free, and our traveler has a place to stay.

The traveler is simply placed into room 1.

However, next there comes a crowd of people. Not just a finite number of them—an *infinite* number of people! Can the manager rearrange the rooms so that each person is given a room? The manager is a clever guy, so what he does is to ask each person that is in a room to move into a room whose room number is double their existing room number. In other words, $f(x) = 2x$. Everyone does this, and that leaves an infinite number of rooms (the odd numbered-rooms) left over for the new guests. Therefore, he puts each of the arriving guests in one of the infinite odd-numbered rooms now available. For each arriving individual (the individual indicated by x), their room number will be $f(x) = 2x - 1$.

Next, however, instead of just an infinite number of guests, there comes an infinite number of carriages. Each carriage holds ten guests! Now, to make enough room, he has each existing guest go to a room number that is 11 times their existing room number ($f(x) = 11x$). Then, for each carriage, their room number is their carriage number times 11, and each person in the carriage adds their position ($1 - -10$) to their room number (for carriage x and seat n, $f(x, n) = 11x + n$).

So, the manager is quite tired at this point. But, what comes along? A long line of special carriages. Here, we have an infinite number of carriages. Not only that, each carriage carries an infinite number of guests!

Can the manager give everyone a seat? The manager thinks about it for a while, and he comes up with a scheme. (I told you he was clever!) Every carriage gets assigned a unique prime number because there are an infinite number of primes. The first prime number, 2, is reserved for existing hotel guests. Then, each member of the carriage's room number is their carriage's prime number raised to the power of their seat number. So, if you are in the fourth carriage, you will have the fifth prime number (because the first prime is for guests), which is 11. If you have the 20th seath in the fourth carriage, your new room number is 11^{20}. If you are an existing guest, your new room number is merely $f(x) = 2^x$.

As you can see, the hotel can accommodate a huge number of guests, meaning that it is has the same number of rooms as the guests that come in. So, even, as in the last example, when we have infinity times infinity, that is really just the same size as infinity.[5]

Hilbert's Hotel represents what is known as **countably infinite** numbers. The reason that they are called "countable" even though you can't actually count them is that each member of the infinity could be paired up with a counting number. So, just like the comparison of goats, since we can match each element with a counting number, the set has the same size of infinity as the counting numbers.

However, there are, in fact, other sizes of infinity. But we'll get to that later.

---

[5]Some people view mathematical games like this as being inconsequential to reality. But, in fact, I have actually made use of this kind of thinking in my work in computer programming. One time, I had a computer database system, where a database table was keyed with *two* separate values. However, the software system that I had to integrate with required that the database table be keyed with a *single* value. Therefore, I had to come up with a matching function that took the two numbers I started with and match it to a single counting number. This is known as Cantor pairing.

The standard method for combining two numbers in this way is to take two numbers, a and b, and produce the combined number c using the following formula:

$$c = \frac{1}{2}(a + b)(a + b + 1) + b$$

Additionally, let's say that you don't know how many keys will combine together (and, therefore, you need to allow for infinite keys). This is similar to the situation with an infinite number of carriages carrying an infinite number of guests. You could use a solution similar to the solution we used in the Hotel example, where each type of key (i.e., the carriage) gets a unique prime number. Then, the value of the key (i.e., the seat of the person in the carriage) tells you what power to raise the prime number. Then, all of the resulting numbers get multiplied together. The result is a unique key based on the contribution of all of the potentially infinite number of keys available.

If you didn't follow that, that's okay (that's why I put it in a footnote), but I did want to point out that mathematics is often *built* by just playing around with numbers and ideas, but that doesn't mean that the results are only toys (though there isn't really anything wrong with that, either). Many of these ideas wind up being very useful in some field or another.

27.5   Ordinal vs. Cardinal Numbers

Georg Cantor solved many of the weird paradoxes created by the concept of infinity by separating out **ordinal** from **cardinal** numbers. An ordinal number refers to a number that can be placed into an ordering. That is, after 1 comes 2, after 2 comes 3, etc.

A cardinal number refers to how "big" a number is. 2 is bigger than 1, 3 is bigger than 2, etc. "Bigness" refers to *how many* items a set of that size contains. That is, a set of three items can contain more items than a set of two items.

Now, it may seem strange that we are making this distinction between ordinals and cardinals. Don't they ultimately refer to the same property? For finite numbers, ordinality and cardinality are the same. However, for **transfinite numbers** (i.e., non-finite numbers), these two concepts diverge! In fact, most of the paradoxes of infinity are resolved once we allow ordinality and cardinality to be different things.

In Hilbert's Hotel, a distinct number (i.e., ordinal) of guests arrived each time (infinity, infinity squared, etc.). However, in each case, the total cardinality (bigness) of the number of guests remained the same (i.e., we could fit them all into the existing rooms through rearrangement).

The notation for infinity in ordinary mathematics is usually ∞. However, when Cantor separated out ordinal and cardinal infinities, he used different symbols for each of these. We will use the symbol ω (the Greek lower-case omega) to represent the scale of ordinal infinity.[6] Because it is an ordinal, it can be involved in arithmetic operations. You can have 2ω, ω^2, and the like. All of these are different transfinite *ordinal* numbers, but they all share the same *cardinality*.[7]

As mentioned, for finite numbers, cardinal and ordinals are the same. However, for infinite numbers, the cardinality ("bigness") of many (but not all!) infinite sets are the same. Cantor called the first infinite cardinal $\aleph_0$. The letter is the Hebrew letter "aleph," and this number is known as "aleph-null" or "aleph-nought" or "aleph-zero". $\aleph_0$ is the cardinality of the infinite set of integers. As mentioned, this is sometimes called a **countable infinity** because it is the infinity that can be matched to the counting numbers.

27.6   Infinities of Different Sizes

Now, we have seen how to show that two sizes of infinite sets are identical. If we can have a mapping that goes from every member of a set to a unique member of the other set, and if we can make the mapping in

---

[6]There is a large number of technical issues when dealing with numbers beyond infinity. Different mathematicians have defined the meanings of these "numbers" in a variety of different ways, and they have defined operations such as addition and multiplication differently when dealing in the infinite. In some of these definitions, addition is no longer commutative (i.e., $\omega + 1$ is not the same as $1 + \omega$), while in other definitions, they are. That doesn't really matter here (we are using the commutative versions, though), but I wanted you to know that it can get weird, and technical issues can cause problems with edge cases. This book focuses on common, practical uses, rather than getting every possibility accounted for. Additionally, many books represent the type of infinity we are referring to as H. I find ω to be better because it connects with other similar notions of infinity, and doesn't use a standard letter that you might already be using for something else.

[7]If you are looking for a way to imagine the difference between ordinal and cardinal numbers, one way that I like to think of them is that the cardinal numbers answer the "how many?" question, while the ordinal numbers answer the "how frequently?" question. That is, let's say that we use ω to represent the ordinality of the integers. Generally, in the system outlined in this chapter, ω is somewhat of an "arbitrary" infinity rather than a specific one, but choosing a specific reference point will help us understand the concept. So, we will call the positive integers as having an occurrence of ω. The odd integers occur half as often, so they can be represented as 0.5ω. If you threw a dart at the integers, the chances of hitting an odd one is 50% (i.e., 0.5). This is because, since we defined in this footnote that ω is the ordinality of the integers, and $\frac{\omega}{2}$ is the ordinality of the odd integers, then $\frac{\frac{\omega}{2}}{\omega} = 0.5$.

However, if we arranged our numbers in a different way, we could alter those odds. For instance, if we wrote the numbers out like 1, 2, 4, 3, 6, 8, 5, 10, 12, . . ., then the odd numbers are only occurring in one out of three locations, and if I threw a dart at this new dartboard, I would only hit an odd number $\frac{1}{3}$ of the time. So, as you can see, the relative sizes of infinite numbers are arrangement-dependent.

both directions, then the sets are the same size. However, our lack of ability to create such a mapping does not mean that the sets are a different size.

In order to show that an infinite set is of a different size than another infinite set, we have to *prove* that there *is no possible mapping* in one direction. That is a difficult goal, but one in which the mathematician Georg Cantor achieved. Cantor was able to prove that the set of real numbers is a larger infinity than the set of integers.

The next level of infinity is Aleph-one (written as $\aleph_1$). This level of infinity is the size of the set of real numbers. It is often referred to as an "uncountable infinity." The next size of infinity is $\aleph_2$, though I cannot for the life of me imagine what this looks like.

Aleph numbers are not numbers in the traditional sense. That is, they don't name a number of things which can be added, divided, multiplied, etc. Instead, they provide a way of speaking about the size of things which are infinite. They are known as cardinalities because they tell you the size of a set, but without actually being a number.

While a lot of this is strange and counter-intuitive, the main points to know are that:

1. With infinities, cardinal numbers and ordinal numbers have different meanings. Recognizing this fact eliminates a lot of the confusion and paradoxes surrounding them.

2. Infinities *do* come in different sizes (cardinalities), but most of the ones we think about are either countable ($\aleph_0$) or uncountable ($\aleph_1$) infinites.

3. Infinities require special rules to manipulate.

27.7 The Hyperreals—Adding Infinities and Infinitesimals to the Number Line

There have been many attempts to add infinities and infinitesimals to the number line. What I am describing in this section should not be considered a rigorous treatment, but one that is good enough to work with. Different ideas about infinities, infinitesimals, and how to model them lead to different rules, different notation, etc.

The extension of real numbers to include infinities and infinitesimals is known as the **hyperreal** numbers. To imagine a hyperreal number, think about about a decimal number. Let's look at the number 0.01. This is a "unit" number (1) shifted two digits to the right of the decimal. If I square the number, the actual value will be four digits to the right of the decimal:

$$0.01^2 = 0.0001$$

Now, let's go the other way. If I have the number 100 (1 shifted left two digits), then 100^2 will be shifted left four digits to the left of the decimal:

$$100^2 = 10000$$

Now, a real number has an infinite number of digits. The number 0.1 is really $0.100000000\dots$. Even if all the digits are just zero, they are there because we are dealing with the real number line. Likewise, a real number has an infinite number of digits in front of it. So, when we say something like 1.2, what we really mean is $\dots 00000000000001.2000000000000\dots$. Additionally, we can represent real numbers as being quantities multiplied by 10^n, where the n tells us where to shift the number. I can represent the number 0.0000000553 as being $5.53 \cdot 10^{-8}$. The 10^{-8} tells me where and how to shift the number.

With the hyperreals, we have some additional ways of shifting a number. In addition to the infinite decimal expansion of a real number, a hyperreal number has decimal expansions that occur *before* it and *after* it.

A number that is to the left of the infinite expansion is an infinite number. When I say that it is "to the left" of the real number, I mean that there are an infinite number of zeroes on the left-hand side of the number, and *then* you have our number. So, ω represents the infinite number size, just like 10 represents the finite digit size.

To get an idea of what ω is like, think of ω as the number that represents the counting numbers. I can multiply it by a real number and get some type of infinite number. Just like $5.53 \cdot 10$ represents 5.53 shifted to the left 1 digit, 5.53ω represents the number 5.53 shifted to the left an infinite number of digits.[8]

If we wanted to shift 5.53 to the left 7 digits, we could write this as $5.53 \cdot 10^7$. Similarly, if we wanted to shift 5.53 to the left by 7 sets of infinite digits, we would write it as $5.53\omega^7$. ω is essentially acting as the "unit" of infinity that we want to shift the number by.

Likewise, we can shift the number to the right as well. If we wanted to shift 5.53 fifteen digits to the right, we would write $5.53 \cdot 10^{-15}$. Just like before, we can shift it to the right an infinite number of digits as well, creating an infinitely small number. Just like shifting the number individual digits, if we want an infinitely small number, like 5.53 shifted infinitely far to the right, we would just put negative exponents on the unit of infinity. So, an infinitesimal could be written like $5.53\omega^{-2}$, which essentially means 5.53 shifted to the right by an infinite number of digits, twice.

Now, unit infinitesimals are so useful, that we often write them as its own number, ϵ.[9] So, instead of writing ω^{-1} we would write ϵ.

So, ϵ^2 is the same as ω^{-2}, which is just a real number twice shifted to the right an infinite number of spaces.[10]

When dealing with infinities and infinitesimals *as hyperreals*, they can be treated as largely well-behaving algebraic entities. Their exponents operate just like normal exponents in algebraic and arithmetic expressions. A hyperreal number might be expressed like the following:

$$5.22\omega^3 + 105.2\omega^2 + 0.0002\omega + 5 + 12.3\omega^{-1} + 5.1\omega^{-2}$$

Each order of infinity (i.e., ω^n) is listed with its multiplier.

We will call the highest exponent of ω in an expression the "order" of infinity of the expression.[11] The expression above is a third-order infinity.

The typical real numbers you have dealt with your whole life all have a zero order of infinity.

Orders of infinity below the primary order of infinity are often ignored in a final result because the lower orders of infinity are essentially irrelevant in the result (they are, quite literally, infinitely less significant).

The most important piece of dealing with expressions involving infinities and infinitesimals is to realize that, at the end, if you have a positive order infinity, your value is infinite. If you have a negative order infinity, your value is infinitesimal.

---

[8]Technically, it isn't shifting by an infinite number of digits, because that would imply that ω is a power of ten, and we have no idea if ω is a power of ten or not. Nonetheless, I think that thinking of it this way is extremely helpful for conceptualizing what it is that ω is doing.

[9]Note that ϵ is used for many similarly microscopic things in mathematics, but even when similar not all of them are equivalent.

[10]It is probably more accurate to say that it is shifted *beyond* an infinite number of spaces. That is, it is shifted *past* the end of the real expansion, not as the tail end of it.

[11]This is also known as the "degree."

Take, for instance, the following expression:

$$2\omega^2 \cdot 3\omega^{-3}$$

What happens here? Well, the exponents of ω combine. This leads to the value $6\omega^{-1}$. In other words, an infinitesimal.

Since an infinitesimal is infinitely close to zero, then for all practical purposes your result is zero.

Now, let's look at another one:

$$\frac{0.124\omega^3}{\omega^2}$$

The result is 0.124ω. Since ω is the same as ω raised to the first power, you have a first order infinity.

Sometimes all we want is an answer in the real numbers—the specific infinity or infinitesimal is not interesting to us. If we are reducing a hyperreal number into the real number line, then infinitesimals (numbers with their highest-order infinity being negative) can be thought of as zero, and infinities (numbers with their highest-order infinity being positive) can be thought of as either $+\infty$ or $-\infty$ depending on the sign of the highest-order value. If the number is a zero-order infinity, then, in this reduction, any additional infinitesimal is disregarded.

In hyperreals, this operation is known as finding the **standard part** of a hyperreal number. The operation is often abbreviated as st().

The following are examples of the st() operation:

- st(5.1) = 5.1 (the standard part of a real number *is* the real number)

- $\text{st}(\omega^2 - 5 + 2\omega^{-1}) = \infty$ (the standard part of a hyperreal with a positive order is ∞)

- $\text{st}(-3.1\omega^5 + 100\omega + 53 + 2\omega^{-1}) = -\infty$ (the sign of ∞ depends on the sign of the highest order of infinity)

- $\text{st}(195\omega^{-1} + 0.3\omega^{-2}) = 0$ (the standard part of an infinitesimal (negative order infinity) is zero)

- $\text{st}(5 - 45\omega^{-1}) = 5$ (the standard part of a real number, even with infinitesimals added to it, is just the real part)

So, while non-rigorous, this gives us a general method to think and work with infinities and infinitesimals in much the same way that we work with ordinary real numbers, using many of the same intuitions.

27.8 Hyperreal Arithmetic

The practice of algebra should allow you to easily perform arithmetic in the hyperreal system. For the most part, you can treat ω as if it were a unit of measure, even though it actually specifies a unit of infinity. It is probably easiest to also treat it as if it were a variable.

To do hyperreal arithmetic, simply take an expression in terms of ω and then just simplify the expression to the extent possible.

—   Example 27.1

Simplify $3.1\omega^2 + 2.2\omega^2 + 5$.

Since we are treating the ω just as if it were a variable, we can combine the two coefficients of ω^2, yielding:

$$5.3\omega^2 + 5$$

That is as far as the number should be reduced. However, if the standard part was asked for, since it has a positive order, and the coefficient of the highest power of ω is positive, the standard part is ∞.

—   Example 27.2

Calculate $\frac{4\omega^2 - 6 + 3\omega^{-2}}{2\omega^2}$ and find the standard part.

Since the bottom part of the fraction is just a single term, it can be divided through the whole fraction:

$$\frac{4\omega^2 - 6 + 3\omega^{-3}}{2\omega^2} = \frac{4\omega^2}{2\omega^2} - \frac{6}{2\omega^2} + \frac{3\omega^{-3}}{2\omega^2} \qquad \text{split the fraction}$$

$$= 2 - 3\omega^{-2} + \frac{3}{2}\omega^{-5} \qquad \text{simplify powers}$$

This is the final hyperreal number. Next we need to find the standard part.

Since this number is of order zero, then 2 is the standard part.

—   Example 27.3

Find the standard part for $\frac{2 + 5\omega^2}{3\omega^5}$.

Since the denominator of the fraction is a single term, simply divide by the term and simplify:

$$\frac{2 + 5\omega^2}{3\omega^5} = \frac{2}{3\omega^5} + \frac{5\omega^2}{3\omega^5} \qquad \text{split the fraction}$$

$$= \frac{2}{3}\omega^{-5} + \frac{5}{3}\omega^{-3} \qquad \text{simplify}$$

Since all of the powers of ω are negative, this is an infinitesimal value. Therefore, the standard part of this is 0.

27.9 Hyperreals and Differentials

I wanted to take a moment and point out the strong connection between differentials and hyperreal numbers. Remember, a differential is essentially an infinitely small change.

In other words, a differential is what happens when the change in the variable is not a real number, but a hyperreal number, with an order of −1. When we put dx and dy into ratio with one another, we usually get a standard value back. This is exactly like what happens if we put two hyperreals with an order of −1 in ratio with one another. The ω^{-1} for each of them will cancel each other out, leaving just a real value for the standard part.

Higher order differentials (see Appendix B) such as d^2y and dx^2 will be hyperreals of order −2. Again, when two hyperreals of order −2 are put into ratio with each other, the ωs cancel each other out. In fact, anytime the ωs are of the *same* order they will cancel each other out, and produce a number whose standard part is a real value.

27.10   Do Infinities and Infinitesimals Exist?

I do not claim to know if infinites and infinitesimals exist in the physical world. However, they do seem to exist mentally. As mentioned at the beginning of this chapter, logical processes tend to be based on the concept of infinity. Therefore, our mind seems to know infinity to some degree. It is possible that infinity is how we get to know the finite. That is, we view the finite "from above," from the perspective of infinity.[12]

Another option (though I can't for the life of me remember who wrote this), is that *everything* is infinite. The idea is this—if objects were not infinite, they could not touch—they would be lost as points in space. Instead, everything is infinite, and the sizes of things are just the relationships between different infinities pressed against each other.

There are still others who view that, at least in the physical world, there are no "completed" infinities, but there are things for which there is an endless supply, such as time. At any particular point, we are at a finite point in time. However, there is no limit to the amount of time that will occur, so, in that sense it is infinite.

Nonetheless, whether infinity exists in the physical world or not, in mathematics infinity allows us to think more clearly about a number of processes. We have already looked at how infinite series can be used to model certain functions. We will look at other places where the concept of infinity will help us understand certain principles that are more difficult without it.

Review

In this chapter, we learned:

1. Infinity is not an esoteric concept—instead, most logical thought stems from the fundamental concept of infinite sets.

2. Infinity brings with it many paradoxes, but many are resolved by separating out the concept of ordinal and cardinal numbers.

---

[12]This makes sense of the concept of the human as both a physical and spiritual being. Being spiritual beings, we have the perspective of thought from infinity. Being physical beings, we use the concept of infinity to make sense of the finitude around us.

3. With finite numbers, ordinal and cardinal numbers are identical. With infinite numbers, the concepts diverge.

4. Cardinality is the "bigness" of a set. Ordinality is a specific position within a series or collection.

5. Infinite cardinalities are known as aleph numbers.

6. $\aleph_0$ is the first infinite cardinal—the size of the set of all counting numbers. Sets of this cardinality are known as "countable infinities."

7. Numerous infinite ordinals resolve to the same cardinal.

8. Infinite sets with the same cardinality are identified by finding a matching procedure that can match every distinct member of each set with a distinct member of the other set.

9. A set that is larger than a countable infinity is known as an "uncountable infinity."

10. The hyperreal numbers are an extension to the reals which allow the manipulation of infinities and infinitesimals in a similar way to the standard real numbers.

11. ω is often used as the unit ordinal infinity. Orders of infinity are marked by ω raised to a positive power (for infinities) or a negative power (for infinitesimals).

12. ϵ is often used as a stand-in for ω^{-1} because it is so frequently used.

13. A hyperreal ordinal is simply written as a series of terms for each level of infinity present.

14. A real number is merely a hyperreal with a level of infinity of zero. An infinitesimal is a hyperreal with a negative level of infinity. An infinite is a hyperreal with a positive level of infinity.

15. The standard part operator st() converts a hyperreal number to its nearest real number.

16. The standard part of an infinitesimal is simply zero.

17. The standard part of an infinity is either $+\infty$ or $-\infty$ depending on the sign of the highest-order infinity.

18. The standard part of a zero-order infinity is just the real part of the number.

19. Differentials can be considered hyperreal infinitesimal values.

20. Just like hyperreals, differentials of the same order can be put into ratio with each other to produce a number whose standard part is a real number.

21. Whether or not infinities and infinitesimals exist in the physical world is an open question, but they certainly allow logical operations and mathematics to work much more cleanly.

Exercises

Label the order of infinity for each hyperreal number:

1. $\omega^3 - \omega^2 + 32 + 0.1\omega^{-1}$

2. $5.2 - 0.3\omega^{-1} + 200\omega^{-2}$

3. $3.2\epsilon + 1.2\epsilon^2$

Find the standard part of each number:

4. $3\omega^2 + 5 - 52^{-1}$

5. $-3\omega^2 + 200\omega + 1000 + 20000\epsilon + 11100\omega^{-2}$

6. $5 + 1.2\omega^{-2}$

7. $\omega^{-5} - \omega^2$

8. $0.0035 + 100.3\epsilon$

9. $\epsilon + 2.34$

Perform the following arithmetic. Find the hyperreal value. Then find the standard part.

10. $\frac{\omega^2 - 3}{\omega^5}$

11. $(1.2\omega - 5)^2$

12. $\frac{\sqrt{\omega^2 + 3\omega^2} + 6}{\omega}$

Answer the following questions:

13. Why do first order differentials generally produce a real value when put into ratio with each other.

14. If an infinitesimal is added to a real number, what happens to the standard part of the number?

Chapter 28

Limits: Finding Impossible and Non-Existent Values of Functions

This chapter deals with the concept of a *limit*. A limit is an operation in mathematics where we find out the value that a function is headed towards. This operation is useful when the value *at* a location cannot be computed directly, but where the function itself is certainly headed *towards* an identifiable value.

28.1 Why We Need Limits

Consider the equation $y = \frac{\sin(x)}{x}$. The graph looks like this:

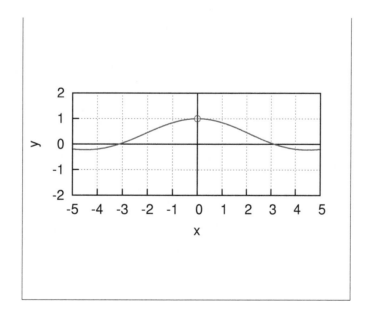

That dot right at $(0, 1)$ represents the fact that the function is undefined at this point. We can see where this missing point occurs just by just plugging in values. If x is 0 then the equation is $y = \frac{\sin(0)}{0} = \frac{0}{0}$. This is known as a **indeterminate form** because there is no way to identify its value.

349

This puts a "hole" in the graph. However, you can pretty clearly see that even though there is a hole in the graph because the function is not defined at $x = 0$, there *is* a reasonable value which we could plug into the hole just by continuing the function at that point.[1]

If you look, the y value is pretty clearly hitting at or near 1 at $x = 0$. When we look at where a graph is *going*, regardless of whether or not it arrives there, what we are looking at is known as the **limit** of a function.

In this case, we would say that "the limit of $\frac{\sin(x)}{x}$ as x approaches 0 is 1." In other words, as x gets closer and closer to 0, the y value gets closer and closer to 1.

Even though the function technically never hits the point $x = 0$, the function can be evaluated at $x = 0$ using limits. The limit we have come up with so far is more-or-less an educated guess, though we will shortly establish some techniques for finding these values.

Technically, limits also exist even when values are defined. In other words, most of the graph contains values. These values are also limits of the function at that point.

For instance, for this function, at $x = \pi$, $\frac{\sin(\pi)}{\pi} = 0$. Because that is also where the graph *looks like* it is going, then it is both the actual value *and* the limit of the function.

For more "normal" functions, the value of the function for a given x value and the limit of the function for that x value *are the same value*. However, the purpose of a limit is to be able to evaluate scenarios where this isn't the case.

28.2   Limit Notation and Simple Limits

For this section, we will analyze the limit of the following equation:

$$y = \frac{x^2 - 1}{x - 1}$$

Note that, at $x = 1$ the equation becomes $\frac{0}{0}$. However, if you graph the equation, you can see that it plots to a line that has a hole in it right at $x = 1$:

---

[1]This is technically known as a **removable discontinuity**. Although it is discontinuous at this point, it is pretty obvious what the point looks like it is going to be. Additionally, if this point is defined, the function actually is continuous.

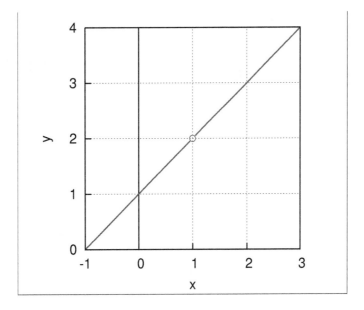

We can very clearly see that this graph is heading towards a y value of 2 at the hole. Therefore, we say, "the limit of $\frac{x^2-1}{x-1}$ as x approaches 1 is 2." We would write this as follows:

$$\lim_{x \to 1} \frac{x^2 - 1}{x - 1} = 2$$

So, the "lim" notation denotes a limit, and below that you put the variable you are using for the limit, and what value it is going to. Then, to the right of this, you write the function that you are taking the limit of.

Solving limits can be a tough problem. This book is not intended as a full discussion of limit theory, but we will look at some of the more common solutions.

Often, a function has a hole in it because the denominator goes to zero. In this equation, at $x = 1$ the denominator $(x - 1)$ goes to zero. Is there any way to rewrite the equation so that it doesn't have a denominator or so that the denominator does not go to zero?

Let's factor the numerator of the function to see if we have any common factors that we can use to get rid of the denominator: $x^2 - 1 = (x + 1)(x - 1)$. Aha! We have $x - 1$ as a factor in both the numerator and the denominator! Therefore, we can manipulate the function to get rid of the denominator:

$$f(x) = \frac{x^2 - 1}{x - 1}$$
$$= \frac{(x + 1)(x - 1)}{x - 1}$$
$$= x + 1$$

As you can see, after manipulating the equation, we found a new form of the same equation that did not have a hole in the graph.

There are many limits that can be found in this way.

— Example 28.1

Find the following limit:

$$\lim_{x \to 2} \frac{x^2 - 5x + 6}{x - 2}$$

We can verify that at $x = 2$ this gives us a problem value:

$$f(x) = \frac{x^2 - 5x + 6}{x - 2}$$

$$f(2) = \frac{2^2 - 5 \cdot 2 + 6}{2 - 2}$$

$$= \frac{4 - 10 + 6}{0}$$

$$= \frac{0}{0}$$

So, is there a way to factor the numerator to get rid of the denominator? $x^2 - 5x + 6$ factors into $(x - 3)(x - 2)$. Therefore, we can cancel out $x - 2$ from the top and bottom, leaving just $x - 3$.

Therefore, we evaluate the limit by just using $x - 3$. Since $x = 2$, the value will be -1.

In other words,

$$\lim_{x \to 2} \frac{x^2 - 5x + 6}{x - 2} = -1$$

28.3   Limits of Strange Functions

In addition to the simplistic forms of limits we have seen so far, there are more bizarre ones that we can dream up.

For example, we can think of the following function:

$$f(x) = \begin{cases} \frac{1}{2}x & \text{if } x \neq 3 \\ 4 & \text{if } x = 3 \end{cases}$$

In this function, $f(x)$ is indeed a function of x, and for the most part it forms a straight line. However, right at $x = 3$, for that very point, the y value is altered.

This creates a graph like the following:

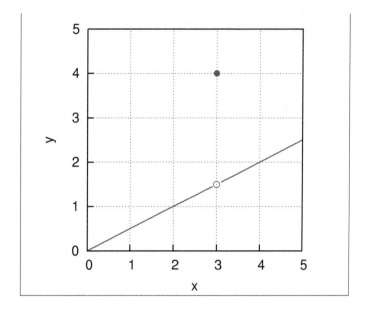

The open circle represents the point that is missing, and the filled circle represents the point that is added. For this function, there *is* a value for the function at $x = 3$, and there *is* a limit for the function at $x = 3$, but *they are not the same.* $\lim_{x \to 3} f(3) = 4$ but $\lim_{x \to 3} f(x) = 1.5$.

You might be thinking that this is a contrived example, and you are correct. However, the point is to make sure you don't confuse the concept of a limit with the actual value of a function at a particular point. The limit is where it *looks like* it is going, while the value is where the function *actually goes.*

Think also about this function:

$$f(x) = \begin{cases} x^2 & \text{if } x < 2 \\ \frac{x}{3} & \text{if } x >= 2 \end{cases}$$

This yields a graph that looks like this:

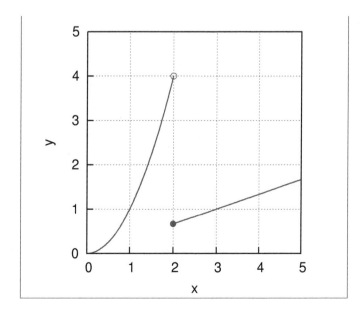

In this graph, the value at $x = 2$ is definitely $\frac{2}{3}$. You can see this in both the formula and the graph. Where $x = 2$ the formula to use is $\frac{x}{3}$. Additionally, the limit coming from the right-hand side is also headed towards the same point, and the filled circle tells us it reaches that point.

However, when coming from the left-hand side, it *looks like* the function is headed towards 4. In other words, there are two different limits occurring at this point. From the left, the function limits to 4, but from the right, the function limits to $\frac{2}{3}$.

The limit when coming from the left is known as the left-hand limit and the limit when coming from the right is called the right-hand limit. We denote these limits using a + (for a right-hand limit) or a − (for a left-hand limit) superscript on the text below the limit operator.

So, for this function, we would say the following:

$$\lim_{x \to 2^-} f(x) = 4$$

$$\lim_{x \to 2^+} f(x) = \frac{2}{3}$$

This says that the left-hand limit is 4 and the right-hand limit is $\frac{2}{3}$.

Additionally, we *could* have a function where the limit on the left is different than the limit on the right, and *neither* of them actually hit the actual value of the function.

Imagine the following function:

$$f(x) = \begin{cases} x^2 & \text{if } x < 2 \\ 2 & \text{if } x = 2 \\ \frac{x}{3} & \text{if } x > 2 \end{cases}$$

This function looks like this:

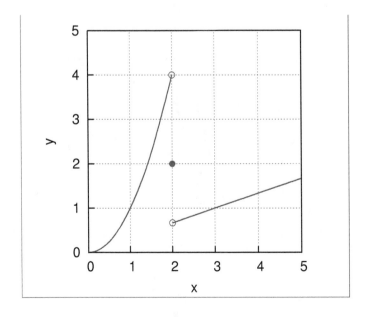

We would describe the limit behavior of this function as follows:

$$\lim_{x \to 2^-} f(x) = 4$$

$$\lim_{x \to 2^+} f(x) = \frac{2}{3}$$

$$f(2) = 2$$

We must remember that a limit can be different depending on which side it is coming from and that a limit can in fact be distinct from the value that the function itself produces.

28.4 The Derivative as a Limit

In this book, we have typically looked at the derivative as being the slope between two points that are infinitely close together (in other words, that are nearly 0 units apart). Another way of thinking of the derivative is in terms of a limit.

If we used the slope formula on two points that are exactly the same, we would always wind up with $\frac{0}{0}$. You can see this with the formula: $m = \frac{y_0 - y_0}{x_0 - x_0} = \frac{0}{0}$. This is not a good result because $\frac{0}{0}$ can actually mean anything.

However, with limits, instead of looking at *exactly* where a function occurs, we can look at *where it is heading*, even if that destination winds up not technically existing. Therefore, we can think of the slope as the *limit* of the slope between two points on a curve as they get closer and closer together. That is, if h, is the distance between the x value of two points, then the derivative is the *limit* of the slope between these two points as h approaches zero.

The general equation for the derivative that we learned (Equation 7.4) is as follows:

$$y' = \frac{f(x + h) - f(x)}{h}$$

Now, we said that after doing this, we simply replace h with 0 and see what happens.

A more precise way of defining the derivative can be achieved using limits is as follows:

$$y' = \lim_{h \to 0} \frac{f(x + h) - f(x)}{h} \tag{28.1}$$

In other words, if h is the difference in x values between two points, the derivative is the limit of the slope between these two points as h approaches zero.

This doesn't make a lot of difference to the *practice* of calculus. However, some mathematicians do not like the use of infinitesimals (values infinitely close to 0 but not actually 0), and this provides a formal way of analyzing derivatives without them.

Personally, I'm a big fan of infinities and infinitesimals, but it is good to be aware of other ways that people have considered the subject of calculus.

28.5   Other Definitions Using Limits

Early on we defined some terms using general ideas and language. The first of these terms was **continuity**. We say that a graph is continuous if we can draw it without picking up the pencil.

That is a good definition, but oftentimes mathematicians want more precise definitions. Limits provide a good way of defining some of these terms. It gives us a way to provide a concrete, mathematical definition of "not picking up your pencil."

When you draw a graph without picking up your pencil, the place where the graph *looks like* it is going is the same place where it *actually* goes. In other words, the limit is the same as the value. Additionally, this is true coming from the left as well as the right.

Therefore, we can define a continuous function as being one where the limit of the function and the function are always the same number! In other words, a graph is continuous if, for every value for which the graph is defined (which we will call c), the following holds true:

$$\lim_{x \to c^+} f(x) = \lim_{x \to c^-} f(x) = f(x)$$

Likewise, a graph is **smooth** if the place where the derivative is heading is the same as the place where the derivative actually goes. In other words, for every value for which the graph is defined (which we will call c), the following holds true:

$$\lim_{x \to c^+} f'(x) = \lim_{x \to c^-} f'(x) = f'(x)$$

28.6   Calculating Limits Using Infinitesimals

Another way of evaluating limits is using infinitesimals. Dividing by zero is only really a problem *at* zero. Dividing by zero is essentially meaningless. However, if you just want the value *near* zero, that's another story.

How might you see what the behavior of something is *near* zero without *actually* arriving at zero? Usually, if setting x to a particular value causes an expression to hit zero, then bumping it just by a tiny amount will cause the value to be non-zero. Using what we learned in Chapter 27, we can add or subtract a tiny amount, ϵ (i.e., ω^{-1}). This will move the expression off of the problematic value, but still be infinitely close to the actual value you are looking for. Since you are only an infinitely small length away, then the standard part of the result will be the limit.

Also note that since the right-hand and left-hand limits may be different, all limits evaluated using ϵ should be evaluated for *both* the right-hand and left-hand limits. The right-hand limit can be found by adding ϵ to x, and the left-hand limit can be found by subtracting ϵ from x.

—   Example 28.2

Evaluate the limit $\lim_{x \to 5} \frac{x^2 - 25}{2x - 10}$.

At $x = 5$, this becomes $\frac{0}{0}$, which can't be evaluated directly. Therefore, we will use limits to solve this. Note that if x is just a tiny bit away from 5, it will no longer be a zero denominator. Therefore, we will evaluate the right and left hand limits by adding and subtracting ϵ to x.

We will start with the right-hand limit, which we will find by adding ϵ to x (which is 5).

$$\lim_{x \to 5^+} \frac{x^2 - 25}{2x - 10} = \frac{(x + \epsilon)^2 - 25}{2(x + \epsilon) - 10}$$

$$= \frac{5^2 + 2 \cdot 5 \cdot \epsilon + \epsilon^2 - 25}{2(5 + \epsilon) - 10}$$

$$= \frac{25 + 10\epsilon + \epsilon^2 - 25}{10 + 2\epsilon - 10}$$

$$= \frac{10\epsilon + \epsilon^2}{2\epsilon}$$

$$= \frac{10\epsilon}{2\epsilon} + \frac{\epsilon^2}{2\epsilon}$$

$$= 5 + \frac{1}{2}\epsilon$$

The hyperreal we ended up with is $5 + \epsilon$. This can also be written as $5 + \omega^{-1}$, but, if you know you are just dealing with infinitesimals, it is often easier just to use ϵ.

Since the hyperreal is zero-order, the standard part of this hyperreal is just the real number 5.

We can now do the same thing for the left-hand limit. This is done by replacing x with $x - \epsilon$ and solving.

$$\lim_{x \to 5^-} \frac{x^2 - 25}{2x - 10} = \frac{(x - \epsilon)^2 - 25}{2(x - \epsilon) - 10}$$

$$= \frac{5^2 - 2 \cdot 5 \cdot \epsilon + \epsilon^2 - 25}{2(5 - \epsilon) - 10}$$

$$= \frac{25 - 10\epsilon + \epsilon^2 - 25}{10 - 2\epsilon - 10}$$

$$= \frac{-10\epsilon + \epsilon^2}{-2\epsilon}$$

$$= \frac{-10\epsilon}{-2\epsilon} + \frac{\epsilon^2}{-\epsilon}$$

$$= 5 - \frac{1}{2}\epsilon$$

Again, the standard part of this expression is 5. Therefore, since both the right-hand and left-hand limit point to the same value, the limit of the expression as x approaches 5 is 5

Review

In this chapter, we learned:

1. The limit of a function for a given value of x is the y value that a function is *headed towards* in the immediate surrounding context of that x value.

2. A limit is usually stated as "the limit of the function $f(x)$ as x approaches the value c is (the result)."

3. Limits are important because sometimes functions can have values, or at least act like they have values, for points for which the values cannot be calculated directly from the formula.

4. For most values of most functions, the limit of the function for a given value of x is the same as the actual value at x.

5. Many simple limits can be figured out by rewriting the function to remove a problematic denominator.

6. In some functions, for a given value of x, the limit of the function coming from the right (known as the right-hand limit) is not the same as the limit coming from the left (known as the left-hand limit).

7. In some functions, for a given value of x, the function has a defined value for x which is not a limit for either the left or right hand sides.

8. Many intuitive definitions for common ideas like continuity and smoothness can be made more explicit and analytical by defining them in terms of limits.

9. A function is continuous over a region if, for every point in the region, the limit as x approaches the point from the left is the same as the limit as x approaches the point from the right. Both of these should be the same as the actual point reached.

10. A function is smooth over a region if, for every point in the region, the limit of the slope (i.e., derivative) as x approaches the point from the left is the same as x approaches the point from the right.

11. A limit of a function that normally reaches an invalid value (such as $\frac{0}{0}$ can often be found by altering it by adding (for the right-hand limit) or subtracting (for the left-hand limit) an infinitesimal such as ϵ to the x value and then evaluating.

12. When evaluating a limit, you should be sure to check both the right-hand and left-hand sides of the limit to make sure they point to the same value. If they do not, then the left-hand and right-hand limit have to be specified separately.

13. The derivative can be defined in terms of limits. The derivative is the slope between two points where the distance between the x value approaches zero.

Exercises

1. In the following graph, what is the limit as x approaches 2 from the left and the right? What is the actual value of the function at $x = 2$? Write the answer using limit notation.

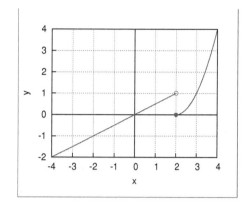

Evaluate the following limits without using ϵ:

2. What is $\lim\limits_{x \to 5} 4x$?

3. What is $\lim\limits_{x \to 0} \frac{x^3}{x-1}$?

4. What is $\lim\limits_{x \to 5} \frac{x^2 - 25}{x - 5}$?

5. What is $\lim\limits_{x \to 2} \frac{x^2 - 3x + 2}{x - 2}$?

Solve the following limits by adding in ϵ (remember to take both the right-hand and left-hand limits):

6. Find $\lim\limits_{x \to 2} \frac{x^3 - 8}{6x - 12}$

7. Find $\lim\limits_{x \to -2} \frac{x^3 + 8}{x + 2}$

8. Find $\lim\limits_{x \to 0} \frac{x}{x^2}$.

9. Find $\lim\limits_{x \to 1} \frac{(x-1)^2}{x-1}$.

Chapter 29

Limits: Finding Results Near Infinity

In this part of the book, we are spending a lot of time thinking about the infinitely big and the infinitely small. In this chapter we will look at what I think is the most important use of limits—examining the infinite.

Interestingly, a lot of functions have values that are very stable out towards infinity, even if they aren't very stable elsewhere. Let's say that we have the following function: $f(x) = \frac{x^2+5}{2x^2-1000x-300}$. What is the value of this function at infinity (i.e., where $x = \infty$)?

We can notate this question using limit notation. We can write this as:

$$\lim_{x \to \infty} \frac{x^2 + 5}{2x^2 - 1000x - 300}$$

What we will find is that, in a number of cases, the limit towards infinity is actually easier to compute than most other values.

29.1   Simple Infinite Limits Using Hyperreals

Many simple limits towards infinity can be solved just by using hyperreals and then taking the standard part, similar to what we did in Chapter 28. However, instead of adding an infinitesimal to x, we are going to substitute x with a particular hyperreal value for infinity. Since ω in the hyperreals is one possible value for ∞ in the reals, ∞ can be substituted with ω, and we can evaluate using our standard rules of ω.

Let's look at the following limit:

$$\lim_{x \to \infty} \frac{1}{x}$$

If we substitute ω in for infinity we get:

$$\lim_{x \to \infty} \frac{1}{x} = \frac{1}{\omega}$$
$$= \omega^{-1}$$

Using our rules of hyperreals, you will notice that the standard part of this number is zero. Therefore, we can say that the limit is zero.

Limits to infinity can be a real number, they can be zero, they can be positive infinity or negative infinity, or they can be undefined.

— **Example 29.1**

Find $\lim x \to \infty \frac{x^2-3}{x}$.

To solve this, we will replace x with ω and use our rules for hyperreals:

$$\lim_{x\to\infty} \frac{x^2 - 3}{x} = \frac{\omega^2 - 3}{\omega}$$
$$= \frac{\omega^2}{\omega} - \frac{3}{\omega}$$
$$= \omega - 3\omega^{-1}$$

This is a hyperreal of order one. Since the order is positive, the standard part of this is an infinity. Since the coefficient of the highest order term is positive, it is a positive infinity, or ∞.

— **Example 29.2**

Find $\lim x \to \infty \frac{2x-3}{5x}$.

To solve this, we will replace x with ω and use our rules for hyperreals:

$$\lim_{x\to\infty} \frac{2x - 3}{5x} = \frac{2\omega - 3}{5\omega}$$
$$= \frac{2\omega}{5\omega} - \frac{3}{5\omega}$$
$$= \frac{2}{5} - \frac{3}{5}\omega^{-1}$$

This is a zero order hyperreal, so that means that the standard part is simply $\frac{2}{5}$.

29.2 Looking at the Infinite

What's interesting about examining infinity is that things that are important on the short term cease to be important at all when talking about infinity. Let's look at the function we saw in at the beginning of the chapter to see what we are talking about:

$$f(x) = \frac{x^2 + 5}{2x^2 - 1000x - 300}$$

Let's look at the top half of the fraction: $x^2 + 5$. Now, at $x = 0$ the expression is $0 + 5$. The dominating part of that expression is the 5. The x plays no part.

At $x = 2$, it becomes $4 + 5$. Here, the x and the 5 are about equally important to the final outcome.

At $x = 3$, it becomes $9 + 5$. Here, the x is twice as dominant as the 5.

Let's look out further, at $x = 1000$. Here, the expression becomes $1000000 + 5$. The x^2 is totally dominating the expression, and the 5 is more-or-less a rounding error—essentially inconsequential to the value. As x gets bigger, this will become more and more the case. The 5 is essentially inconsequential to the formula as x gets bigger.

Now let's look at the denominator: $2x^2 - 1000x - 300$.

At $x = 0$, none of the x terms have any consequence. The value is -300. At $x = 2$, the middle term dominates: $8 - 2000 - 300 = -2292$. From here for quite a ways, the middle term will continue to dominate.

Now, let's fast-forward to $x = 10000$. What happens here? You get $200000000 - 10000000 - 300 = 189999700$. Now, the first term ($2x^2$) is starting to dominate. This term will continue to get more and more prominent as x gets larger and larger.

Infinity is unfathomably large. Therefore, if anything has *any* sort of long-term advantage, it will win out in the long run.

Now, in the numerator of our function ($x^2 + 5$), as x gets larger and larger, the 5 gets less and less important. So, when we get close to infinity, the x^2 is *infinitely* more important than the 5, so we can simplify the numerator to x^2! Likewise, on the denominator ($2x^2 - 1000x - 300$), when we get close to infinity, the only term that really matters is $2x^2$—the other terms become less and less important, and, at infinity, are *infinitely* less important.

Therefore, as x approaches infinity, the only relevant term on the top is x^2 and the only relevant term on the bottom is $2x^2$. Therefore, our problem reduces to:

$$\lim_{x \to \infty} \frac{x^2}{2x^2}$$

By simply dividing out x^2 from both sides, this reduces to $\frac{1}{2}$.

Therefore, we can say:

$$\lim_{x \to \infty} \frac{x^2}{2x^2} = \frac{1}{2}$$

So, for any polynomial fraction, you can find the limit behavior at infinity by reducing the numerator and denominator to only their most significant (i.e., highest power) factors.

— Example 29.3

Find $\lim\limits_{x \to \infty} \frac{2x^2 - 6x^4 + x - 10}{2x^4 + 3x^3 + 3x^2 - 10x - 20}$.

Because we are taking a limit to infinity, the lesser factors drop off. The highest factor on the numerator is $-6x^4$, and the highest factor on the denominator is $2x^4$. Therefore, for an infinite limit, we can reduce this to:

$$\lim_{x \to \infty} \frac{-6x^4}{2x^4} = \frac{-6}{2}$$
$$= -3$$

29.3　Infinite Limits on Unbalanced Polynomial Fractions

If the numerator and denominator of a fraction are polynomials of different degrees then the limit will tend towards either zero or positive or negative infinity.

If the denominator has the higher degree, then the limit will be zero. To understand why, imagine the term $\frac{1}{x}$. As x gets larger and larger, our 1 gets divided into more and more pieces, so the pieces themselves get smaller and smaller. If 1 is divided into an infinite number of pieces, it gets infinitely small (i.e., an infinitesimal). In other words, it gets infinitely close to zero. Therefore, whenever the denominator has a higher degree, after dividing out, the denominator will have some x left over, so it will act like $\frac{1}{x}$.

—　　Example 29.4

Find $\lim\limits_{x \to \infty} \frac{x^3 - x^2 + 100}{x^5 - 200x^2}$

If we reduce this for evaluation, we get:

$$\lim_{x \to \infty} \frac{x^3}{x^5}$$

If we divide this out, we get:

$$\lim_{x \to \infty} \frac{1}{x^2}$$

Therefore, as x approaches infinity, the value of this function will approach zero. This is the same as our rules for hyperreals.

Thus:

$$\lim_{x \to \infty} \frac{x^3 - x^2 + 100}{x^5 - 200x^2} = 0$$

If the numerator has the higher degree, the function will go towards either positive or negative infinity. Whether it is positive or negative will depend on the sign of the largest term of *both* the numerator and the denominator.

— **Example 29.5**

Find $\lim\limits_{x \to \infty} \frac{2x^5 - x^3}{5x^4 + 500}$

Since we are looking at infinite limits, the numerator and denominator reduce to their highest degree term. This gives us $\lim\limits_{x \to \infty} \frac{2x^5}{5x^4}$. If we divide out both sides, that leaves us with $\frac{2x}{5}$. As x gets closer and closer to infinity, the numerator will grow to infinity.

Thus we can say:

$$\lim_{x \to \infty} \frac{2x^5 - x^3}{5x^4 + 500} = \infty$$

29.4 Applying Infinite Limits to Life

When we look at infinite limits, what is it that we are seeing? In the long run, a function will be dominated by the highest-degree factor. In the long run, the lower-degree factors don't even merit consideration.

However, in the near-term, oftentimes the lower-degree factors dominate. When we looked at $\frac{x^2 + 5}{2x^2 - 1000x - 300}$, the lower terms definitely dominated near zero. On the denominator, the middle term dominated for a long, long time. However, no matter how big your other terms are, in the long run, the result will be controlled by the dominating factors.

Virtue is based on living according to things which dominate in the long term. We can see from math that if we focus on what is most significant, that wins out over the long term. In the short term, it may seem to be unproductive or unfruitful. However, what limits show us is that all of the local vicissitudes in life don't really matter in long-term decision-making, What really matters is the dominant factor.

The lesser terms may seem important. They may look important. They may *feel* important. They may impact your life more *right now*. However, taking a long-term view tells us that we should not worry about the here and now, but focus on the important things such as virtue, which will have everlasting importance.

Take, for instance, Jesus' commandment to "do unto others as you would have them do unto you." In the short term, this is usually a detriment to yourself. I am doing something for someone else, and therefore they are getting my time and/or my stuff. I'm not getting squat.

The problem is, if I focus on myself, and if everybody else focuses on themselves, and we do that for a long time, then everybody winds up fighting each other for every little table scrap. We are all concerned about our own stuff, and everybody lives in a society where nobody is looking at for anybody else. However, if you choose to follow what Jesus says and "do unto others as you would have them do unto you," then at least the people around you will get the benefit of living in a society where someone cares about them in a significant way. Some of them may see that, and then they may choose to live in a similar way themselves. Eventually, if the whole society "does unto others" in this way, everybody prospers (eventually). In this scenario, *everybody* gets to live in a society where everybody cares for each other.

However, you can't get there just thinking about the near-term. If everyone's concern was just for their immediate benefit, "do unto others" would fail as a concept. However, when everyone looks to the long-term benefit rather than the short-term, then the whole society prospers in the long-term. For the people who first start the trend, the outcome is not necessarily good (we crucified Jesus, just as a reminder). However, if you keep in mind the long-term goal, then you can see that the way to really impact the future is to focus on what has significant lasting value rather than what is immediately gratifying.

Similarly, the Bible says to seek God's kingdom. According to the Bible, God's kingdom is an *everlasting* kingdom. Therefore, the rules are meant to not optimize for the moment, but optimize for the infinite limit. Understanding and applying the concepts of limit behavior will help us see which things we need to focus on and which things we need to let go of.

Oftentimes in our lives, we get stuck because all we can see is the present moment and maybe a few years or a few decades in the future. The Bible tells us that this is but a brief, fleeting moment in the scheme of things. If we focus on the here and now we will miss the things of long-term importance, and they will be all that matters in the future. The importance of the other things will become infinitely less as time progresses to infinity.

Likewise, we can use this perspective of God's kingdom when analyzing public policies. We need to not look towards the short-term gains, but towards long-term ones. There are many political systems that focus almost entirely on short-term effects. John Maynard Keynes criticized the long-term view by saying, "The long run is a misleading guide to current affairs. In the long run we are all dead."

Keynes is actually right to some extent. The long run *is* a misleading guide to current affairs, *if the most important things are the current affairs.* However, if the goal is to optimize the long run, then spending too much time worrying over the current affairs seems like a counterproductive practice. Today will pass, our policies should focus on the future.[1]

You can also see this in congressional budget planning in the United States. The congress often does ten-year budget plans. The problem, though, is that a ten-year budget can be used to mask long-term difficulties.

For instance, if you want to spend a lot but tax a little, you can simply start taxing early, but save the spending for later years. To put it in simple terms, let's say I need a ten dollars a year for a benefit. However, I only want to tax five dollars a year. Well, what I can do is to delay the benefits by five years. That way, it looks like it breaks even on a ten-year budget. However, in the long run, it is unsustainable, because every year after that, I am going to be taxing five dollars but spending ten. I can claim a "balanced budget" when I pass such a bill, because congress only looks at the ten-year claims.

While a ten-year budget may have some practical benefits, the real examinations should be on the limit behavior of policies and spending. What these policies look like in ten years is important, but what they look like way down the road, especially into future generations, is more important. The behavior towards infinity could be calculated using limits, but, sadly, it isn't.

Additionally, if you noticed, analyzing the infinite behavior of functions is often *easier* than analyzing their short-term behaviors, because fewer factors dominate the long term. Oftentimes, people trying to point us in the wrong direction will state a multiplicity of shoft-term factors that they want us to think about to make the issues seem complicated. However, often, the number of factors which are important for the long term are very small and manageable.

Thinking about limit behavior towards infinity is not only beneficial for the long-term, but, as the mathematics of limits show, is often simpler.

---

[1]Just to be precise, Keynes' actual view was that we should focus on the "middle term"—that is, he wasn't espousing hedonism, but rather that today's policies should be for today's people. That is, for Keynes, since we will all be dead by the time that the long term comes around, having plans that focus on the long term (i.e., when we are long past dead) are pretty useless for the people today. I don't think that middle-term thinking is necessarily bad in all cases, but the long term should always dominate our considerations.

29.5   Non-limiting Functions

Some functions do not show long-term limiting behavior. Others will have a long-term limiting behavior that restricts to a range of values rather than a specific value.

For instance, the function $\sin(x)$ vacillates back-and-forth between -1 and 1 forever. That means it will never *converge* on any particular value. So the limit of $\sin(x)$ as x approaches infinity is actually the range of -1 to 1.

This doesn't mean that all functions involving $\sin(x)$ will have this behavior, though. Think about the function $\frac{\sin(x)}{x}$. As x approaches infinity, $\sin(x)$ will waffle between -1 and 1, but the denominator will approach infinity. Since the range of the numerator, $\sin(x)$, is restricted, that means that the long-term limit of this function will be 0. This is because, as the denominator increases in value, the numerator will be divided into smaller and smaller pieces. The biggest piece the numerator could possibly be is 1, and the standard part of $\frac{1}{\omega}$ is zero.

29.6   Integrating to Infinity

Now that we know how to evaluate functions at infinity, it turns out that we can even take definite integrals of certain functions all the way out to infinity.

Take a look at the graph of the equation $y = \frac{1}{x^2}$:

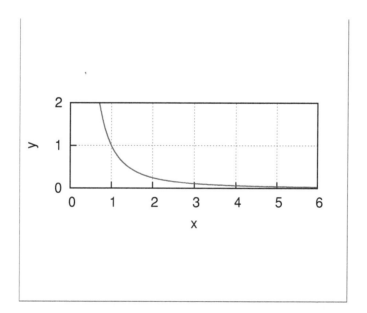

As the graph goes further to the right, notice how the y value gets closer and closer to zero. It never actually reaches zero, but zero is the limit (which you can check yourself if you wish). In fact, even though there is an infinitely long space to the right which has some tiny area, the *total* area of the space in the tail actually has a finite value![2]

Remember, we can use Equation 18.1 to measure the area under a curve using an integral. Using the same techniques here, we can find the area of the tail from $x = 1$ to $x = \infty$. The only difference is that we will have

---

[2]If you actually measure the area up through $x = 0$, the area is infinite again. However, for any positive x value, the total area is finite. We will measure from $x = 1$ in the equations that follow.

to evaluate the infinite behavior using limit reasoning. These are often called **improper integrals** because of the squeamishness of previous mathematicians about infinity, but there is nothing wrong or improper about them.

$$\text{area} = \int_{x=1}^{x=\infty} \frac{1}{x^2}\, dx$$

$$= \int \frac{1}{x^2}\, dx \Bigg|_{x=1}^{x=\infty}$$

$$= -\frac{1}{x}\Bigg|_{x=1}^{x=\infty}$$

If we substitute ω for ∞ we can see how this will work in the long run:

$$\text{area} = -\frac{1}{x}\Bigg|_{x=1}^{x=\infty}$$

$$= -\frac{1}{\omega} - -\frac{1}{1}$$

$$= -\frac{1}{\omega} + 1$$

$$= 1 - \omega^{-1}$$

Here we end up with a hyperreal value. The standard part of this value is merely 1.

Therefore, the area under the curve $y = \frac{1}{x^2}$ from $x = 1$ to $x = \infty$ is 1 square unit.

In order to do problems like this, the normal constraints of calculus apply—the functions need to be smooth and continuous throughout the region you are integrating. Also, just like other limits, it is possible (or even likely) that the value at infinity will either be infinite in one direction or the other, or even indeterminate.

However, if you have an equation that is smooth all the way from $-\infty$ to $+\infty$ then you can actually take the integral to infinity on both sides! Unfortunately, the functions for which this is actually doable are extremely difficult to work with. But it is possible!

29.7   Integrals Through Infinity

Another kind of integral that has been called "improper" are integrals which pass *through* infinity. That is, the graph has vertical asymptotes and becomes infinite at some point. In order to solve these, you must first identify where the asymptote occurs. Then you can separate this into two integrals—one going from the lower bound of the definite integral to the asymptote, and one going from the asymptote to the upper bound of the integral. Then, take the integral of both sides. Finally, add the results together.

You may have to use limits or hyperreals in order to do this successfully.

There are many pitfalls and special situations for this kid of integral, so the present book is not covering this type of integral in depth, nor will the exercises have you doing problems of this kind. I just wanted to make sure you were aware that such integrals existed, and how they might be handled.

Review

In this chapter, we learned:

1. The behavior of functions near infinity can be examined using limits.

2. Some infinite limits can be evaluated by merely substituting in ω and evaluating using the rules of the hyperreals.

3. As x approaches infinity, only the highest-power terms remain important.

4. A polynomial fraction can be reduced to just the highest-power terms on the numerator and denominator in order to find the limit as it approaches infinity.

5. If the numerator of a polynomial fraction has a higher degree than the denominator, then the limit as x approaches infinity will be positive or negative infinity.

6. If the denominator of a polynomial fraction has a higher degree than the denominator, then the limit as x approaches infinity will be zero.

7. Some functions have no specific limit as x approaches infinity.

8. Limits show that long-term and short-term behavior of functions may be radically different.

Exercises

Evaluate the following limits:

1. Find $\lim\limits_{x \to \infty} \frac{3x^5 - 2x^3 + 60x^2 - 300}{4x^5 + 5x^5 - 33x^3 + 1000x}$

2. Find $\lim\limits_{x \to \infty} \frac{5x^3 - 3x^2 + 600}{6x^4 - 500x + 10}$

3. Find $\lim\limits_{x \to \infty} \frac{10x^7 + 600x^3 + 231x^2}{5x^7 - 20x^3 + 209}$

4. Find $\lim\limits_{x \to \infty} \frac{32x^6 - 65x^4 + 33}{88x^5 + 23x^4 - 25x^3 + 22x^2 + 100}$

5. Find $\int_5^\infty \frac{7}{x^3}\,dx$

6. Find $\int_0^\infty x^2\,dx$

7. Find $\int_{-\infty}^{-3} 2x^{-5}$

8. Find $\lim\limits_{x \to \infty} \frac{2x^3 - 5x^9 + 3x^2 + 500}{3x^5 - 2x^4 + 12x^2 + 8x^9 - 5000}$

9. Find $\lim\limits_{x \to -\infty} \frac{x^4 + x^5}{x^3 - 5x^4}$

10. Find $\lim\limits_{x \to \infty} \frac{\sin(x)}{x}$

Chapter 30

Limits: Difficult Limits with L'Hospital

In this chapter, we will look at a method which uses differentials to simplify the process of taking certain types of limits.

30.1 Indeterminate Forms

When analyzing equations at certain points, often times you wind up with what is known as an **indeterminate form**. An indeterminate form means that the result has no actual meaning. The common indeterminate forms are $\frac{0}{0}$, $\frac{\infty}{\infty}$, $0 \cdot \infty$, $\infty - \infty$, 0^0, 1^∞, and ∞^0. These are indeterminate because they can actually result in any real value or none at all.

For example, take $\frac{0}{0}$. How many times can you divide 0 evenly into 0-sized parts? Well, you can do it once, or you can do it a million times. All of those are valid answers. So, even though you have numbers, $\frac{0}{0}$ does not give you any information about a solution. Ultimately, each of the indeterminate forms allows you to substitute it for any possible answer or none at all.

So, if you have a formula that winds up with a result that is an indeterminate form, then you still don't know what the answer is. For instance, let's look at the following function:

$$f(x) = \frac{e^x - 1}{x}$$

Let's evaluate at this function where $x = 0$.

$$f(x) = \frac{e^x - 1}{x}$$
$$f(0) = \frac{e^0 - 1}{0}$$
$$= \frac{1 - 1}{0}$$
$$= \frac{0}{0}$$

So, as you can see, a simple evaluation of this function leads to an indeterminate form. Now, however, let's graph the function. Below is the graph of that same function:

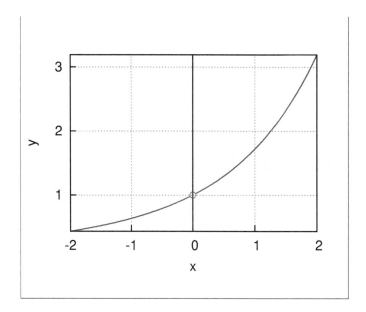

As you can see, the function *looks* like it should have a value at that location. As we have seen in previous chapters, when we have an equation appears to have a value at a point, when the graph seems to be *going to* a point on the graph, we can often evaluate such a function at that point using a limit.

30.2   L'Hosptal's Rule

Oftentimes our standard limit tools don't do the job for indeterminate forms, or at least not easily enough. If the limit we are looking at is of the form $\frac{0}{0}$ or $\frac{\infty}{\infty}$, there is a special rule that allows use to solve for the limit more easily, known as **L'Hospital's Rule** (pronounced "Low Pit All").[1] L'Hospital's Rule states that if we have one of these two indeterminate forms, we can find the limit by simply creating a new fraction made by taking the differential of the top (numerator) and the differential of the bottom (denominator) of the original fraction and evaluating again.

So, in our original equation, we had:

$$f(x) = \frac{e^x - 1}{x}$$

Therefore, to apply L'Hospital's Rule, we take the differential of the numerator and divide it by the differential of the denominator.

The top of the fraction is $e^x - 1$. The differential of this is just $e^x \, dx$.

The bottom of the fraction is simply x. The derivative of this is just dx.

Therefore, we can find the derivative by evaluating $\frac{e^x \, dx}{dx}$ at 0. This is is easy to evaluate. First, we will use basic algebra to reduce the fraction:

$$\frac{e^x \, dx}{dx} = \frac{e^x}{1} = e^x$$

---

[1] L'Hospital's Rule applies for $\frac{\infty}{\infty}$ regardless of whether either infinity is positive or negative.

Now we will just substitute in 0 for x:

$$e^0 = 1$$

So, the value (Technically, the limit) of our original function at $x = 0$ is 1.

The official form of L'Hospital's Rule is:

$$\text{If } \lim_{x \to c} f(x) = \lim_{x \to c} g(x) = 0 \text{ or } \infty$$

$$\text{Then } \lim_{x \to c} \frac{f(x)}{g(x)} = \lim_{x \to c} \frac{d(f(x))}{d(g(x))} \tag{30.1}$$

In other words, if you are trying to evaluate a function at a particular x value and you wind up with a fraction of either $\frac{0}{0}$ or $\frac{\infty}{\infty}$ (and *only* those values), you can apply this rule. The rule says that we can, for this point only, rewrite our fraction by replacing it with a new fraction made from taking the differentials of the numerator and the denominator. This new fraction can then be evaluated at x to give you your answer.

Now, there are some prerequisites to using L'Hospital's Rule:

1. It only applies to fractions.

2. The fraction has to result in an indeterminate form at the point we are looking at (either $\frac{0}{0}$ or $\frac{\infty}{\infty}$).

3. Both the top and bottom of the fractions have to be continuous and differentiable (smooth) at the point where we are looking for the limit.

4. Both the numerator and denominator of the fractions have to have limits that exist. If the function is differentiable, this is usually the case.

However, when those are satisfied, you can use L'Hospital's Rule with confidence. Sometimes you will get another indeterminate form. In such a case, you can simply apply L'Hospital's Rule again to get your answer, until you reach a form that is not indeterminate. However, if you try to apply L'Hospital's Rule where there is not an indeterminate form, *you will not get a correct answer.*

— **Example 30.1**

Find the following limit:

$$\lim_{x \to 0} \frac{x \tan(x)}{\sin(3x)}$$

So, in the numerator we have a zero because x is going to zero. In the denominator we have zero because $\sin(0) = 0$. Thus we have the indeterminate form $\frac{0}{0}$. This means we can apply L'Hosptal's Rule.

Therefore:

$$\lim_{x \to 0} \frac{x \tan(x)}{\sin(3x)} = \lim_{x \to 0} \frac{D(x \tan(x))}{D(\sin(3x))}$$

$$D(x \tan(x)) = x \sec^2(x) + \tan(x)$$

$$D(\sin(3x)) = 3 \cos(3x)$$

$$\lim_{x \to 0} \frac{x \sec^2(x) + \tan(x)}{3 \cos(3x)} = \frac{0}{1} = 0$$

Thus, the limit of $\frac{x \tan(x)}{\sin(3x)}$ as x approaches 0 is 0.

30.3 Proving L'Hospital's Rule

L'Hospital's Rule is a little counterintuitive. Why does this work? And why only for indeterminate forms? The proof itself makes the result a little more clear.

The simplest proof to show is for the case of $\frac{0}{0}$. We are trying to show the following:

$$\lim_{x \to c} \frac{f(x)}{g(x)} = \lim_{x \to c} \frac{f'(x)}{g'(x)}$$

In theory, we can prove an equality like this either by converting the left-hand side into the right-hand side, *or* by converting the right-hand side into the left-hand side. We will do the latter because it allows us to make use of a lot more knowledge about the functions.

In order to convert the right-hand side into the left-hand side, we need to expand the right-hand side of this equation using our trusty general definition of the derivative (Equation 7.4):

$$f'(x) = \frac{f(x + h) - f(x)}{h}$$

So, we can then apply this equation to the right-hand side of our equation to convert $f'(x)$ and $g'(x)$ into formulas involving just $f(x)$ and $g(x)$:

$$\frac{f'(x)}{g'(x)} = \frac{\frac{f(x+h)-f(x)}{h}}{\frac{g(x+h)-g(x)}{h}}$$

We can then manipulate this a bit to get rid of the bare hs:

$$\frac{\frac{f(x+h)-f(x)}{h}}{\frac{g(x+h)-g(x)}{h}} = \frac{h \cdot (f(x + h) - f(x))}{h \cdot (g(x + h) - g(x))} = \frac{f(x + h) - f(x)}{g(x + h) - g(x)}$$

Now, we need to remember that $f(0)$ and $g(0)$ *are both zero*! Remember, that's why we did this rule to begin with, because we found out that they are zero. Therefore, we can rewrite this with $f(x)$ and $g(x)$ replaced with zeroes:

$$\frac{f(x+h) - f(x)}{g(x+h) - g(x)} = \frac{f(x+h) - 0}{g(x+h) - 0} = \frac{f(x+h)}{g(x+h)}$$

Now, since this is based on the derivative, we know that h is going towards zero. Therefore, we can say that:

$$\lim_{h \to 0} \frac{f(x+h)}{g(x+h)} = \frac{f(x)}{g(x)}$$

Therefore, we can see that in the special case of $\frac{0}{0}$, the $\frac{f(x)}{g(x)}$ is equivalent to $\frac{f'(x)}{g'(x)}$.

This also gets us the case of $\frac{\infty}{\infty}$ as well, because what is $\frac{0}{0}$ except $\frac{\frac{1}{\infty}}{\frac{1}{\infty}}$!

You may have noticed that, in the beginning of the chapter, we talked about L'Hospital's rule in terms of differentials, and now we are talking about it in terms of derivatives. However, in functions of a single variable, a ratio of differentials is the same as the ratio of derivatives. The ratio of differentials is $\frac{f'(x)\,dx}{g'(x)\,dx}$. However, just by reassociating the fraction, this becomes $\frac{f'(x)}{g'(x)}\frac{dx}{dx} = \frac{f'(x)}{g'(x)}$. Thus, you can view L'Hospital's rule either as taking differentials or derivatives, and they will both give you the same answer.

30.4 Other Indeterminate Forms

While L'Hospital's Rule can only be used *directly* for the forms $\frac{0}{0}$ and $\frac{\infty}{\infty}$, if you have one of the other indeterminate forms, you can usually transform it into a form that is workable with L'Hospital's Rule. To understand these transformations, you just have to realize that $0 = \frac{1}{\infty}$ and $\infty = \frac{1}{0}$.

30.4.1 Indeterminate Forms of the Type $0 \cdot \infty$

The first type we will look at is of the type $0 \cdot \infty$. The way to work this type of a problem is to realize that, 0 can, in some ways, be viewed as the reciprocal of ∞. Therefore, $0 \cdot \infty = 0 \cdot \frac{1}{\frac{1}{\infty}}$. This is equivalent to $\frac{0}{0}$.

To see how to do this in real life, let us take a look at a particular problem:

$$\lim_{x \to 0^+} x \ln(x)$$

Note that we have to take the right-hand limit because $\ln(x)$ is undefined to the left of 0. However, as x approaches 0, $\ln(x)$ approaches infinity, so this expression becomes $0 \cdot \infty$. This is an indeterminate form (see Section 30.1) but it does not match the form needed for L'Hospital's Rule.

However, note that we said that $0 = \frac{1}{\infty}$. Therefore, if we transformed the left-hand side of this expression to its $\frac{1}{\infty}$ form, then we could simply multiply it through to get $\frac{\infty}{\infty}$.

So, instead of x we will substitute in $\frac{1}{\frac{1}{x}}$. You can see that this is equivalent to x (two reciprocals give you back the original number), but it is written so that the bottom half will evaluate to infinity ($\frac{1}{0}$ yields infinity). Now, this is the *exact equivalent* of the previous expression.

However, it can be substituted it in for the previous expression and get a form workable by L'Hospital's Rule:

$$\lim_{x \to 0^+} x \ln(x) = \lim_{x \to 0^+} \frac{1}{\frac{1}{x}} \ln(x) = \lim_{x \to 0^+} \frac{\ln(x)}{\frac{1}{x}}$$

This is exactly equivalent to our first expression, but it is now in a form for which L'Hospital's Rule works.

$$\lim_{x \to 0^+} \frac{\ln(x)}{\frac{1}{x}} = \lim x \to 0^+ \frac{\frac{1}{x}}{\frac{1}{-x^2}} \qquad \text{use L'Hospital's rule}$$

$$= \lim x \to 0^+ \frac{-x^2}{x} \qquad \text{convert to a nicer fraction}$$

$$= \lim x \to 0^+ - x \qquad \text{divide by } x$$

$$= 0 \qquad \text{evaluate}$$

30.4.2   Indeterminate Forms of the Type $\infty - \infty$

The form $\infty - \infty$ can be solved by transforming each infinity into $\frac{1}{0}$ and then joining the fractions through cross-multiplication. Let's look at the following limit to see how this works:

$$\lim_{x \to 0} \frac{1}{x} - \frac{1}{\sin(x)} = \infty - \infty \qquad \text{Indeterminate form}$$

$$\lim_{x \to 0} \frac{1}{x} - \frac{1}{\sin(x)} = \lim_{x \to 0} \frac{\sin(x) - x}{x \sin(x)} \qquad \text{cross-multiply to make a single fraction}$$

$$\frac{\sin(x) - x}{x \sin(x)} = \frac{0}{0} \qquad \text{confirm that this is a matching indeterminate form}$$

$$\frac{\sin(x) - x}{x \sin(x)} = \lim_{x \to 0} \frac{\cos(x) - 1}{x \cos(x) + \sin(x)} \qquad \text{apply L'Hospital's Rule}$$

$$= \frac{\cos(0) - 1}{0 \cos(0) + \sin(0)} \qquad \text{substitute}$$

$$= \frac{0}{0} \qquad \text{another indeterminate form}$$

This resulted in an indeterminate form, but that's just fine, because we can apply L'Hospital's rule again!

$$\lim_{x \to 0} \frac{\cos(x) - 1}{x \cos(x) + \sin(x)} = \lim_{x \to 0} \frac{-\sin(x)}{-x \sin(x) + \cos(x) + \cos(x)} \qquad \text{re-apply L'Hospital's Rule}$$

$$= \frac{-\sin(0)}{0 \sin(0) + \cos(0) + \cos(0)} \qquad \text{evaluate at 0}$$

$$= \frac{0}{0 + 1 + 1} \qquad \text{evaluate sine and cosine}$$

$$= \frac{0}{2} = 0 \qquad \text{final result}$$

30.4.3 Indeterminate forms of Type 1^∞, 0^0, and ∞^0

The exponential versions of indeterminate forms are a little tougher to analyze because you have to use logarithms to convert them. Let's look at one of the form ∞^0:

$$\lim_{x\to 0} \frac{1}{x}^x$$

Let's assume the result is some constant C. Then we can convert this to an equation:

$$C = \lim_{x\to 0} \frac{1}{x}^x$$

If we keep in mind that we are solving for C, then we can take the logarithm of both sides:

$$\ln(C) = \lim_{x\to 0} \ln\left(\frac{1}{x}^x\right) \qquad \text{take the logarithm of both sides}$$

$$= \lim_{x\to 0} x \ln\left(\frac{1}{x}\right) \qquad \text{remove exponent through logarithm rules}$$

$$= 0 \cdot \infty \qquad \text{this form is convertible to L'Hospital's Rule}$$

$$= \lim_{x\to 0} \frac{1}{\frac{1}{x}} \ln\left(\frac{1}{x}\right)$$

$$= \lim_{x\to 0} \frac{\ln(\frac{1}{x})}{\frac{1}{x}} \qquad \text{form for L'Hospital's Rule}$$

Now we can apply L'Hospital's rule to obtain a result:

$$\ln(C) = \lim_{x\to 0} \frac{\ln(\frac{1}{x})}{\frac{1}{x}}$$

$$= \lim_{x\to 0} \frac{-\frac{1}{x}}{-\frac{1}{x^2}} \qquad \text{applying L'Hospital's Rule}$$

$$= \lim_{x\to 0} \frac{x^2}{x} \qquad \text{rearranging the fraction}$$

$$= \lim_{x\to 0} x \qquad \text{simplifying}$$

$$\ln(C) = 0 \qquad \text{intermediate result}$$

To get the final result back, we just exponentiate both sides:

$$\ln(C) = 0$$

$$e^{\ln(C)} = e^0 \qquad \text{exponentiate both sides}$$

$$C = 1 \qquad \text{final result}$$

Don't forget the step at the end! If you used a logarithm to pull an exponent out in front, don't forget to reverse this at the end to get the final result!

Using these techniques, you can usually find the limit of indeterminate forms.

One important note, however—the result of an indeterminate form may wind up being infinity. That is perfectly acceptable—it is a determinate result. You only re-apply L'Hospital's Rule if the result is *indeterminate* (i.e., one of the forms discussed in Section 30.1).

All of the exponential indeterminate forms, 1^∞, 0^0, and ∞^0 can be evaluated in this way. The steps are:

1. Assuming the result is equal to some constant C.

2. Take the logarithm of both sides.

3. The logarithm form can then be converted into $\frac{0}{0}$ or $\frac{\infty}{\infty}$ for L'Hospital's rule.

4. Once in the proper form for L'Hospital's rule, apply L'Hospital's rule to get a result.

5. Since you took the logarithm of C in step 2, you now need to exponentiate both sides to get the result.

If Step 4 results in another indeterminate form, you can repeat Step 4 (or, depending on the particular form, Steps 1–4) as many times as necessary.

30.5   Summary of Indeterminate Forms

While the canonical L'Hospital's Rule is applied to indeterminate forms of the form $\frac{0}{0}$ or $\frac{\infty}{\infty}$, we have seen that, by transforming them about a bit, we can apply L'Hospital's rule to all seven types of indeterminate forms.

Figure 30.1 shows the transformations discussed in this chapter. To use the table, start by using the first column to figure out which form applies to your particular problem. Then, use the second column to assign a label of A or B to each part of your problem, according to its form. Finally, use the formula in the third column to apply L'Hospital's rule to your problem.

C is the resulting number. Notice that some of the forms result in $\ln(C)$ rather than C. In those cases, you will need to exponentiate your result to get rid of the $\ln()$ and get the final C value.

———   Example 30.2

Find $\lim\limits_{x \to -\infty} x\,e^x$.

Since the infinity is negative, this has the form of $\infty \cdot 0$ because x will become a negative infinity, and $e^{-\infty}$ is essentially zero. Looking at Figure 30.1, you can see that, for this form, we set A to the zero term and B to the infinite term.[a] Therefore, $A = e^x$ and $B = x$.

Figure 30.1: L'Hospital's Rule Applied to Various Indeterminate Forms

Form	A and B	Solution Method
$\frac{0}{0}$	$\frac{A}{B}$	$C = \frac{\mathrm{d}(A)}{\mathrm{d}(B)}$
$\frac{\infty}{\infty}$	$\frac{A}{B}$	$C = \frac{\mathrm{d}(A)}{\mathrm{d}(B)}$
$0 \cdot \infty$	$A \cdot B$	$C = \frac{\mathrm{d}(B)}{\mathrm{d}\left(\frac{1}{A}\right)}$
$\infty - \infty$	$A - B$	$C = \frac{\mathrm{d}\left(\frac{1}{B} - \frac{1}{A}\right)}{\mathrm{d}\left(\frac{1}{AB}\right)}$
1^{∞}	A^B	$\ln(C) = \frac{\mathrm{d}(\ln(A))}{\mathrm{d}\left(\frac{1}{B}\right)}$
0^0	A^B	$\ln(C) = \frac{\mathrm{d}(\ln(A))}{\mathrm{d}\left(\frac{1}{B}\right)}$
∞^0	A^B	$\ln(C) = \frac{\mathrm{d}(\ln(A))}{\mathrm{d}\left(\frac{1}{B}\right)}$

Using the rule, we find:

$$C = \frac{\mathrm{d}(x)}{\mathrm{d}\left(\frac{1}{e^x}\right)}$$

$$= \frac{\mathrm{d}(x)}{\mathrm{d}(e^{-x})}$$

$$= \frac{\mathrm{d}x}{-e^{-x}\,\mathrm{d}x}$$

$$= -\frac{1}{e^{-x}}$$

$$= -e^x$$

As x approaches $-\infty$, this becomes:

$$C = -e^x$$

$$= -e^{-\infty}$$

$$= -\frac{1}{e^{\infty}}$$

$$= 0$$

---

[a]Note that technically this form will work either way (with either term being A or B), but we just picked the one to match what is given in the table. Additionally, on occasion, it will matter how you convert this into a standard form for L'Hospital's Rule. However, those are pretty exceptional circumstances, and we will only note them here.

--- **Example 30.3**

Find $\lim\limits_{x \to 1}(2x - 2)^{x-1}$.

If $x = 1$, this is of the form 0^0. Therefore, find the 0^0 form in the table. Here, set $A = 2x - 2$ and $B = x - 1$. Using the rule, we can see that:

$$\ln(C) = \frac{d(\ln(A))}{d\left(\frac{1}{B}\right)}$$

$$= \frac{d(\ln(2x - 2))}{d((x - 1)^{-1})}$$

$$= \frac{2\frac{1}{2x-2}\,dx}{-(x - 1)^{-2}\,dx}$$

$$= -\frac{\frac{2}{2x-2}}{(x - 1)^{-2}}$$

$$= -\frac{2}{2x - 2}(x - 1)^2$$

$$= -\frac{1}{x - 1}(x - 1)^2$$

$$= -(x - 1)$$

$$= 1 - x$$

As x approaches 1 this becomes:

$$\ln(C) = 1 - 1$$

$$= 0$$

However, on the left we have $\ln(C)$ rather than C, so we need to exponentiate both sides:

$$\ln(C) = 0$$

$$e^{\ln(C)} = e^0$$

$$C = 1$$

Therefore, the limit is 1.

Review

In this chapter, we learned:

1. An indeterminate form is the evaluation of a function which leads to on of the following results: $\frac{0}{0}$, $\frac{\infty}{\infty}$, $0 \cdot \infty$, $\infty - \infty$, 0^0, 1^∞, and ∞^0.

2. An indeterminate form is indeterminate because, if evaluated literally, it could result in any value whatsoever.

3. To find the value of a function at a point which yields an indeterminate form, a limit can be used.

4. L'Hospital's Rule states that the limit of an expression of the form $\frac{f(x)}{g(x)}$ which yield an indeterminate form of the forms $\frac{0}{0}$ or $\frac{\infty}{\infty}$ is simply the derivative of the top divided by the derivative of the bottom, or $\frac{f'(x)}{g'(x)}$.

5. Indeterminate forms of the form $0 \cdot \infty$ can be converted into a form workable by L'Hospital's Rule by applying the equivalencies $0 = \frac{1}{\infty}$ and $\infty = \frac{1}{0}$.

6. Indeterminate forms of the form $\infty - \infty$ can be oconverted into a form workable by L'Hospital's rule by applying the above equivalencies and cross-multiplying to yield a fraction that is also an indeterminate form.

7. Indeterminate forms of the exponential variety can be solved by taking the logarithm of the form and then using logarithm rules to get rid of the exponent. When doing this, the answer is the *logarithm* of the limit, so you have to exponentiate it to get a final result.

Exercises

Find the following limits using L'Hospital's Rule:

1. $\lim\limits_{x \to 4} \frac{x^2 - 16}{x - 4}$

2. $\lim\limits_{x \to 0} \frac{\sin(x)}{x}$

3. $\lim\limits_{x \to 0} \frac{2x - \sin(x)}{x}$

4. $\lim\limits_{x \to 1} \frac{x^2 - 1}{x^2 + 3x - 4}$

5. $\lim\limits_{x \to \infty} x \, e^{-2x}$

6. $\lim\limits_{x \to 0} \frac{\sin(x^2)}{x \tan(x)}$

7. $\lim\limits_{x \to \infty} \frac{e^{3x}}{4x + 200}$

8. $\lim\limits_{x \to \infty} \frac{3x + 2^x}{2x + 3^x}$

9. $\lim\limits_{x \to 5^+} \frac{x}{x - 5}$

10. $\lim\limits_{x \to \infty} (1 + \frac{1}{x})^x$

11. $\lim\limits_{x \to \infty} (2 + \frac{1}{3x})^x$

Chapter 31

Conclusion

You made it to the end!

I hope you realize how far you have come in the way that you think about mathematics. You have been asked to think about problems in new ways, even using new numbers. You have looked at the infinitely small and the infinitely large. You have learned how to make the impossible possible.

Calculus is not the end of math, it is merely the gateway that lies between the rote application of memorized formulas and the ability to think about problems and numbers creatively. Calculus gives you not only the formulas you need for the future, but also the process of thinking that you will need on the road ahead.

Yes, you have learned fundamental operations of calculus, which allow you to look at slopes, find maximas and minimas, evaluate areas under curves, and find volumes of strange shapes. However, the process of learning calculus has also taught you to:

1. Bridge between static and dynamic representations of problems. Differentials convert static equations into dynamic ones, and integrals go the other way.

2. Convert estimates into rigorous formulas by reducing the problem to smaller and smaller subproblems and then adding (integrating) over the infinitely small subproblems.

3. Remove barriers on impossible problems by identifying the assumptions that make the problem impossible.

4. Make rigorous use of infinitely small and infinitely big values.

5. Evaluate the long-term results of equations, even out to infinity.

6. Evaluate non-existent points on a graph, and make sense of seemingly non-sensical results such as $\frac{0}{0}$ and $\infty - \infty$.

These are great tools to have, whether you pursue mathematics long-term or not. If you pursue a career as a manager, you will need to be able to switch between thinking of the dynamic aspects of the business and the static aspects of the business. Even if you don't explicitly use derivatives and integrals to do this, your experience with derivatives and integrals should give you an improved intuitive sense. Understanding the nature of long-term behavior and its results will help you no matter what you do in life, as it will help you both mentally and morally. Knowing how to get past impossible problems will help you in every challenging area of your life.

So, whether you continue to pursue mathematics further, or decide that this is plenty for you, I hope you take the lessons you have learned here to heart, and find ways to apply them to all of your life.

Sincerely,

Acknowledgements

I wanted to take the time at this point to say thank you to the people who helped make this book possible. First, I want to thank my wife Christa for her participation in this book. She took my class, read the book, worked the problems, and made suggestions over the whole book.

Second, I want to thank my students (and other test readers) over the last several years. They were my guinea pigs. The whole process of the book started with my deviations from the existing textbook many years ago, and has slowly built up. Over the past two years, students have put up with half-baked ideas, partially-finished (or non-existent) chapters, and other problems that come from using a book in progress. All of them were gracious and helpful, pointing out where the book needed improvements.

Third, I want to thank my cover designers. Christopher Doehling is the artist behind the robot graphics on all of the books, and he is fantastic—not only does he do great work he is great to work with. He seems to just get what I'm trying to accomplish and makes the perfect illustration each time. I also want to thank Jayleen Pepito for doing the layout and numerous small production art tasks. Every time I need something Jayleen has made it happen.

Fourth, I want to thank Chris Peter for supplying the graphics for a few of the chapters. Some of the more advanced graphs I just could not get to work, and Chris made it look easy.

Fifth, I wanted to thank the other people who inspired me on my mathematical journeys overall. Mathematics is not my primary subject, but I have appreciated the encouragement and feedback from many engineers and mathematicians along the way who treated me as a colleague rather than an outsider. These include Eric Holloway, Asatur Khurshudyan, Bob Marks, Winston Ewert, George Montañez, Daniel Lichtblau, Logan Gaastra, Salvador Cordova, David Nemati, Bob Herrmann, David Paige, and Jerome Keisler. Thank you all for your help and patience.

Next, I want to thank my readers! Thank you for taking the time to pick up the book and join me in this adventure. While I hope that most of you did so enthusiastically, I'm sure some of you also did so under duress. Nonetheless, it was for you all that this effort was made. I hope this book has made calculus a joy for you rather than a struggle.

Above all, I want to give thanks to God who makes everything possible. The One bigger than the infinities and smaller than the infinitesimals. The One who reaches out for us when we don't even know we need to reach out to Him, sending Jesus to die for our sin when we didn't even know we needed saving. The world is logically understandable because it was built from God's own Logos. Without that, there would be nothing to calculate.

For all of you, I am continually thankful.

Part V

Appendices

Appendix A

Guide for Instructors

I wrote this book specifically for a regular introductory Calculus class that I teach. The goal of this appendix is to help you understand where I am coming from, what I am doing, and how to make the best use of the book.

A.1 What Makes This Book Different

I love calculus. I really do. I think that it is a beautiful and amazing subject. I want my students to see that beauty and all of the amazing things that are going on.

However, every time I tried to teach from a textbook, I found that the authors of the textbook must have had as their number one goal that they must make students hate calculus. It was both maddening and saddening. So many students get so lost in the beginning of calculus (i.e., during limits) that they spend the rest of their time struggling. And for what purpose?

This book doesn't skip limits, but it recognizes that although limits are a necessary requirement for the *proof* of derivatives, it actually gets in the way in the *learning* of derivatives. Now, I think that limits are important, too, and they aren't left out of the book. They are merely moved to a place where students are more likely to appreciate them.

Most of the decisions of what to cover and when are based on considerations like these. I always ask myself, "what are students *ready* for?" and "what will give the most bang for the buck *at this point*?" You can decide if I have chosen wisely or foolishly, and rearrange your teaching how you wish (I know I did that myself when teaching other books).

A.2 Simplifying Calculus

Calculus has developed over a long history. During that history, many individual techniques have been developed. Some of them overlap considerably.

In fact, in a basic calculus course, students are often taught three entirely different methods of performing differentials! There is explicit differentiation, implicit differentiation, and multivariable differentiation, all of which are taught as if they were almost entirely different beasts.

In this book, we have refactored the process. There is a single, unified method for finding a derivative, and the method is identical for all of these situations. Although we use explicit differentiation as a kind of "training wheels" for new calculus students, starting in Chapter 10 these are all converted to differential rules. The process given is to take a differential and then solve for whatever derivative you are looking for.

For instance, given $y = x^2$, we would first take the differential, which gives $dy = 2x\,dx$ and then solve for the derivative by dividing both sides by dx. The idea that you can take a differential *without* finding a full derivative takes some calculus teachers by surprise. However, the process simplifies everything.

For instance, take $y^2 = x^3$. Instead of an implicit derivative, we will do the same process—find the differential, then take the derivative. The differential $2y\,dy = 3x^2\,dx$. To find the derivative, just solve for $\frac{dy}{dx}$, which yields $\frac{dy}{dx} = \frac{3x^2}{2y}$. Doing it in this way makes the whole process much more understandable for students.

Other simplifications have been employed. For instance, instead of teaching logarithmic differentiation, we simply give the "generalized power rule." Most students and teachers are unaware that there is a simple, straightforward rule for differentiating u^v. While the proof for the differential of u^v is interesting, forcing students to perform this operation every time they need to differentiate something looking like u^v is terribly time-consuming. Considering that we don't force students to re-invent any other differentiation rule, I find it odd that logarithmic differentiation is taught so often when a simple rule will do.

The chain rule is also simplified. Technically, it doesn't need to be its own rule. Substitution is one of the foundation stones of mathematics. Therefore, rather than having a new, specialized rule, students learn to use substitution and apply it everywhere. We do show them that there is a "chain rule" which also does this, but the focus is just on substitution, as that carries over to a much wider variety of situations.

Finally, we introduce the hyperreal number system. This system simplifies many things that students find difficult in calculus, from how limits work to what are differentials. By introducing a number line which explicitly includes infinitesimals, students can have a more concrete understanding of the terms they are dealing with. Using hyperreals for limits also makes the demonstration and proofs of limits much more simple.

On the integral side, while most calculus books focus on the integral as being the area under the curve, a more general idea of the integral as being an infinite sum is introduced in this book, with the area under the curve being just a special case. Thinking of the integral as an infinite sum simplifies a number of the more advanced integral topics.

A.3   What is Important in Calculus?

There are lots of important topics in calculus. However, there are two topics which I think are the most important, but they unfortunately receive the least attention in calculus.

The first is the expansion of your mathematical imagination. The great tools of science and mathematics are not in laboratories, they are inside the imaginations of scientists and mathematicians.

Proofs are important, but they are secondary. Without imagination, you would have nothing to prove, and you wouldn't know how to begin to do so. Imagination is how you reach beyond what you already know. It is how discovery is made.

Proofs allow us to tell ourselves and others whether our imaginations are worthwhile. Some of the things we imagine are pure junk, while others are pure gold. Proofs help us to sort through that. Proofs also tell us the limitations of the things we imagine. They help us say, "oh yeah, in order to prove this theorem I have to assume these other things first." These are all good and beneficial things. However, the productive part is in the imagination.

Therefore, the entire wording of the book asks students to use their imagination. Typically, mathematical writing just lays it out, assuming that students know how to imagine it. Some students know to do this instinctively. However, other students, you actually have to *tell them* to think. They don't even know that they should be imagining these processes.

Because of this, throughout the book there are things where I tell students to "think about" whatever. You might view these as throwaway phrases, but the goal is to help students take ownership of their own imagination. It trains them to start *thinking* about mathematics rather than just trying to apply formulas by rote. The rote application of formulas works for arithmetic, but calculus requires thinking, and thinking requires training students to use their imagination.

The second, though related, thing that I try to teach students is how to build their own formulas. Really, most people don't use calculus, they use formulas that were built using calculus. Therefore, an important part of teaching calculus is to teach students how to build their own formulas.

This can actually be done in algebra as well, but few books and teachers want to take the time, and students may not be intellectually mature enough at that point anyway. However, calculus provides the perfect setup for creating formulas because it is itself a set of metaformulas–formulas about formulas—which allow for creating new formulas from thought processes.

It's hard to come up with something genuinely new, but nonetheless we try to get students to arrive at new material which is not commonly found in textbooks. After showing how to generate the vertex formula for quadratic equations, students have a review problem that asks them to generate the vertex formula for cubic equations. Students are repeatedly asked to take steps that they used to solve a problem and convert it into a formula that they can use going forward.

Many mathematics textbooks don't like that approach because it limits the amount of problems that they can give. If the students develop a formula, then students can get the answer right by using the formula instead of calculus! I don't myself view this as a problem. I hope that students learn to be creative and imaginative enough to do this all the time.

As for specific calculus content, the book has three areas of focus—derivatives, integrals, and infinities. These three all relate to each other. Obviously derivatives and integrals go together hand-in-hand, but most calculus books try to remove the infinite from calculus. Instead, this book dives head first, forcing students to think about the issues and paradoxes surrounding infinities, and then showing how the separation of ordinal and cardinal infinities solve most of those paradoxes, and how the hyperreal number system allows us to use infinities and infinitesimals fairly seamlessly with the rest of mathematics.

The book also includes a lot of topics about problem-solving, and how ideas from calculus can aid in problem-solving. In Chapters 18 and 20, students are shown how to break problems down into smaller, more tractable problems, and how estimates can be made convertible into more exact values. The integral is a special case of this, and shows that if you can make your subproblems infinitely small, the integral can be used to add them back up again. Likewise, Chapter 25 shows a general method for solving impossible problems.

These are the sorts of things that will grow your students imaginations so that they can tackle any problem, mathematical or otherwise.

A.4 The Solution Guide

There is a companion solution guide for this text. Many teachers try to hide the solution guide from their students. I recommend the opposite approach. Students should always refer to the solution guide. It has important material they may have missed in their reading of the chapter, and helps them walk through how to apply the material.

Students should be encouraged that they should try to solve the problem first on their own, and then, if the solution guide shows that they are wrong, they should copy down *both* the solution from the guide *and its explanation.* Going this direction, imagine how much more calculus your students would know if they skipped doing the problems and instead recopied the entire solution manual! So, using the solution guide shouldn't be a problem—they just need to show their work. If they got the answer wrong, they should force themselves to copy every word and every step of the solution guide.

A.5 Teaching Schedule

This book was written to be taught over a one-year period of thirty weeks. The class I wrote this for met once a week for an hour. For small classes, this is enough time for basic instruction on the topics. Different skill levels of students may require more time for review and explanation, but for a small, self-motivated class of students, the course can be done with one hour of instruction per week.

The first few classes covered multiple chapters each week, covering Part 1 in four weeks. Depending on your students' level of knowledge coming into the class, this is likely sufficient. After that, a new chapter is presented each week, though you can make exceptions for difficult content. The goal is to finish Part 2 by week 14 so that the material can be tested on during week 15.

The second semester covers Parts 3 and 4. Chapter 26 covers a lot of topics and could last for multiple weeks for in-depth coverage. I, however, usually pick and choose topics based on the interests of the class and the time available. These topics are interesting but not critically important for first year students, so the goal for this chapter is more exposure than mastery. I usually combine Chapter 24 into one of the other chapters as well because, if students understand integration really well, numeric integration is just an obvious way to approximate it. Therefore, I tend to focus on a true understanding of the integral rather than worrying too much if students recognize how to approximate it.

Additionally, there is a lot of supplemental material in the appendix. One important function of the appendix is that it includes items that are likely needed for standardized tests, but not really essential to understanding calculus itself. Appendix readings can be interspersed with regular readings as needed, and are often referenced from the text itself.

I would appreciate any feedback you have in teaching this book. It will make future editions even better! Feel free to send all feedback and comments to cgucomments@bplearning.net.

Appendix B

Liebniz Notation of Higher Order Differentials

In this appendix, I want to discuss a topic that I feel is very important, but that you probably couldn't care less about—the Leibniz notation for higher order differentials and derivatives. This is a topic that has created a great amount of confusion in the world of mathematics, and I wanted to spend some time clearing it up.

Unfortunately, the standard way of notating second (and higher) derivatives is, well, I guess *wrong* is probably the best way to say it. However, even though it is wrong I have to show it to you because every single book you will read at this time has it written this way.

B.1 The Current Standard Notation for the Second Derivative

As we have seen throughout the book, the way that the first derivative is notated in Leibniz notation is as a fraction of differentials:

$$\frac{dy}{dx}$$

This is the derivative of y with respect to x.

The second derivative is merely the derivative of the derivative. So far, what we have been doing when we want a second derivative is to create a new variable to represent the variable, and then taking the derivative of that new variable. So, if we say $z = \frac{dy}{dx}$, then the second derivative is the derivative of z with respect to x, or $\frac{dz}{dx}$.

However, most books and papers use a special (and, as we will see, incorrect) notation for this second derivative. The notation for the second derivative of y with respect to x is usually given as:

$$\frac{d^2y}{dx^2}$$

The third derivative is given as:

$$\frac{d^3y}{dx^3}$$

And so on. Pay particular attention to where the numbers are placed in the numerator and the denominator. Their placement indicates vastly different meanings.

In Chapter 10, we noted that dy does *not* mean some variable d multiplied by some variable y. Instead, dy is shorthand for "the differential of y," or $d(y)$. Similarly, d^2y does *not* mean that we are squaring some variable d. Instead, it is a shorthand for the differential of the differential. It means that we are applying the differential *twice* to y. In other words, $d^2y = d(dy) = d(d(y))$.

However, in the denominator, the dx^2 does in fact mean that we are squaring dx.

So, in short, if the superscripted number is after the d, then that means that the number indicates how many times the differential operator is applied. If the superscripted number is after the whole differential (i.e., after the variable name), the number indicates the power to which the differential is raised.

In terms of hyperreal numbers (Chapter 27), *both* the second differential *and* the square of the first differential are both second order infinitesimal hyperreals. Therefore, when placed in ratio with each other, you will usually get a real valued result.

Before we go further, *remember that this notation is incorrect.* However, it is is important to note how the notation works so that we can better see what the correct notation for the second derivative is.

B.2   Why the Second Derivative Notation Fails

It is important to take a minute to provide an example of why $\frac{d^2y}{dx^2}$ is not a valid representation for the second derivative. Let's look at a simple example with two simple equations:

$$y = x^3$$

and

$$x = t^2$$

Let's now find the first and second derivatives of y with respect to x using the standard notation:

$$y = x^3$$

$$\frac{dy}{dx} = 3x^2$$

$$\frac{d^2y}{dx^2} = 6x$$

Now, let's take the first and second derivatives of x with respect to t:

$$x = t^2$$

$$\frac{dx}{dt} = 2t$$

$$\frac{d^2x}{dt^2} = 2$$

If we took the notation of the second derivative of y with respect to x ($\frac{d^2y}{dx^2}$) seriously, we could convert this derivative into the second derivative of y with respect to t by multiplying it by $\left(\frac{dx}{dt}\right)^2$. In other words, we *should* be able to do:

$$\frac{d^2y}{dx^2}\left(\frac{dx}{dt}\right)^2 = \frac{d^2y}{dt^2}$$

Now, since $\frac{dx}{dt} = 2t$, then that means that $\left(\frac{dx}{dt}\right)^2 = 4t^2$. Therefore, we should be able to multiply $\frac{d^2y}{dx^2}$ by $4t^2$ to get the second derivative of y with respect to t. If we did that, we would get:

$$\frac{d^2y}{dx^2} = 6x \qquad\qquad \text{the original second derivative}$$

$$\frac{d^2y}{dx^2}\left(\frac{dx}{dt}\right)^2 = 6x \cdot 4t^2 \qquad\qquad \text{multiply each side by } \left(\frac{dx}{dt}\right)^2$$

$$\frac{d^2y}{dt^2} = 6x \cdot 4t^2 \qquad\qquad \text{simplify the left side}$$

$$\frac{d^2y}{dt^2} = 6t^2 \cdot 4t^2 \qquad\qquad \text{replace } x \text{ with its value in terms of } t$$

$$\frac{d^2y}{dt^2} = 24t^4 \qquad\qquad \text{simplify the right-hand side}$$

So, according to this calculation, the second derivative of y with respect to t is $24t^4$.

Now, let's go about it a different way. Let's begin by replacing x with t^2 in the *original* equation, and then find the second derivative. Here is the calculation:

$$y = x^3 \qquad\qquad \text{the original equation}$$

$$y = (t^2)^3 \qquad\qquad \text{because } x = t^2$$

$$y = t^6 \qquad\qquad \text{simplified}$$

$$\frac{dy}{dt} = 6t^5 \qquad\qquad \text{first derivative}$$

$$\frac{d^2y}{dt^2} = 30t^4 \qquad\qquad \text{second derivative}$$

So, with the same starting equations, we found two *conflicting* values for the second derivative of y with respect to t. In the first case, we found that $\frac{d^2y}{dt^2} = 24t^4$, and in the second case we found that $\frac{d^2y}{dt^2} = 30t^4$.

The consensus from mathematicians has been that this is because the second derivative doesn't really express a fraction. It is merely *written* as a fraction to remind us of how it is constructed, but, in reality, we should not consider $\frac{d^2y}{dt^2}$ to be a true fraction. Therefore, when we manipulated it as if it were a fraction, the operation was invalid.

However, another alternative (and the one that I hold to) is that the real problem is that the notation for the second derivative is simply incorrect.

B.3   An Improved Notation for the Second Derivative

So, what should the notation for the second derivative be? Let's start by remembering what the parts of the notation mean. Indeed, d^2y means taking the differential of y twice. Essentially, d^2y is a synonym for $d(d(y))$ and also for $d(dy)$.

On the other hand, dx^2 means to take the whole differential, dx, and square it. In other words, dx^2 means $(dx)^2$.

Now, the second derivative of y with respect to x is the result of taking the derivative of the first derivative $\left(\frac{dy}{dx}\right)$. When we take the derivative, what operations do we do? Well, we first take the differential, and then we divide by dx.

Therefore, let's look and see what happens when we do that to $\frac{dy}{dx}$. Let's start by taking the differential of $\frac{dy}{dx}$:

$$d\left(\frac{dy}{dx}\right) = \frac{dx\,d(dy) - dy\,d(dx)}{dx^2} \qquad \text{application of the quotient rule}$$

$$= \frac{dx\,d^2y - dy\,d^2x}{dx^2} \qquad \text{rewriting } d(dy) \text{ as } d^2y$$

That is the differential of the derivative. The full derivative is found by dividing by this result by dx. This will yield:

$$d\left(\frac{dy}{dx}\right) = \frac{dx\,d^2y - dy\,d^2x}{dx^2} \qquad \text{result from previous operations}$$

$$\frac{d\left(\frac{dy}{dx}\right)}{dx} = \frac{dx\,d^2y - dy\,d^2x}{dx^3} \qquad \text{divide both sides by } dx$$

$$= \frac{dx\,d^2y}{dx^3} - \frac{dy\,d^2x}{dx^3} \qquad \text{splitting the fraction}$$

$$= \frac{d^2y}{dx^2} - \frac{dy}{dx}\frac{d^2x}{dx^2} \qquad \text{simplifying}$$

This last form is what I think of as the "real" second derivative. In other words:

$$y'' = \frac{d\left(\frac{dy}{dx}\right)}{dx} = \frac{d^2y}{dx^2} - \frac{dy}{dx}\frac{d^2x}{dx^2}$$

This is a lot more complicated than the standard notation (i.e., $\frac{d^2y}{dx^2}$), but it comes with the advantage that it actually works like a fraction.

Higher derivatives than the second derivative are derived using the same logic (applying the basic differential rules to the previous derivative), and therefore the resulting formula gets more and more complicated.[1]

B.4 Using the New Notation

So, going back to our example equations of $y = x^3$ and $x = t^2$, can we use our new notation to correctly transform the second derivative of y with respect to x into the second derivative of x with respect to t?

Let's start by just writing down our derivatives using the new notation:

$$y = x^3$$

$$\frac{dy}{dx} = 3x^2$$

$$\frac{d^2y}{dx^2} - \frac{dy}{dx}\frac{d^2x}{dx^2} = 6x$$

$$x = t^2$$

$$\frac{dx}{dt} = 2t$$

$$\frac{d^2x}{dt^2} - \frac{dx}{dt}\frac{d^2t}{dt^2} = 2$$

---

[1]For more information on this method of notating the second derivative, see the paper "Extending the Algebraic Manipulability of Differentials" by Jonathan Bartlett and Asatur Zh. Khurshudyan (https://arxiv.org/abs/1801.09553).

The new notation for the second derivative is more messy and a little unwieldy, but, since it has the benefit of being algebraically correct, we can use it to transform the second derivative of y with respect to x into the second derivative of y with respect to t. In other words, we want to find $\frac{d^2y}{dt^2} - \frac{dy}{dt}$.

The procedure is a bit complex. You can skip it if you find it confusing. It is merely here to show that it works.

$$\frac{d^2y}{dx^2} - \frac{dy}{dx}\frac{d^2x}{dx^2} = 6x \qquad \text{The second derivative of } y \text{ with respect to } x$$

$$\left(\frac{d^2y}{dx^2} - \frac{dy}{dx}\frac{d^2x}{dx^2}\right)\left(\frac{dx}{dt}\right)^2 = 6x \cdot 4t^2 \qquad \text{multiply both sides by } \left(\frac{dx}{dt}\right)^2$$

$$\frac{d^2y}{dt^2} - \frac{dy}{dx}\frac{d^2x}{dt^2} = 6t^2 \cdot 4t^2 \qquad \text{simplify}$$

$$\frac{d^2y}{dt^2} - \frac{dy}{dx}\frac{d^2x}{dt^2} = 24t^4$$

This next step will be a bit of a doozy. We are going to add to both sides the product of the first derivative of y with respect to x and the second derivative of x with respect to t:

$$\frac{d^2y}{dt^2} - \frac{dy}{dx}\frac{d^2x}{dt^2} + \left(\frac{dy}{dx}\right)\left(\frac{d^2x}{dt^2} - \frac{dx}{dt}\frac{d^2x}{dt^2}\right) = 24t^4 + 3x^2 \cdot 2 \qquad \text{applying the operation mentioned above}$$

$$\frac{d^2y}{dt^2} - \frac{dy}{dx}\frac{d^2x}{dt^2} + \frac{dy}{dx}\frac{d^2x}{dt^2} - \frac{dy}{dx}\frac{dx}{dt}\frac{d^2x}{dt^2} = 24t^4 + 6(t^2)^2 \qquad \text{simplifying}$$

$$\frac{d^2y}{dt^2} - \frac{dy}{dx}\frac{dx}{dt}\frac{d^2x}{dt^2} = 24t^4 + 6t^4$$

$$\frac{d^2y}{dt^2} - \frac{dy}{dt}\frac{d^2x}{dt^2} = 30t^4$$

This matches what we found for the second derivative of y with respect to t when we replaced t at the beginning of the operation.

B.5   How Mathematicians Have Gotten By Without the Right Notation

You may be wondering how mathematicians managed to get by without the right notation for so long. It is actually pretty straightforward. First of all, by denouncing the treatment of the second derivative as an actual fraction, mathematicians prevented themselves from doing most operations that would get them into trouble. That is, as long as someone just wrote down $\frac{d^2y}{dx^2}$ as the second derivative, but never tried to pull those two pieces apart, no errors would ensue. It might technically be wrong but not in a way that leads to errors.[2]

However, there were some times when mathematicians *needed* to pull them apart. Most notably, as in our example above, when switching the independent variable used in the second derivative. What they did in these cases was to develop secondary formulas which allowed them to perform these transformations. The formula for switching out the independent variable is known as Faà di Bruno's formula, and it is equivalent to performing the operations we specified above.

---

[2] As an example of why this wouldn't lead to errors, remember that notation is essentially the "name" that is given to an entity. People with glasses are often called "four-eyes." It isn't technically true that they have four eyes. If you tried to count their eyes, you wouldn't get 4 as an answer. However, if you just call them "four-eyes," but don't actually try to do computations with the number 4, then it doesn't lead to errors.

B.6   Why Was the Notation Wrong in the First Place?

You may also be wondering why the notation was wrong in the first place.[3] While I am not a historian of mathematics, I have some hunches. Don't take these as gospel—a true historian of mathematics could probably give a more correct account. However, for the sake of satisfying curiosity, here is what I think may have happened.

First of all, there was a split in the notation for calculus. One school of thought used Leibniz notation used differentials (i.e., $\frac{dy}{dx}$), and the other used Newtonian/Lagrangian notation (i.e, y' or some other variant of this). Generally speaking, the ones who believed in differentials as true algebraic entities used Leibniz notation, and those who only believed that the full derivative itself was valid used Newtonian notation.

Calculus was originally developed for physics in the 17th century. In physics, the independent variable is almost always "time." Therefore, all of the derivatives have some form of dt in the denominator. Euler developed many rules for simplifying differential equations (i.e., advanced equations involving differentials). Remember, this was before relativity—before any physics existed in which time might flow more quickly or slowly. Since (as Euler thought) time flowed at a constant rate, that means that dt is a constant. If you remember from our differential rules, the differential of a constant is always zero. Therefore, since $d^2t = d(dt)$, and dt is a constant, that means that $d^2t = 0$.

Now, let's say that we have a second derivative of y with respect to t, where t is time. How is that written? $\frac{d^2y}{dt^2} - \frac{dy}{dt}d^2tdt^2$. Now, if $d^2t = 0$, this can be simplified. What does it simplify to?

$$\frac{d^2y}{dt^2} - \frac{dy}{dt}\frac{d^2t}{dt^2} = \frac{d^2y}{dt^2} - \frac{dy}{dt}\frac{0}{dt^2}$$
$$= \frac{d^2y}{dt^2} - 0$$
$$= \frac{d^2y}{dt^2}$$

What do you see? This is the same notation as the "faulty" form of the second derivative that everyone uses! As you can see, if the variable that the derivative is taken with respect to is changing at a constant rate, then the "faulty" form of the second derivative is equivalent with the "true" form of the second derivative.

Since calculus was mostly physics, and since physics had not progressed to recognize the fluctuations in the movement of time, the simplified form of the second derivative worked just fine for most occasions.

Now, in England, where they were mostly using the Newtonian/Lagrangian notation for derivatives, they fell behind those who were using Leibniz notation elsewhere in Europe. So, in the mid-1800s, there was a large switch from using Newtonian notation to using Leibniz notation. However, the *understanding* of the derivative did not similarly switch. Just at the time when everyone switched over to using the notation of Leibniz, they also switched over to using the *understanding* of the Newton school, which downplayed the significance of differentials as independent units.[4]

Therefore, since nobody was *expecting* differentials to be well-behaved, nobody paid much attention to the fact that the differentials in the second derivative couldn't be manipulated algebraically.[5] Therefore, the fact that it didn't work, rather than sparking someone to fix the problem, simply reinforced the idea that

---

[3]Some mathematicians have objected to my use of the word "wrong." Their viewpoint is that it is "just notation" and therefore can't technically be wrong. My viewpoint is that of a teacher. If a student writes something as a fraction, but it isn't a correct fraction, but there is in fact a correct way to write it as a fraction, then what they have written is wrong.

[4]The person most responsible for this was probably George Berkeley who derided infinitesimals by saying, "They are neither finite Quantities nor Quantities infinitely small, nor yet nothing. May we not call them the Ghosts of departed Quantities?"

[5]For teachers who are familiar with higher levels of calculus, a similar but not identical problem exists with partial differentials. You cannot use partial differentials algebraically, but the reason is merely that the notation used is problematic. Using improved notation, partial differentials can be algebraically manipulated just as easily.

differentials shouldn't be treated as true algebraic units. It formed a self-fulfilling prophecy of sorts. And, since they had Faà di Bruno's formula, they could manipulate differentials in the way that is of the most practical importance (though it is really amazing how few mathematicians actually know Faà di Bruno's formula).

Appendix C

Well-Known Calculus Theorems

While I believe that the loose approach of this book will help people gain the fundamental ideas of calculus faster and internalize them better, the more traditional propositional approach to calculus still has its place. In academic mathematics, oftentimes all statements must be proved, whether by direct proof, appealing to an axiom, or appealing to a theorem which has already proven your point. For those who are building new areas of mathematics, this task is vital, as it ensures that each new postulate in the mathematical canon is well grounded and logically coherent. For those merely *using* mathematics, it is usually sufficient to have an intuitional knowledge of the subject.

Therefore, this appendix will identify several common theorems that the more deductively-inclined students may wish to learn in order to help prove the truth of their usage of calculus.

C.1 Basic Ideas, Definitions, and Foundational Theorems

C.1.1 Interval Notation

Intervals are discussed frequently but informally throughout the book. Interval notation is fairly simple. If I want to talk about a range of values between 3 and 5 which include the numbers 3 and 5, I would write that as $[3, 5]$. This is known as a **closed interval** because the endpoints (3 and 5) are included in the interval.

If, instead I wanted to talk about a range of values between 3 and 5 which didn't include the numbers 3 and 5, I would write that as $(3, 5)$. In other words, it is including 3.01, 3.0000001, 3.0000000000001, etc., but 3 itself is outside of the interval. This is known as an **open interval** because the endpoints (3 and 5) are not included in the interval.

Intervals can also be half-open, which means that it includes one of the endpoints but not the other. An interval between 3 and 5 which includes 5 but not 3 is written as $(3, 5]$. An interval which includes 3 but not 5 is written as $[3, 5)$. Essentially, if a side is open, it is marked with a parenthesis, and if it is closed, it is marked with a bracket. Infinities are never closed. So, if I wanted to specify the intervale from 10 (inclusive) to infinity, I would write $[10, \infty)$. Because of this, theorems which apply to closed intervals (i.e., $[a, b]$) do not necessarily apply when one or more sides are infinite, because those are not closed intervals.

Many of the theorems use this notation to specify the intervals that they are valid for. For instance, if we are discussing "$f(x)$ on the interval $[a, b]$," that means that we are thinking of a graph for $y = f(x)$, and we are drawing the graph from $x = a$ to $x = b$.

Note that many functions have a requirement that $f(x)$ be *continuous* on the interval $[a, b]$, but be differentiable (i.e., smooth) on the intervale (a, b). This allows you to pick two points, and, as long as you can show that it is smooth *between* those two points, you don't necessarily have to show that it was smooth outside of those points.

C.1.2   Continuous and Differentiable Functions

$f(x)$ is a true **function** if it returns at most one value for any given x. Most theorems are directly valid only for true functions, but many non-true-functions can be pulled in as well using the Implicit Function Theorem (see Appendix C.1.5).

A function is **continuous** if you can draw it without picking up your pencil. More technically, a function is continuous on $[a, b]$ iff, for every point c in the interval (a, b),

$$\lim_{x \to c} f(x) = f(x). \tag{C.1}$$

A function is differentiable on $[a, b]$ iff, for every point c in the interval (a, b),

$$\lim_{h \to 0^+} \frac{f(x + h) - f(x)}{h} = \lim_{h \to 0^+} \frac{f(x) - f(x - h)}{h}, \tag{C.2}$$

and the formula above is defined for every point on the interval (i.e., the value must exist and must be non-infinite).

C.1.3   The Intermediate Value Theorem

The intermediate value theorem says that if $f(x)$ is continuous on the closed interval $[a, b]$, and c is any number between $f(a)$ and $f(b)$, then there exists some x in the interval $[a, b]$ such that $f(x) = c$.

Another way to state this is to say that if a function is continuous from a to b, then it will hit every value between $f(a)$ and $f(b)$ for some x between a and b.

The most confusing thing about this theorem is that it is so obvious that stating it sounds funny. However, it is an important theorem for proving things about continuous functions. It is also known as **Bolzano's Theorem**.

C.1.4   The Squeeze Theorem

The Squeeze Theorem states the behavior of a function that is bounded by two other functions. Let's start with the function $f(x)$ that is continuous and differentiable. If, over an interval (a, b), $f(x)$ is always bounded from above by $g(x)$ and bounded from below by $h(x)$, then, if $g(x)$ and $h(x)$ have a limit at some point c, $f(c) = g(c) = h(c)$.

Using limits, we can say that if $g(x) \geq f(x)$, $h(x) \leq f(x)$, and $\lim_{x \to c} g(x) = \lim_{x \to c} h(x)$, then $\lim_{x \to c} f(x) = g(x) = h(x)$.

C.1.5   The Implicit Function Theorem

The Implicit Function Theorem says that many implicit and non-true-functions can act like a true explicit function for a large subset of their values. Essentially, if the function has only one derivative over a particular segment of its graph, then it acts like a function at that point.

The idea is that, as long as the function can be zoomed in sufficiently to look like a function, then for all practical purposes it is a function. The reason why this works is that we can actually always posit additional variables that would make it act like a function at that point.

For instance, take the unit circle. For most of its x values, there are 2 possible y values. This can be written explicitly as $y = \sqrt{1 - x^2}$, but the square root function can return two values. Therefore, $y = f(x)$ is ambiguous, because for any given x there could be two different values.

However, we could be explicit. We could create a multivariable function such that

$$f(x, q) = \begin{cases} +\sqrt{x}, & \text{if } q = 0 \\ -\sqrt{x}, & \text{if } q = 1 \end{cases}$$

This is indeed a true function of two variables. Additionally, because the q parameter is constant (except during the crossover points), it does not affect the derivative (again, except during the crossover points). Therefore, it can be ignored during differentiation.

Basically, the implicit function theorem says that even if a function isn't a true explicit function, if it acts as if it were a true explicit function when zoomed in, we can pretend that there is a hidden variable that went unnamed which is converting the not-true-function function into a true explicit function.

C.2   Derivative Theorems

C.2.1   Mean Value Theorem

The Mean Value Theorem states that, given a graph of $y = f(x)$ which is both continuous in the interval $[a, b]$ and differentiable (i.e., smooth) on the interval (a, b), there exists some value c in the interval where the slope on the graph is equivalent to the direct slope between the the points a and b.

In other words, there must exist some c in the interval such that

$$f'(c) = \frac{f(b) - f(a)}{b - a} \tag{C.3}$$

The way to understand this is to see that, if a graph is smooth and continuous, then, as the slope of the graph changes, the slope is going to hit all of the values between the beginning and ending of the change.

So, you have three possibilities. The first is that the graph can go directly in a line from a to b. In this case, since it is a line, the slope of *all* of the points in (a, b) is the same, and it is equal to the slope between the points. The second one is that the slope will begin at a with the slope larger than the full slope between the two points, with the graph's direction pointing *above* point b. However, since the graph has to smoothly hit b, it now has to overcompensate and have a slope less than the whole slope in order to hit its target. Therefore, the intermediate value theorem says that since the derivative is itself a smooth function (this from the notion of differentiability), then it will attain every value from the overshoot to the compensating undershoot, which will include the whole slope from a to b. This same reasoning applies to if the graph began undershooting and had to overshoot to compensate.

C.2.2   Rolle's Theorem

Rolle's Theorem is just a special case of the Mean Value Theorem. Rolle's Theorem states that if a continuous, differentiable function hits the same value (i.e., y-value) more than once on the interval $[a, b]$, then there is at least one value c in the interval such that the slope at c is zero, (i.e., $f'(c) = 0$). In other words, the curve has to be flat at some point or points in the interval.

This can be shown because, if we restrict the interval to just the points that have equivalent y values, the slope between those two points will be zero, and the mean value theorem says that there must be at least one point in this restricted interval where the slope is the same as the whole slope between the two points (which will be zero).

C.2.3   The Boundedness Theorem

The Boundedness Theorem says that if a function is smooth in the interval $[a, b]$ and differentiable on the interval (a, b) then that function will have a non-infinite range on the interval $[a, b]$.

Note that since this theorem is defined on a closed interval, it is only valid as long as a and b are non-infinite, and this one is especially tricky in this regard. This is because a function cannot get infinitely large or infinitely negative on a finite range if the slope is only attaining finite values throughout the slope.

C.2.4   Extreme Value Theorem

The Extreme Value Theorem follows directly from the Boundedness Theorem. Since on a function that is differentiable and continuous on a closed interval there is a bounded range, that means that the range must have a minimum and a maximum value that it will in fact achieve.

Additionally, the Extreme Value Theorem states that if $f(x)$ has an extremum on an open interval (a, b), then the extremum *must* occur at a critical point. This is because if the extremum is not occuring on the exact values a and b but at a different point c, then, if the function is continuous and differentiable, there must be identical values to both the left and right of c. If that is the case, then Rolle's Theorem tells us that we can see that the slope between these two points is 0, and therefore there must be a point between them that attains this same slope.

From this we can deduce that the extreme values of a continuous, differentiable interval will either occur at the edges of the interval or at a critical point. This theorem is what yields the list of things to test for to find extreme values in Chapter 9.

C.2.5   Inverse Function Theorem

The Inverse Function Theorem states that if $f(x)$ is smooth, differentiable, and has a non-zero derivative over the interval (a, b), then $f(x)$ is **invertable**, meaning that a function $g(x)$ exists which takes the value given by $f(x)$ and yields x.

Additionally, if the derivative of $f(x)$ is $f'(x)$ then the derivative of $g(x)$ is $\frac{1}{f'(x)}$.

C.3   The Fundamental Theorems of Calculus

The fundamental theorems of calculus deal with derivatives as fundamental units, while this book deals primarily in differentials. They are provided here for reference, but, personally, I think they are outmoded by viewing the integral in terms of infinite sums rather than as areas. Note that some calculus texts switch the first and second fundamental theorems.

C.3.1 The First Fundamental Theorem of Calculus

The First Fundamental Theorem of Calculus states that one of the antiderivatives of a function $f(x)$ can be used to calculate the area under the curve $f(x)$ with a fixed lower and variable upper bound of integration. We will call this function $F(x)$.

This is often written as[1]

$$F(x) = \int_a^x f(t)\, dt. \tag{C.4}$$

Because of this, we also know that $F'(x) = f(x)$.

C.3.2 The Second Fundamental Theorem of Calculus

The Second Fundamental Theorem of Calculus tells us that, with some special trickery, we can actually use *any* of the antiderivatives of $f(x)$ to find the area under the curve.

If $F(x)$ is *any* antiderivative of $f(x)$, then the area under the curve $f(x)$ on the interval $[a, b]$ is given by $F(b) - F(a)$, no matter which antiderivative is used. This is written as

$$\int_a^b f(x)\, dx = F(x) \Big|_a^b = F(b) - F(a). \tag{C.5}$$

C.4 Sequences and Series

A **sequence** is a set of distinct values (called **terms**) given in a particular order. For instance, $23, 100, 0.5$ form a sequence. A sequence is said to be a **defined sequence** if a given term in a sequence can be computed from its position. For instance, $1, 4, 9$ form a defined sequence where, for any position n, the term u_n for the sequence is given by $u_n = n^2$. An **infinite sequence** is a sequence that goes on forever without termination.

A **series** is a sequence of terms that are added together. Series are often written as

$$\sum_{n=1}^m f(x) \tag{C.6}$$

where $f(x)$ is the definition of the series. An **infinite series** is a series with an infinite number of terms (where $m = \infty$). A **partial sum** of a series is the value of a (usually infinite) series up to a particular position within the sequence of numbers. For instance, given the series $1 + 4 + 9 + \ldots$, the partial sum of the series up to the position $n = 5$ is $1 + 4 + 9 + 16 + 25 = 55$.

C.4.1 Convergence and Divergence

A series **converges** if there is a finite value a for which

$$\lim_{n \to \infty} u_1 + u_2 + u_3 + \ldots + u_n = a. \tag{C.7}$$

A series **diverges** if a goes to positive or negative infinity, or there is no single value that the limit becomes closer to.

---

[1]Note that in this equation, $f(x)$ is written as $f(t)$. This is because we are distinguishing between the parameter of f, which is varying continually on the function, and the parameter of F, which is fixed at the value x. The name of the variable for f doesn't matter, as long as it isn't used for anything else.

An example of a convergent series is

$$\sum_{n=1}^{\infty} \frac{1}{2^n} = \frac{1}{2} + \frac{1}{4} + \frac{1}{8} + \frac{1}{16} + \ldots = 1. \tag{C.8}$$

An example of a divergent series is

$$\sum_{n=1}^{\infty} n = 1 + 2 + 3 + \ldots = \infty. \tag{C.9}$$

A geometric series is a series given in the form

$$\text{sum} = \sum_{n=1}^{\infty} a \cdot r^n \tag{C.10}$$

where a and r are constants. All geometric series are convergent for $-1 < r < 1$ and divergent for $r \geq 1$ and $r < -1$. $r = -1$ is a more complicated topic.

C.4.2 Tests for Convergence

Determining whether a limit converges or diverges can be difficult. A **convergence test** is a way to know whether a given series converges or diverges.

The following convergence tests can help to determine if a series converges:

1. A series converges if it is the sum of two series that each converge.

2. A series of positive numbers converges if its terms past a particular n are all less than some other series that is known to converge (due to the Squeeze Theorem).

3. For a series of positive numbers where you have two terms u_n and u_{n+1}, find r such that $r = \lim_{n \to \infty} \frac{u_{n+1}}{u_n}$. If $r < 1$ the series will converge, if $r > 1$, the series will diverge, and if $r = 1$ it is unknown.

4. For a series of positive numbers where each term u_n is given by $f(n)$, the series converges if $\int_a^{\infty} f(x)\, dx$ yields a real, non-infinite number.

5. For a series with both positive and negative terms, the series will converge if a series made from the absolute values of the terms will converge.

A series is said to be **conditionally convergent** if the series converges but the series formed from the absolute values of the terms diverge (otherwise, a convergent series is called **absolutely convergent**).

C.4.3 Manipulating Terms of Series

Absolutely convergent series are very resilient to manipulating the terms of the series. Rearrangements (i.e., swapping positions of different terms of the series), reassociations (parenthesizing the series in different ways), and spacings (adding zeroes into the series at one or more points) do not affect the value of absolutely convergent series.

However, all of these can in fact affect the values of conditionally convergent series, and even of divergent series (to the extent that they can be said to have a value). For instance, $1 + 2 + 3 + \ldots$ is *not in any way* the same series as $1 + 0 + 2 + 0 + 3 + 0 + \ldots$ despite the fact that the only thing added are zeroes.[2]

---

[2]For more information on evaluating divergent series, see "Hyperreal Numbers for Infinite Divergent Series," (https://arxiv.org/abs/1804.11342).

Appendix D

Additional Uses of the Derivative

This appendix provides several mathematical techniques that derivatives can be used for. These are the techniques which you can use at the level of knowledge presented in this book. Further uses of the derivative are available in higher-level calculus-oriented courses.

D.1 Finding Small Changes

Remember that a differential is an infinitely small change in a variable. The derivative is the relative rates of change of two variables at an instantaneous moment. Beyond this infinitely small region, derivatives and differentials are no longer perfectly accurate.

Nonetheless, for smooth continuous functions, you can use really small changes in x to stand in for the differential dx. How well this works depends on the function itself, but nonetheless, if you want to approximate how much changing one value will affect another, you can take a differential equation or a derivative, substitute in a small value for x and dx (and whatever other variables are needed), and calculate what the resulting dy will be.

This is not a perfect estimation, as calculus only truly deals with infinitesimals. Nonetheless, it is usually good enough for estimation and approximation purposes.

D.2 Estimating Values

There are innumerable uses of the previous section. One big one is the ability to estimate values of known but difficult functions.

Would you like to know what the square root of 16.1 is without a calculator? We *could* use the method of infinite series (see Chapter 25), and convert the square root function to an infinite series of polynomial terms, and then use the first however many terms we wanted.

However, there is a simpler method we can utilize which just uses the derivative.

The basic function we are looking for is:

$$y = \sqrt{x}$$

Now, we know the value of $\sqrt{16}$—it is just 4. Therefore, the value of $\sqrt{16.1}$ is the square root of 4, *plus a little bit*. In other words, plus a *small change*.

While not exact, a *small change* is essentially what a differential is! So, what we want to do is find what is dy when x is 16 and dx is 0.1. So, we just need to take a differential:

$$y = \sqrt{x} \qquad\qquad \text{the original function}$$

$$dy = x^{\frac{1}{2}} \qquad\qquad \text{rewritten for the power rule}$$

$$dy = \frac{1}{2}x^{\frac{-1}{2}}\,dx \qquad\qquad \text{power rule}$$

$$dy = \frac{dx}{2\sqrt{x}} \qquad\qquad \text{rewritten and simplified}$$

So, if $x = 16$ and $dx = 0.1$, we can find dy by just plugging in the numbers:

$$dy = \frac{dx}{2\sqrt{x}}$$

$$dy = \frac{0.1}{2\sqrt{16}}$$

$$dy = \frac{0.1}{8}$$

$$dy = \frac{1}{80}$$

$$dy \approx 0.0125$$

That means that if we add 0.1 to $\sqrt{16}$, then we add 0.0125 to the result. So, since $\sqrt{16} = 4$, we can say that $\sqrt{16.1} \approx 4.0125$. My calculator gives the result as 4.012480529547776, so our estimate is pretty close.

Note that, since this is a differential, the closer to 16 the x value is, the more accurate our result will be. Likewise, as we drift from 16, our answer will be further and further from the true value.

For instance, if we try to get $\sqrt{16.00001}$, our formula will give 4.00000125 while the calculator gives 4.000001249999805—almost an exact match. However, if we try to get $\sqrt{19}$, our formula will give 4.375 while the calculator gives 4.358898943540674. That might be good enough for your purposes, but it is important to know the limitations of the method.

D.3   Relative Error

Relative error gives you an estimate of the amount of variance in your result based on the amount of potential error in your inputs. For instance, let's say that you were measuring the radius of a sphere (let's say it measures as 6in, but you are only certain of the value to within $\frac{1}{2}$ of an inch. For that amount of variance, how much might our measurement of the volume of the sphere be off?

dr is the change in the radius (r), and dv is the change in the resulting volume. What we are looking for is how much our v value *might change* in response to a *change* in r values. In other words, we want to know what dv is, if r is 6in and dr is $\frac{1}{2}$.

Well, the volume of a sphere is given as $v = \frac{4}{3}\pi r^3$. The derivative of that is $dv = 4\pi r^2\,dr$. So, if we measured

6in, and we were off by $\frac{1}{2}$in, then we can estimate how much that affected dv as:

$$dv = 4\pi r^2\, dr$$

$$dv = 4\pi (6\text{in})^2\, (\frac{1}{2}\text{in})$$

$$dv = 72\pi\text{in}^3$$

$$dv \approx 226.1947\text{in}^3$$

So, if we measure the radius as 6in, a measurement error of a half inch will result in approximately 226.1947 cubic inches of error in the resulting volume calculation. Again, this is only approximate, because dv and dr are calculated as if they were infinitesimals, and we are giving them as real numbers.

The number we calculated was the total error. Oftentimes we need **relative error**, which is the error divided by the calculated value. In this case, the calculated volume (at radius 6in) is 904.752in^3. Therefore, the relative error is $\frac{226.1947}{904.752} \approx 0.25$. As a percentage (termed **percentage error**) it is a 25% error.

We can actually calculate a formula for the relative error by recognizing that relative error is $\frac{dv}{v}$. We can therefore solve for that:

$$v = \frac{4}{3}\pi r^3 \qquad\qquad \text{volume formula}$$

$$dv = 4\pi r^2\, dr \qquad\qquad \text{differential}$$

$$\frac{dv}{v} = \frac{4\pi r^2\, dr}{v} \qquad\qquad \text{divide by } v \text{ for relative error}$$

$$\frac{dv}{v} = \frac{4\pi r^2\, dr}{\frac{4}{3}\pi r^3} \qquad\qquad \text{substute } v \text{ for its formula on the right}$$

$$\frac{dv}{v} = \frac{3\, dr}{r} \qquad\qquad \text{simplified}$$

So, our relative error for this measurement will always be $\frac{3\, dr}{r}$. We can check this with our previous measurements. If the radius is 6in and the measurement error is 0.5in then the relative error will be $\frac{3(0.5)}{6} = 0.25$.

D.4 Plotting Unknown Functions from Their Derivative

If you know the derivative of a function, you can use it to plot an estimate of the function itself. This is useful in two situations. The first one is that if you *only* know the derivative, but don't know the main function, this will give you a basic picture of what the main function looks like. The second one is if the derivative of the function is more simple than the main function, it can simply be easier to graph using this method.

The way that the method works is to start at a given point (the method assumes that you know at least one valid point of the main function). Then, you calculate the slope using the derivative. Then, you generate a plot point a short distance away using the derivative to tell you where the next point is. Finally, you start over again using the new plot point.

As an example, you can plot $y = x^2$ this way, starting at $(0, 0)$. The derivative is $\frac{dy}{dx} = 2x$. Therefore, starting at $(0, 0)$, the slope will be 0. So, we will increase x by a small amount (say, 0.1) and use the slope to tell us how much to increase our y value (which will be 0 in this case).

So, the next point is $(0.1, 0)$. If we plug this into the derivative formula, the slope is 0.2. Therefore, if we move over by 0.1, we will move up $0.2 \cdot 0.1 = 0.02$. So now, our next point is $(0.2, 0.02)$.

The slope at this new point, using the derivative, is 0.4. Therefore, if we move the x value over 0.1, then the y value will change $0.4 \cdot 0.1 = 0.04$ units. So, the next point will be $(0.3, 0.06)$.

If we continue this repetition from $x = 0$ to $x = 3$ we will get a graph that looks like this (the dotted line represents the true graph):

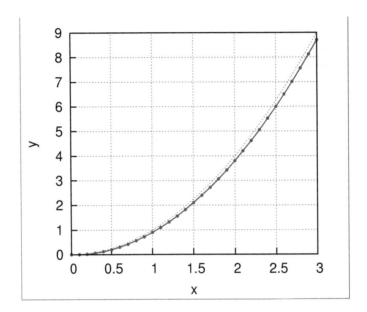

As you can see, this method for drawing the derivative can get pretty close to the true graph.

D.5   Constructing Functions Using the Graph of the Derivative

If you only have a *graph* of the derivative, and not the equation itself, you can still estimate the shape of the original function to some degree.

Essentially, you look at the graph of the derivative. For any x value where the derivative is positive, that means the original function is *increasing* (i.e., it has a positive slope). For any x value where the derivative is negative, that means the original function is *decreasing* (i.e., it has a negative slope).

Wherever the derivative crosses the x-axis, that will be a top or a bottom of the function. If you think about the "second derivative test" from Chapter 9, you can see that if the derivative passes downward across the x-axis, then that represents a local maxima of the original function. If, instead, it crosses upward across the x-axis, then that represents a local minima of the original function.

Wherever the derivative itself has a maxima or minima, that represents an **inflection point** where the original graph switches from being **concave up** to **concave down** or vice-versa. Concave up means that the graph is shaped like a U in that area, and concave down means that the graph is shaped like an upside-down U in that area. Basically, "up" or "down" refers to the direction that the opening of the U-shape is pointing. An inflection point is the point where the graph switches from concave up to concave down.

To see what an inflection point looks like (in the main graph, not the derivative), take a look at the following graph, where the dot marks the inflection point. To the right of the inflection point, the graph is concave up and to the left of the inflection point the graph is concave down.

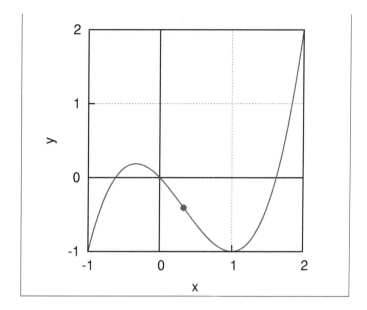

D.6   Finding Inverse Functions Using the Derivative

One interesting use of the derivative is finding an inverse function (see Section 4.6 for a refresher). We noted that when you look at an inverse function graphically, it is basically the original function, but with the xs and ys swapped. What is interesting is that, because of this, the *derivative* of the inverse function is simply the inverse of the derivative of the original function.

So, for instance, the derivative of $y = x^2$ is $\frac{dy}{dx} = 2x$. For the inverse function, we swap our ys and our xs, and then use the reciprocal on the right-hand side. Therefore, we would see that $dydx = \frac{1}{2y}$. Now, we can integrate to find the equation:

$$dydx = \frac{1}{2y}$$

$$2y\,dy = dx$$

$$\int 2y\,dy = \int dx$$

$$y^2 = x + C$$

$$y = \sqrt{x + C}$$

We can also use a particular point to solve to see that $C = 0$ for our equation.

Now, that was a lot of work, and we already really knew what the answer was going to be. However, for some problems, this is an easier method than trying to find the inverse function algebraically.

Appendix E

Additional Uses of the Integral

This appendix contains some specific applications for the integral which I did not have room for in the main text, but I find interesting enough to be included.

E.1   Finding the Total Work Performed

Any time you want to find the "total" of something, it means that something is being added together. Sometimes when we total, we total up individual values, such as totalling up the cost of items in an order. Other times, however, we are totalling up a *continuous* sum. This usually means that an integral will be needed.

In this case, we will be looking at totalling the "work" needed to lift an object an arbitrarily large distance from a gravitational body.

E.1.1   The Concept of "Work" in Physics

In Physics "work" is calculated as the *force F* (in Newtons) multiplied by the *distance D*, which yields a result in Joules.

In physics, the gravity between two objects (i.e., between the object and the earth) is given by the formula $F_g = G\frac{m_1 \cdot m_2}{r^2}$, where F_g is the force in Newtons, G is the gravitational constant, m_1 and m_2 are the masses of each object in kilograms, and r is the distance between the objects. For our problem, most of these are held constant. G is always a constant, $6.674 \cdot 10^{-11}$. m_1 is the mass of the earth, which is $5.972 \cdot 10^{24}$ kilograms. The distance between the earth and earth's surface at sea level is $6.371 \cdot 10^6$ meters. So, at any particular distance from the earth's surface, the gravity will be:

$$F_g = 6.674 \cdot 10^{-11} \frac{5.972 \cdot 10^{24} \cdot m_2}{(6.371 \cdot 10^6 + h)^2}$$

This approximately reduces to:

$$F_g = \frac{3.986 \cdot 10^{14} \cdot m}{(6.371 \cdot 10^6 + h)^2}$$

where m is the fixed mass of our object in kilograms, and h is the height of the object in meters at the current time. So, using our mass of 3 kilograms, the equation becomes:

$$F_g = \frac{3.986 \cdot 10^{14} \cdot 3}{(6.371 \cdot 10^6 + h)^2}$$

$$= \frac{1.1958 \cdot 10^{15}}{(6.371 \cdot 10^6 + h)^2}$$

So, for instance, at 20,000 meters, the force would be:

$$F_g = \frac{1.1958 \cdot 10^{15}}{(6.371 \cdot 10^6 + 20000)^2}$$

$$= \frac{1.1958 \cdot 10^{15}}{(6.371 \cdot 10^6 + 20000)^2}$$

$$\approx 29.61 \text{ Newtons}$$

However, as we move up and up, the force itself will be continuously varying with h.

We, however, are not trying to find the force, we are trying to find the *work*, which is $F \cdot h$. The problem is, since h is continuously varying, and F is a function of h, we cannot perform a simple multiplication.

E.1.2   Totaling Work Across a Varying Force

If I were to lift a 3 kilogram object 100,000 meters, then the total work performed would be all of the force I applied to the object across that 100,000 meters. The problem, however, is that as I lift the object, the force of gravity (and therefore the force I need to lift against gravity) changes.

To sum up the total work, therefore, we need to find the work performed at infinitely small increments of height, and do an infinite sum of them. An infinitely small increment of height would be termed dh. Therefore, since the equation for work in this case is $F \cdot h$, for an infinitely small increment of h, the work performed would be $F \cdot dh$. Since F is a function of h, we can write this as

$$\frac{1.1958 \cdot 10^{15}}{(6.371 \cdot 10^6 + h)^2} dh$$

Since we want a sum of all of the work done across a continuous range of heights, we can write it as an integral:

$$\int \frac{1.1958 \cdot 10^{15}}{(6.371 \cdot 10^6 + h)^2} dh$$

Since the goal is to find out how much work it would take to lift the object from the ground up 100,000 meters, we would use a definite integral from 0 to 100,000:

$$\int_0^{100000} \frac{1.1958 \cdot 10^{15}}{(6.371 \cdot 10^6 + h)^2} dh$$

To solve this integral, the first thing to do is to move the constants outside the integral, and rewrite the fraction using negative exponents:

$$work = \int \frac{1.1958 \cdot 10^{15}}{(6.371 \cdot 10^6 + h)^2} dh$$

$$= 1.1958 \cdot 10^{15} \int \frac{1}{6.371 \cdot 10^6 + h)^2} dh \qquad \text{constant multipler rule}$$

$$= 1.1958 \cdot 10^{15} \int (6.371 \cdot 10^6 + h)^{-2} dh \qquad \text{rewrite fraction as negative exponent}$$

At this point, we can find the integral much easier if we use u-substitution, letting $u = 6.371 \cdot 10^6 + h$ and $du = dh$. Therefore, the integral becomes:

$$1.1958 \cdot 10^{15} \int_{h=0}^{100000} u^{-2} du$$

This we can integrate with the power rule, yielding:

$$1.1958 \cdot 10^{15} \cdot -1 \cdot u^{-1} \Big|_{h=0}^{100000}$$

Substituting $u = 6.371 \cdot 10^6 + h$ back in, we get:

$$work = 1.1958 \cdot 10^{15} \cdot -1 \cdot (6.371 \cdot 10^6 + h)^{-1} \Big|_{h=0}^{100000}$$

$$= \frac{-1.1958 \cdot 10^{15}}{6.371 \cdot 10^6 + h} \Big|_{h=0}^{100000}$$

When we evaluate this at 0 and 100000, we get:

$$work = \frac{-1.1958 \cdot 10^{15}}{6.371 \cdot 10^6 + h} \Big|_{h=0}^{100000}$$

$$= \frac{-1.1958 \cdot 10^{15}}{6.371 \cdot 10^6 + 100000} - \frac{-1.1958 \cdot 10^{15}}{6.371 \cdot 10^6 + 0}$$

$$\approx -184793695 - -187694240 \qquad \text{approximating to whole numbers}$$

$$\approx 2900545 \text{ Joules}$$

Therefore, the total work required to lift the object was approximately 2,900,545 Joules.

E.1.3 Finding a General Formula for Work Performed

If you wanted to derive a general formula for the previous problem, how would you do it? Section 9.4 gave a general method for making general solutions to problems.

First, we look for the values that are constant for that problem. In this case, there are two—the mass of the object and the height to lift the object. We will denote them with capital letters to remind ourselves that they should be treated as constants during calculus operations: M and H.

Now, we need to work the problem using M and H instead of the actual constants. Note that h will still be used for the continuously-varying height for integration, it's just that H will be used as a stand-in for the stopping point. So, when we use h it is a variable, and when we use H it is a constant.

We will replace m with M in the force equation, giving us:

$$F_g = \frac{3.986 \cdot 10^{14} \cdot M}{(6.371 \cdot 10^6 + h)^2}$$

Therefore, the work for each infinitesimal dh will be:

$$\frac{3.986 \cdot 10^{14} \cdot M}{(6.371 \cdot 10^6 + h)^2}dh$$

Therefore, to find an equation for the final value, we simply need to integrate this from 0 to H:

$$\text{work} = \int_0^H \frac{3.986 \cdot 10^{14} \cdot M}{(6.371 \cdot 10^6 + h)^2}dh \qquad \text{basic integral}$$

$$= 3.986 \cdot 10^{14} M \int_0^H (6.371 \cdot 10^6 + h)^{-2}dh \qquad \text{simplify the integral}$$

$$u = 6.371 \cdot 10^6 + h \qquad \text{create a } u\text{-substitution}$$

$$du = dh$$

$$work = 3.986 \cdot 10^{14} M \int_0^H u^{-2}dh$$

$$= 3.986 \cdot 10^{14} M \cdot u^{-1}\Big|h = 0^H \qquad \text{integrating for } u$$

$$= 3.986 \cdot 10^{14} M \cdot -1 \cdot (6.371 \cdot 10^6 + h)^{-1}\Big|h = 0^H \qquad \text{substituting back}$$

$$= \frac{-3.986 \cdot 10^{14} M}{6.371 \cdot 10^6 + h} \qquad \Big|h = 0^H \text{simplifying}$$

$$= \frac{-3.986 \cdot 10^{14} M}{6.371 \cdot 10^6 + H} - \frac{3.986 \cdot 10^{14} M}{6.371 \cdot 10^6 + 0} \qquad \text{evaluate at the limits set by the evaluation bar}$$

$$= \frac{-3.986 \cdot 10^{14} M}{6.371 \cdot 10^6 + H} - \frac{-3.986 \cdot 10^{14} M}{6.371 \cdot 10^6} \qquad \text{simplifying}$$

Therefore, the final formula for total work to lift an object of mass M against the earth's gravity from sea level a distance of H meters is:

$$\text{work} = \frac{-3.986 \cdot 10^{14} M}{6.371 \cdot 10^6 + H} - \frac{-3.986 \cdot 10^{14} M}{6.371 \cdot 10^6} \qquad\qquad \text{(E.1)}$$

So, if anyone wants you to lift an object of a given mass a large distance, you can use this formula to determine how much work it will take!

As an example, to lift a 100kg mass 200,000 meters, we would do:

$$work = \frac{-3.986 \cdot 10^{14} M}{6.371 \cdot 10^6 + H} - \frac{-3.986 \cdot 10^{14} M}{6.371 \cdot 10^6} \qquad \text{our new formula}$$

$$= \frac{-3.986 \cdot 10^{14} \cdot 100}{6.371 \cdot 10^6 + 200000} - \frac{-3.986 \cdot 10^{14} M}{6.371 \cdot 10^6} \qquad \text{substituting in our values}$$

$$\approx 190426865 \text{ Joules}$$

If you ever wondered how people came up with the formulas in your Physics textbook, this is how. While some of the basic truths were found by experiment, many of the practical equations and corollaries were found by applying calculus to the basic formulas in order to find new ones.

Here, we took the definition of work (force multiplied by the distance) and the formula for gravitational force, and used it to formulate an integral to find the total force required to move one object away from the other. We then used that integral to find a general formula for this action.

E.1.4   To Infinity

We can also look at this to see how much work it would take to remove an object from earth's gravitational force completely. We can use our tools of infinity to simply evaluate Equation E.1 where the height is infinity. Substituting w for height gives us the formula:

$$\text{work} = \frac{-3.986 \cdot 10^{14} M}{6.371 \cdot 10^6 + H} - \frac{-3.986 \cdot 10^{14} M}{6.371 \cdot 10^6} \qquad \text{starting equation}$$

$$= \frac{-3.986 \cdot 10^{14} M}{6.371 \cdot 10^6 + w} - \frac{-3.986 \cdot 10^{14} M}{6.371 \cdot 10^6} \qquad \text{substitute } w \text{ for } H$$

$$= 0 - \frac{-3.986 \cdot 10^{14} M}{6.371 \cdot 10^6} \qquad \text{A number divided by } w \text{ is zero}$$

$$= \frac{3.986 \cdot 10^{14} M}{6.371 \cdot 10^6} \qquad \text{Simplifying}$$

Therefore, the total work to lift something completely out of earth's gravitational field from the surface is:

$$\text{work} = \frac{3.986 \cdot 10^{14} M}{6.371 \cdot 10^6} \qquad (E.2)$$

So, if I have a ball that weighs 2 kilograms, the amount of work required to get it out of Earth's gravitational field is:

$$\text{work} = \frac{3.986 \cdot 10^{14} M}{6.371 \cdot 10^{6}}$$

$$= \frac{3.986 \cdot 10^{14} 2}{6.371 \cdot 10^{6}}$$

$$= \frac{7.972 \cdot 10^{14}}{6.371 \cdot 10^{6}}$$

$$= \frac{7.972}{6.371} 10^{8}$$

$$\approx 1.2513 \cdot 10^{8}$$

$$\approx 125,130,000$$

So, it would take a little over 125 million joules of energy to perform this task.

E.2   Finding RMS Values

You may have heard that the electricity coming out of your wall socket is 120 volts (written as 120V). Where does this number come from? If you look at the electricity on an oscilloscope, you will find that the actual voltage fluctuates between 170V and -170V in a sine wave with 60 oscillations per second. This is known as "alternating current," or AC current. Current from a battery doesn't swing like this, and just stays at a steady voltage. This is known as DC current.

The average voltage for AC current is 0V (because it swings equally positive and negative), and the extremes are at 170V and -170V. So where do thes 120V number come in?

There are many different ways to take averages. It depends on what you are averaging. In this case, what electricians want to do is find an average that (a) doesn't equal zero, and (b) can be compared to DC voltage. Since AC always averages to zero, the "average" voltage doesn't really tell you anything. However, if we just listed peak voltages, we couldn't compare it to DC voltages, because most of the time an AC voltage is *lower* than the peak, while on a DC voltage, it is *always* at the peak.

A way of averaging that takes these into account is known as **RMS voltage**, or "root meam squared." This is a way of averaging where the *squares* of every value are averaged, rather than the values themselves. Then, the whole result is square rooted, to yield the final answer. This procedure gives an average that can be compared across different types of waveforms.

We can use the procedure in Section 23.2 to find the average value for our wave. First, we have to come out with an equation for our wave.

The equation will be:

$$v = 170 \sin(t)$$

Where v is voltage and t is time. For simplicity, I didn't model the fact that the wave cycles 60 cycles per second. It makes the equation harder, but does not affect the average. Instead, we will just measure the average of a single cycle, from $t = 0$ to $t = 2\pi$.

However, what we are *averaging* is not the function itself (it would average to zero), but the average of the *squares* of the function. Therefore, we want the average of the following:

$$(170 \sin(t))^2$$

Or, we can write this as:

$$28,900 \sin^2(t)$$

The averaging procedure that was established in Section 23.2 is given by Equationiu.avgval as:

$$\text{average of } f(x) \text{ from } a \text{ to } b = \frac{\int_a^b f(x)\mathrm{d}t}{b-a}$$

So, in this case, our squared average would be given by:

$$\frac{\int_0^{2\pi} 28,900 \sin^2(t)\,\mathrm{d}t}{2\pi - 0}$$

Then, because RMS takes the square root of the final average, then the final average is given by:

$$\sqrt{\frac{\int_0^{2\pi} 28,900 \sin^2(t)\,\mathrm{d}t}{2\pi - 0}}$$

We can also move the 28,900 outside of the integral sign since it is a constant multiplier. Additionally, we can simplify the denominator. This gives us:

$$\sqrt{\frac{28,900 \int_0^{2\pi} \sin^2(t)\,\mathrm{d}t}{2\pi}}$$

Now, we have a squared factor under a square root. Thus, we can simplify this to:

$$170\sqrt{\frac{\int_0^{2\pi} \sin^2(t)\,\mathrm{d}t}{2\pi}}$$

Now, let's look at the integral in the middle of this mess:

$$\int_0^{2\pi} \sin^2(t)\,\mathrm{d}t$$

To solve this, we will take advantage of the fact that Appendix H.5 gives us a power-reducing formula to get rid of $\sin^2$, and then solve the integral:

$$\int_0^{2\pi} \sin^2(t)\,dt = \int \sin^2(t)\,dt \,\bigg|_0^{2\pi} \qquad\qquad \text{convert to an indefinite integral}$$

$$= \int \frac{1}{2}(dt - \cos(2t)\,dt)\,\bigg|_0^{2\pi} \qquad\qquad \text{power-reducing trig identity}$$

$$= \frac{1}{2}\int dt - \cos(2t)\,dt\,\bigg|_0^{2\pi} \qquad\qquad \text{simplifying}$$

$$= \frac{1}{2}t - \frac{1}{2}\sin(2t)\,\bigg|_0^{2\pi} \qquad\qquad \text{integrating}$$

$$= \frac{1}{2}2\pi - \frac{1}{2}\sin(2(2\pi)) - (\frac{1}{2}(0) - \frac{1}{2}\sin(2(0))) \qquad\qquad \text{apply evaluation bar}$$

$$= \pi - \frac{1}{2}\sin(4\pi) - (0 - 0) \qquad\qquad \text{simplifying}$$

$$= \pi - \frac{1}{2}\sin(4\pi)$$

$$= \pi - 0$$

$$= \pi$$

So, substituting that into our original equation gives us:

$$\text{average} = 170\sqrt{\frac{\int_0^{2\pi}\sin^2(t)\,dt}{2\pi}}$$

$$= 170\sqrt{\frac{\pi}{2\pi}}$$

$$= 170\sqrt{\frac{1}{2}}$$

$$\approx 170 \cdot 0.7071$$

$$\approx 120.207$$

That is the RMS average voltage that is in your wall socket, and precisely how it was calculated.

E.3 Geometries of Revolution

The goal of this appendix is to show how the tools from Chapter 20 can be used to generate the standard volume formulas for standard shapes.

E.3.1 The Volume of a Cone

In Chapter 20, we managed to find the volume of a cone based on a line revolved around the x axis, but it looked almost nothing like the standard formula for the volume of a cone. How do we go from the solid of revolution of a line to the standard formula for a volume of a cone?

One of the differences between what we have calculated and what is normally done with the volume of a cone is that we have started with a line for the side and the height. Usually, instead of a line representing a side, we just get the radius of the base of the cone.

To simplify our lives, we can simply assume that the point of the cone will be at the origin. This means that (a) the limit of integration will start at zero, and (b) the line being revolved will have a y-intercept of zero. Since the height of the cone is merely the x value that it ends on, the other limit of integration will simply be the height of the cone, h.

What about the line? Well, think about the equation for a line. It is normally $y = mx + b$. However, since it is going through the origin, b will be zero. That means that $y = mx$.

So, what is the slope? Well, the radius r of the base of the cone is what the y value will be when $x = h$. Therefore, we can solve for m using these facts:

$$r = mh$$

$$m = \frac{r}{h}$$

Therefore, the equation of the line will be:

$$y = \frac{r}{h}x$$

Now, we can just plug these in to our standard volume of revolution equation, Equation 20.2. Remember, though, that r and h are merely stand-ins for constants!

$$\text{volume} = \int_{x=\text{start}}^{x=\text{finish}} \pi y^2 \, dx \qquad \text{standard equation}$$

$$= \int_{x=0}^{x=h} \pi \left(\frac{r}{h}x\right)^2 dx \qquad \text{make substitutions}$$

$$= \int_{x=0}^{x=h} \pi \frac{r^2}{h^2} x^2 \, dx \qquad \text{square the argument}$$

$$= \int \pi \frac{r^2}{h^2} x^2 \, dx \, \Big|_{x=0}^{x=h} \qquad \text{convert to indefinite integration and evaluation}$$

$$= \pi \frac{r^2}{h^2} \frac{x^3}{3} \Big|_{x=0}^{x=h} \qquad \text{perform integration—remember that } \pi, r, \text{ and } h \text{ are constants}$$

$$= \pi \frac{r^2}{h^2} \frac{(h)^3}{3} - \pi \frac{r^2}{h^2} \frac{(0)^3}{3} \qquad \text{apply evaluation bar}$$

$$= \pi \frac{r^2}{h^2} \frac{(h)^3}{3} - 0 \qquad \text{simplify}$$

$$= \pi \frac{r^2}{h^2} \frac{h^3}{3}$$

$$= \frac{1}{3} \pi r^2 \frac{h^3}{h^2}$$

$$= \frac{1}{3} \pi r^2 h$$

This last equation is the standard equation for the volume of a cone!

So, as you can see, by thinking carefully, and replacing certain pieces of our equation with constant-variables, we can use the integral to generate general equations.

E.3.2 Volume of a Sphere

A similar procedure can be used to find the volume of a sphere.

If you think about it, a sphere is simply a semicircle rotated about the x-axis (any axis, really, but we will focus on the x-axis).

The equation for a circle centered about the origin is $x^2 + y^2 = r^2$, where r is the radius of the circle. To recall *why* this is the case, refer back to Chapter 2. We can solve for y like this:

$$y = \sqrt{r^2 - x^2}$$

We only need the top half of the circle, so we will ignore the negative square roots.

Now, if we turn this on its x axis, we will generate numerous cyclinders dx wide. The equation for the volume of each cylinder is $\pi y^2 dx$. In our case, based on the equation for y above, this becomes:

$$
\begin{aligned}
volume &= \pi y^2 dx \\
&= \pi \sqrt{r^2 - x^2}^2 dx \qquad \text{substitute for } y \\
&= \pi (r^2 - x^2) dx \\
&= \pi r^2 dx - \pi x^2 dx
\end{aligned}
$$

The total volume between two x values a and b will be given by the integral:

$$volume = \int_a^b \pi r^2 dx - \pi x^2 dx$$

Note that, since, for any given equation, r will be constant, r will treated as a constant during the integration.

$$
\begin{aligned}
volume &= \int_a^b \pi r^2 dx - \pi x^2 dx \\
&= \int \pi r^2 dx - \pi x^2 \Big|_a^b \\
&= \pi r^2 x - \pi \frac{x^3}{3} \Big|_a^b
\end{aligned}
$$

Now, if we want to know the volume of the *entire* circle, we need to set a and b to the left and right x values of the circle. Since the circle has a radius r, that means that the leftmost x will be $-r$ and the rightmost x will be r. Therefore, $a = -r$ and $b = r$. This gives us:

$$\text{volume} = \pi r^2 x - \pi \frac{x^3}{3} \Big|_{-r}^{r}$$

$$= \left(\pi r^2 r - \pi \frac{r^3}{3}\right) - \left(\pi r^2(-r) - \pi \frac{-r^3}{3}\right)$$

$$= \pi r^3 - \pi \frac{r^3}{3} - \left(-\pi r^3 + \pi \frac{r^3}{3}\right)$$

$$= \pi r^3 - \pi \frac{r^3}{3} + \pi r^3 - \pi \frac{r^3}{3})$$

$$= \frac{3\pi r^3 - \pi r^3 + 3\pi r^3 - \pi r^3}{3}$$

$$= \frac{4\pi r^3}{3}$$

$$= \frac{4}{3}\pi r^3$$

And that is the equation for the volume of a sphere.

Appendix F

Proofs and Derivations

While there were a few proofs in the main text, the goal of the main text was to help you learn the basics of what calculus is and how to use it. For those interested in a few more details, this appendix provides additional proofs and derivations of the various rules and ideas contained in the rest of the book.

These are not exhaustive, formal proofs. For that we would have to justify domains and ranges, the existence of values at different points, and a bunch of other stuff that, while important, is not of importance to *someone learning introductory calculus*.

F.1   Proof of the Power Rule for Integers

The power rule for integers states that given $y = x^n$, where n is a constant integer, the derivative is $y' = nx^{n-1}$. To understand why this is, we need only look at the general formula for derivatives:

$$y' = \frac{f(x + h) - f(x)}{h}$$

For $y = x^n$, this becomes:

$$y' = \frac{(x + h)^n - x^n}{h}$$

When $(x + h)^n$ is expanded, it can give a somewhat large polynomial if n is large. To deal with this in the general case, we need to go to the binomial expansion, which tells us how to think about the expansion.

The binomial theorem says that for any binomial $(F + S)^n$ (first plus second raised to the nth power), the expanded form will be composed of the following sum of terms (note that $0! = 1$):

$$(F + S)^n = \sum_{k=0}^{n} \frac{n!}{k!(n - k)!} F^{n-k} S^k$$

The first term of this expansion will always be F^n (which means x^n in our case) which you can see by just substituting in 0 for k in the formula above. This becomes:

$$\frac{n!}{0!(n-0)!}F^{n-0}S^0 = \frac{n!}{1 \cdot n!}F^n S^0 = 1 \cdot F^n = F^n$$

Since we are subtracting x^n in the numerator, this first term will always drop off when we simplify the numerator.

You can see by inspection that all of the remaining terms have h raised to some power in their expansion (because $k \geq 1$ for the remaining terms). When we later divide by h, it lowers the power that h is raised to in each term. Since, on the second term ($k = 1$), h is only raised to the first power, that means that we will get rid of h in that term altogether. All of the remaining terms still are multiplied by some power of h.

When doing a derivative, h is considered to be an infinitesimal—a value infinitely close to zero. When you then find the standard part of the solution (see Chapter 27 for more information about hyperreals and standard parts), all of the h values resolve to the closest real number, which is 0. This gets rid of all of the remaining terms that are multiplied by some power of h.

Since the first term was removed by subtraction and the third and following terms were removed because they still have a power of h, this leaves only the second term to be the answer.

We can use the binomial expansion rule to find out what the second term is.

Therefore, the second term (where $k = 1$) of $(x + h)^n$ will look like:

$$\frac{n!}{1!(n-1)!}F^{n-1}S^1$$

The term $\frac{n!}{1!(n-1)!}$ simplifies to n, giving:

$$nF^{n-1}S$$

In this case F is x and S in h, so this gives us as the second term:

$$nx^{n-1}h$$

However, the whole thing is divided by h, leaving us with only nx^{n-1}, which is the power rule for derivatives.

F.2   Proof of the Product Rule

The product rule states that if $d(u \cdot v) = u dv + v du$. To see why this is so, let's try a new technique. What does it mean to be a differential? It is an infinitely small change in the variable. More importantly, however, the differentials are the appropriate *relative sizes* to each other.

Therefore, another way to solve differentials is to simply increase each variable by its differential. If I increase y by dy, x by dx, and so on, then the statement should still remain true. This means that I can do the following transformation:

$$y = u \cdot v \qquad \text{my starting equation}$$

$$(y + dy) = (u + du)(v + dv) \qquad \text{replace all variables with variable + di}$$

$$y + dy = u \cdot v + udv + vdu + dudv \qquad \text{expanded the multiplication}$$

This is very close to the product rule, but not quite.

Since we are searching for dy, we need to subtract y from both sides:

$$y + dy = u \cdot v + udv + vdu + dudv$$

$$dy = u \cdot v + udv + vdu + dudv - y \qquad \text{subtract } y \text{ from both sides}$$

$$dy = u \cdot v + udv + vdu + dudv - u \cdot v \qquad \text{replace } y \text{ with its equivalent}$$

$$dy = udv + vdu + dudv$$

Because dudv is the product of two differentials, they will disappear to zero for nearly every usage (see Chapter 27). Therefore, dudv can be reduced to 0. This gives us the equation for the product rule:

$$dy = udv + vdu$$

F.3 Proof of the Quotient Rule

The quotient rule follows very simply from the product rule. If you have the differential d$(\frac{u}{v})$ you can rewrite this as a simple product, $diff(uv^{-1})$. This can be solved using the product rule:

$$d\left(\frac{u}{v}\right) = diff(uv^{-1})$$

$$w = v^{-1}$$

$$dw = -v^{-2}\, dv$$

$$d\left(\frac{u}{v}\right) = d(uv^{-1}) = d(uw) = u\, dw + w\, du$$

$$= (u)(-v^{-2}\, dv) + v^{-1}\, du$$

$$= \frac{-u\, dv}{v^2} + \frac{du}{v}$$

$$= \frac{-u\, dv}{v^2} + \frac{v\, du}{v^2}$$

$$= \frac{-u\, dv + v\, du}{v^2}$$

$$= \frac{v\, du - u\, dv}{v^2}$$

And that is the quotient rule.

F.4   Proof of the Exponential Rule

The exponential rule states that $d(e^x) = e^x dx$.

The reason for this lies in the definition of e^x. e^x is said to be equal to the following formula:

$$e^x = (1 + \frac{x}{\infty})^\infty$$

Using the binomial expansion (discussed in the Appendix F.1), we can see that the terms of this series will be:

$$e^x = \sum_{k=0}^{\infty} \frac{\infty!}{k!(\infty - k)!} F^{\infty-k} S^k$$

We will then say that $\frac{\infty!}{(inf-k)!} = 1$ because these actually have the same set size, for reasons outside the scope of this book. Likewise, since $F = 1$, then F raised to any power will still be 1 and will just drop off as the identity multiplication. Likewise, $S = x$, so we will simply replace that in the formula. Using these facts gives us this new series:

$$e^x = \sum_{k=0}^{\infty} \frac{x^k}{k!}$$

Therefore, we can inspect the first few parts of the series to get a feel for what this will look like:

$$e^x = \frac{x^0}{0!} + \frac{x^1}{1!} + \frac{x^2}{2!} + \frac{x^3}{3!} + \frac{x^4}{4!} + \frac{x^5}{5!} \cdots$$

Notice how, for each term, the term to the left of it is the derivative of the term on the right. That is,

$$\frac{d}{dx}(\frac{x^5}{5!}) = \frac{5x^4}{5!} = \frac{5x^4}{5 \cdot 4!} = \frac{x^4}{4!}$$

The term on the far left is simple 1, so its derivative is just 0. Therefore, every term simply moves over one. Since it is an infinite sequence, we never run out of terms. Therefore, as you can see, if $y = e^x$ then $\frac{dy}{dx} = e^x$, which means that $dy = e^x dx$.

F.5   Proof of the Logarithm rule

The logarithm rule states that $d(\ln(u)) = \frac{du}{u}$.

To see why this is so, let us first say that

$$y = \ln(u)$$

This also means that, conversely,

$$u = e^y$$

If we take the differential of this, we get

$$du = e^y dy$$

Dividing both sides by e^y, we get

$$\frac{du}{e^y} = dy$$

However, we have already found out that $u = e^y$. Therefore, we can substitute it back in and get the final answer:

$$\frac{du}{u} = dy$$

F.6   Proving the Exponential and Logarithm Rules for Other Bases

The Exponential and Logarithm Rule proofs work for a base of e, but what about other bases? What about 2^x or $\log_5(x)$?

These can be easily worked using logarithm rules (Appendix H.1.4) and exponent rules (Appendix H.1.3). According to the logarithm rules, $\log_5(x)$ is equal to $\frac{\ln(x)}{\ln(5)}$. Therefore, you can convert any logarithm first to its natural log equivalent and then perform a differential.

For 2^x, we can prove it using the exponent rules. We can start by rewriting 2^x in terms of an exponent of base e: $(e^{\ln(2)})^x$. Then, because $(a^b)^c = a^{(bc)}$, we can rewrite this as $e^{\ln(2)x}$. Then, we can solve it using the exponential rule.
$$d(e^{\ln(2)x}) = \ln(2)e^{\ln(2)x} \, dx = \ln(2) \, 2^x \, dx$$

F.7   Proof of the Generalized Power Rule

The generalized power rule is:

$$d(u^v) = v \cdot u^{v-1} \cdot du + u^v \cdot ln(u) \cdot dv \tag{F.1}$$

To understand how this is derived, let us convert it into an equation:

$$z = u^v \tag{F.2}$$

Now, the question is how do we convert an exponent (which we don't yet know how to take the derivative of) into something that we do know. Well, the best way to get rid of an exponent is to use a logarithm. Therefore, we will take the natural log of both sides of the equation.

$$\ln(z) = \ln(u^v) \tag{F.3}$$

$$ln(z) = v \cdot ln(u) \tag{F.4}$$

Now we don't have to deal with the exponent anymore. So now we take the differential of both sides of the equation.

$$d(\ln(z)) = d(v \cdot \ln(u)) \tag{F.5}$$

Using the log rule for the left side and the product rule for the right side, this works out to be

$$\frac{1}{z} \, dz = v \frac{1}{u} \, du + \ln(u) \, dv \tag{F.6}$$

Now the problem is that we have a $\frac{1}{z}$ on the left-hand side. To get rid of it, we will multiply both sides by z.

$$dz = z \frac{1}{u} \, du + z \ln(u) \, dv \tag{F.7}$$

This is better, but now we have a new term, z, on the right-hand side. However, if we look back to equation F.2, we see that z is equivalent to our original expression, u^v. Therefore, this becomes

$$dz = u^v \, \frac{1}{u} \, du + u^v \, \ln(u) \, dv \tag{F.8}$$

Simplifying, this becomes the generalized power rule:

$$d(u^v) = vu^{v-1} \, du + u^v \, \ln(u) dv \tag{F.9}$$

Another equivalent way that this is commonly expressed is

$$d(u^v) = u^v \left(\frac{v}{u} \, du + ln(u) \, dv \right) \tag{F.10}$$

Because the natural log is undefined at zero, this derivative does not exist at zero (or you can think of it as going to negative infinity at zero, since that is what it limits out to). For numbers less than zero, this is only defined when using the complex natural log function.

The basic power rule can be thought of as a subset of this rule. In the power rule, if v is actually a constant (we will call it n for the constant version), and therefore dv is zero, and that entire term drops from the equation:

$$d(u^n) = n \cdot u^{n-1} \cdot du \tag{F.11}$$

F.8   Another Proof of the derivative of e^x

There are several proofs of the derivative of e^x. The easiest one is to use the generalized power rule.

$$d(e^u) = u \cdot e^{u-1} \cdot d(e) + e^u \cdot ln(e) \cdot du \qquad \text{(F.12)}$$

Since e is a constant, $d(e)$ is 0, which drops the whole term. Likewise, $ln(e)$ simplifies to 1, leaving us with only this:

$$d(e^u) = e^u \cdot du \qquad \text{(F.13)}$$

F.9   A Proof of the Generalized Logarithm Rule

The generalized logarithm rule is for taking the differential of functions of the form: $\log_u(v)$, where both the base and the argument are both functions. This proof will be similar to the proof of the Generalized Power Rule.

First we will start with a declaration:

$$z = \log_u(v)$$

Since we do not know how to differentiate this, we will try to find something we can differentiate, such as an exponent. Therefore, we will raise both sides to the u power:

$$u^z = u^{\log_u(v)}$$

$$u^z = v$$

Now we can differentiate both sides with the Generalized Power Rule:

$$d(u^z) = d(v)$$

$$\ln(u)u^z \, dz + zu^{z-1} \, du = dv$$

Since we are trying to find an equivalent for the differential of z, we need to solve for dz:

$$\ln(u)u^z \, dz + zu^{z-1} \, du = dv$$

$$\ln(u)u^z \, dz = dv - zu^{z-1} \, du$$

$$dz = \frac{dv - zu^{z-1} \, du}{\ln(u)u^z}$$

This is all well and good, but it incorporates the z term itself. Therefore, we need to replace z with its equivalent, $log_u(v)$:

$$dz = \frac{dv - zu^{z-1} \, du}{\ln(u)u^z}$$

$$dz = \frac{dv - \log_u(v) \, u^{\log_u(v)-1} \, du}{\ln(u)u^{\log_u(v)}}$$

Therefore, since $dz = d(\log_u(v))$, we can rewrite this as:

$$d(\log_u(v)) = \frac{dv - \log_u(v) \, u^{\log_u(v)-1} \, du}{\ln(u)u^{\log_u(v)}}$$

We can separate the components of this into two parts, like this:

$$d(\log_u(v)) = \frac{dv}{\ln(u)u^{\log_u(v)}} - \frac{\log_u(v)\,u^{\log_u(v)-1}\,du}{\ln(u)u^{\log_u(v)}}$$

$$d(\log_u(v)) = \frac{dv}{\ln(u)u^{\log_u(v)}} - \frac{\log_u(v)\,du}{\ln(u)u}$$

Because $u^{\log_u(v)} = v$, we can simplify this to:

$$d(\log_u(v)) = \frac{dv}{\ln(u)v} - \frac{\log_u(v)\,du}{u\,\ln(u)}$$

Another way to prove this is to use the change-of-base formula to convert the $\log_u()$ into a quotient of two natural log functions using the change of base formula (see Appendix H.1.4).

$$z = \log_u(v)$$

$$z = \frac{\ln(v)}{\ln(u)}$$

$$dz = d\left(\frac{\ln(v)}{\ln(u)}\right)$$

$$w = \ln(v)$$

$$dw = \frac{dv}{v}$$

$$q = \ln(u)$$

$$dq = \frac{du}{u}$$

$$dz = d\left(\frac{w}{q}\right)$$

$$dz = \frac{q\,dw - w\,dq}{q^2}$$

$$dz = \frac{\ln(u)\frac{dv}{v} - \ln(v)\frac{du}{u}}{(\ln(u))^2}$$

$$dz = \frac{dv}{\ln(u)v} - \frac{\ln(v)du}{u\,(\ln(u))^2}$$

The right-hand term *looks* different until you realize that $\frac{\ln(v)}{\ln(u)}$ is just another way of writing $\log_u(v)$ (using the rules of logarithms). The nice thing about this way of writing the formula, however, is that everything in this equation is in terms of the natural log, which is easier to think about, to graph, etc. than a log whose base is a function of one or more variables.

F.10   Integral Proofs Using Integration by Parts

The inverse trigonometric functions are not the result of the differentiation of single, simple functions like $\sin(x)$ and $\cos(x)$ are. Therefore, their integrals have to be proved separately. The proof of several such functions can be done using integration by parts in a very interesting way. We will use $\int \arcsin(x) \, dx$ to demonstrate the general technique.

Normally, integration by parts operates on two functions multiplied together, and choosing one to be u and one to be dv. In the case of $\int \arcsin(x) \, dx$ (and the other inverse trigonometric functions), there is only one term to use in the integration. However, what we can do is take the $\arcsin(x)$ as our u, and then just take the leftover dx as our dv. Then we can use our table of differentials to find $du = \frac{dx}{\sqrt{1-x^2}}$ and then by inspection we can see that if $dv = dx$ then $v = x$.

Therefore, we can say:

$$\int \arcsin(x) \, dx = \int u \, dv \qquad\qquad \text{substitutions}$$

$$= u \cdot v - \int v \, du \qquad\qquad \text{integration by parts}$$

$$= \arcsin(x) \cdot x - \int x \frac{dx}{\sqrt{1-x^2}} \qquad\qquad \text{substituting back in}$$

$$= \arcsin(x) \cdot x - \int \frac{1}{\sqrt{1-x^2}} x \, dx \qquad\qquad \text{simplifying}$$

In this case, if you look, x is *almost* the derivative of $1 - x^2$. If we made $u = 1 - x^2$, then $du = -2x \, dx$, which means that $x \, dx$ (which is the term we actually have) is equal to $\frac{-du}{2}$. Therefore, we can transform this integral as such:

$$\int \frac{1}{\sqrt{1-x^2}} x \, dx = \int \frac{1}{\sqrt{u}} \frac{-du}{2} \qquad\qquad \text{substituting}$$

$$= \int u^{\frac{-1}{2}} \frac{-du}{2} \qquad\qquad \text{simplifying}$$

$$= -\frac{1}{2} \int u^{\frac{-1}{2}} \, du \qquad\qquad \text{constant multiplier rule}$$

$$= -\frac{1}{2} \frac{u^{\frac{1}{2}}}{\frac{1}{2}} \qquad\qquad \text{power rule}$$

$$= -u^{\frac{1}{2}} \qquad\qquad \text{simplifying}$$

$$= -\sqrt{u}$$

$$= -\sqrt{1-x^2} \qquad\qquad \text{substituting back}$$

Now we can substitute this back in to our original integral:

$$\int \arcsin(x) \, dx = \arcsin(x) \cdot x - \int \frac{1}{1-x^2} x \, dx \qquad\qquad \text{original result}$$

$$= \arcsin(x) \cdot x - (-\sqrt{1-x^2}) \qquad\qquad \text{substituting in second integral}$$

$$= \arcsin(x) \cdot x + \sqrt{1-x^2} + C \qquad\qquad \text{constant of integration}$$

Proofs for the other inverse trigonometric functions and the natural log function work similarly.

Appendix G

Additional Things to Know for Standardized Tests

This book is not geared for any specific test. My goal with this book is to describe calculus in the way that is most effective for people to "get" what is happening with calculus. I didn't dumb anything down—the actual problems and equations I put in this book are harder than in many other books. However, some topics I gave short shrift because I felt that they were tangential to the actual learning of calculus.

I do realize, though, that many people learn calculus for the purpose of passing standardized tests on the subject (such as the CLEP, AP, or IB tests). Therefore, this chapter contains an abbreviated summary of those topics which we skipped or covered too briefly which are important for many standardized tests.

The biggest thing about the standardized tests is merely getting used to the type of questions they ask and the way that they ask them. The questions aren't all that hard—you've had to do much harder derivatives and integrals for this book. What they require you to do is to put together a lot of disparate pieces of information together in the same question. Additionally, they do a lot of problems of graph interpretation—given a graph of the derivative, what does this mean about the original function or about the second derivative?

Most of the questions are pretty basic, but require that you look at the question from a slightly different perspective. This chapter aims at helping you apply what you already know to the kinds of questions asked on the test.

G.1   Intervals and Interval Notation

A lot of the questions on the exams deal with specific intervals. This isn't difficult per se, but can sometimes take practice. The main thing to realize is that an interval is given with two values—a start and an endpoint. These are either surrounded by parentheses or brackets (or one of each). The bracket means that the interval includes the specific value named, and a parenthesis means that the interval includes everything up to but not including that number. For instance, the interval $(2, 5]$ means everything starting after two (but not including two—so, for instance, 2.0001 is included) and up to five (including the five itself).

Intervals are usually used to describe the domain of functions, or the range from which they want you to pull your answers. So, for instance, for a question about the sine graph, they may ask you to restrict your answer to looking at the interval $[0, 2\pi)$ in order to be specific about which section of the graph they want you to concern yourself with. Or, if a function has multiple minimas and maximas, they may only want you to find the minima within a certain interval.

G.2   Piecewise Functions

This book hasn't covered a lot of piecewise functions—that is, functions that are governed by different equations on different ranges. Standardized tests tend to use these a lot. The thing to recognize is (a) where the boundary between the pieces occurs, and (b) what is the nature of that boundary.

So, for instance, if you are integrating a piecewise function, you would simply integrate the first function from the beginning of its interval to the end of its interval, then separately integrate the second function, and then add the areas together.

So, given the function:

$$f(x) = \begin{cases} x^2, & x < 2 \\ 2x, & x >= 2 \end{cases}$$

If you wanted to know the area of this function betwen 1 and 5, you would simply integrate the first function from 1 to 2 and the second function from 2 to 5. Note that this is possible because at the point where the function switches from one equation to the other, the value is the same ($(2)^2 = 4$ and $2(2) = 4$. As long as this is true (or, at least, the *limit* is the same) you can do this. If the value of the function was different, then you could not validly take an integral at this point because it would be discontinuous.

You might get asked questions about the continuity of piecewise functions. A piecewise function is continuous if the limit at the crossover point is the same for both functions.

You might get asked questions about the smoothness or continuity of piecewise functions. A piecewise function is smooth if the equations themselves are smooth, and the have the same derivative at the crossover point.

G.3   Some Tricky Details

In this book, I've tried to be very straightforward with the questions and their applications. However, sometimes tests aim to be tricky and ask questions in complicated ways. This is useful because it tests your ability to really think about and analyze concepts deeply. However, it can be somewhat confusing for new students who are just trying to figure out the basics, much less all of the ways that someone can ask a question.

One place where this comes in is in questions asking about the area of a region bounded by a curve and the x-axis, or between two curves. The tricky point is that, if the question doesn't *specify* which one is on top and which one is on the bottom, and just wants the *bounded* region, then you have to do additional calculations to figure out which curve is on top and on the bottom, and also if that changes at any point!

Imagine the curve $y = x^2 - 9$ from $x = 0$ to $x = 9$. The area *under* the curve is a straightforward application of integration. The first part of the curve ($x = 0$ to $x = 3$) has a negative result (because the curve is below the x-axis, the area under the curve is negative), and the second part has a positive result. The definite integral will give you this result naturally:

$$\int_0^9 x^2 \, dx - 9 \, dx = \int x^2 \, dx - 9 \, dx \Big|_0^9 = \frac{x^3}{3} - 9x \Big|_0^9 = \frac{(9)^3}{3} - 9(9) - (\frac{0^3}{3} - 9(0)) = 243 - 81 = 162$$

However, if the question is the area *bounded* by the curve and the x-axis, then, since the question didn't state which one is on top and which one is on the bottom, that means that we have to break this area up into two parts—the part where the curve is on the bottom and the part where the curve is on the top. So, first, you have to figure out where this break occurs. I wrote this so it would be easy to see that the break occurs at $x = 3$ (this gets even harder when you are finding the area between two curves rather than the area bounded by the curve and the x axis).

So, the first integral be from $x = 0$ to $x = 3$, and we will have to take the absolute value of it, since it the direct result of integration will be negative:

$$\int_0^3 x^2 \, dx - 9 \, dx = \int x^2 \, dx - 9 \, dx \Big|_0^3 = \frac{x^3}{3} - 9x \Big|_0^3 = \frac{(3)^3}{3} - 9(3) - (\frac{0^3}{3} - 9(0)) = 9 - 27 = -18$$

So, the definite integral give -18, but we are using the absolute value, which is 18. Now, we do the same for the region from $x = 3$ to $x = 9$:

$$\int_3^9 x^2 \, dx - 9 \, dx = \int x^2 \, dx - 9 \, dx \Big|_3^9 = \frac{x^3}{3} - 9x \Big|_3^9 = \frac{(9)^3}{3} - 9(9) - (\frac{3^3}{3} - 9(3)) = 243 - 81 - (-18) = 180$$

So, the area of this is 180. So, the total area is the result of combining these, so $18 + 180 = 198$.

Anyway, there is no limit to the number of times that the lines in such problems may cross each other, making it more and more complicated. If you are using the integral to find totals (which is more the emphasis in this book), then we just total everything, so we don't worry about crossing axes and that sort of thing—the negatives really just are negative. But, if you use the integral for geometry (i.e., true areas), then adding up areas similar to the way we do it in this section is more appropriate.

G.4   Combining Pieces of Knowledge

One thing that happens a lot in standardized tests is that they will ask questions which combine knowledge from a lot of different sources. For instance, they may give you a definite integral involving sin() or cos() and give you π or $\frac{\pi}{4}$ for the limits of integration. You have to recognize from your trigonometry knowledge what the sine of $\frac{\pi}{4}$ is.

In many standardized tests, knowledge from geometry and trigonometry are intertwined with questions about calculus. For related rates problems, you have to interpret their questions in terms of what you know about geometry. Similarly for integral questions.

Another place where knowledge is asked to be combined is that, in addition to finding derivatives, you are often asked to find equations for tangent lines. This merely combines the derivative (which gives the slope of a tangent line) with knowing how to construct a line given a slope and a point (the point being the point of tangency in question). So, given $y = x^2$, if someone asks you for the equation of the line tangent to the graph at $x = 3$, you first find the slope using the derivative (slope is $2x$ which at $x = 3$ is 6), and then find the point on the graph itself (if $x = 3$ then $y = 9$). Then, the point and the slope can be combined to find the full equation for the line.

G.5   Recognizing Formulas and Theorems

Sometimes on standardized tests you get asked questions in weird ways. The goal of questions such as these are for you to recognize standard definitions and questions given in non-standard ways.

For instance, you may be asked to find:

$$\lim_{c \to 0} \frac{\sin(x + c) - \sin(x)}{c}$$

This appears to be a very difficult limit to perform, until you recognize that it is precisely the form of the limit definition of the derivative (see Equation 28.1)! The only difference is that h is replaced with c. Since the name of the variable doesn't matter, it is identical.

Of course, we know what the derivative of $\sin(x)$ is, it is $\cos(x)$. Therefore, the answer is $\cos(x)$, but it requires that you be able to recognize the problem as a derivative problem.

G.6   Graph Interpretation

Many standard calculus tests ask you to interpret graphs of functions, graphs of integrals, and graphs of derivatives. They want you to (a) recognize and write interval notation, (b) be able to understand the relationship between values on a derivative and what it means for the original function, and (c) recognize important features of graphs such as minima, maxima, concavity, and inflection points.

See Appendix D.5 for more information on this subject.

G.7   Additional Material

Many standardized tests will ask questions on material that I did not include in the main text. However, I have aimed to include everything that is required for standardized tests in the appendices. Therefore, for preparation for a standardized test, I recommend that you read through all of the appendices (except Appendix B because it has non-standard material).

One additional detail that is often on tests but is not covered in the main text of the book is the definition of the **normal line**. The normal line is a line that is perpendicular to the tangent line. The slope of the normal line is the negative reciprocal of the slope of the tangent line.

Appendix H

Mathematical Formulas, Relationships, and Tables

H.1 Algebra Rules

H.1.1 Fundamental Rules of Equations

Fundamental Law of Equality
> For two things that are equivalent (i.e., there is an equal sign between them), the equivalency will remain no matter what operations you do to them, as long as you do the *same* operations to *both* things in the same order (i.e., you do it to both sides of the equation).

Substitution Property of Equality
> Any quantities which are equivalent (i.e., on opposite sides of an equal sign) can be substituted for each other.

Variables Introduction Rule
> An equality with a new (i.e., not otherwise used) variable can be created merely by defining the equivalency. From that point, the variable can be interchanged with its equivalent using substitution.

Variable Sufficiency Rule
> When solving for multiple variables, to solve for all variables of a system having N variables you need *at least N* distinct equations.[1]

H.1.2 Fundamental Rules of Algebraic Manipulation

Identity Rule of Addition
> Any number plus zero is the original number.

Identity Rule of Multiplication
> Any number multiplied by one is the original number.

Additive Inverse Principle
> Adding together a number and its negative always yields zero.

---

[1]There are actually specific exceptoins for this in very special situations, but in general it is a worthwhile guide.

Associative Property of Addition

$$(a + b) + c = a + (b + c)$$

Associative Property of Multiplication

$$(a \cdot b) \cdot c = a \cdot (b \cdot c)$$

Commutative Property of Addition

$$a + b = b + a$$

Commutative Property of Multiplication

$$a \cdot b = b \cdot a$$

Distributive Property of Addition and Multiplication

$$a \cdot (b + c) = a \cdot b + a \cdot c$$

Special note - the identity rule of multiplication has a lot of really fascinating usages. Remember that a lot of different things equal one, so you can get a lot of mileage out of creatively multiplying by very creative versions of 1. All unit conversions are essentially multiplying by different forms of 1. If I have 1 foot, I can convert to feet by multiplying by $\frac{12 \text{ inches}}{1 \text{ foot}}$. This ratio is actually one, because the numerator and the denominator are equivalent. Therefore, multiplying by this ratio is just another form of multiplying by one.

H.1.3   Exponent Rules

- $x^a \cdot x^b = x^{a+b}$

- $(x^a)^b = x^{ab}$

- $\left(\frac{x}{y}\right)^a = \frac{x^a}{y^a}$

- $(xy)^a = x^a y^a$

- $x^{-a} = \frac{1}{x^a}$

- $x^{\frac{a}{b}} = \sqrt[b]{x^a}$

- $x^0 = 1$

- $\frac{x^a}{x^b} = x^{a-b}$

- $\sqrt[n]{x} = x^{\frac{1}{n}}$

Note that, based on the last rule, the exponent rules apply to roots as well, because a root is merely a fractional exponent. Sometimes it is easier to work with powers than roots, so you can simply convert between one and the other as needed.

H.1.4   Logarithm Rules

These rules hold where $b > 1$, $d > 1$, m and n are any positive real number, and j is any real number.

- $\log_b(m \cdot n) = \log_b(m) + \log_b(n)$

- $\log_b(\frac{m}{n}) = \log_b(m) - \log_b(n)$

- $\log_b(m^j) = j \log_b(m)$

- $\log_b(1) = 0$

- $\log_b(b) = 1$

- $\log_b(b^j) = j$

- $b^{\log_b(j)} = j$

- $\log_b(j) = \frac{\log_d(j)}{\log_d(b)}$

- $\ln(m) = \log_e(m)$

- $e^{\ln(m)} = m$

The last rule in the list is merely the natural log function (ln), and the rule simply states that this function is just the regular logarithm but using e (Euler's constant) as a base. The natural log is used so often in mathematics it is given its own notation.

H.1.5 Factorial Rules

- $x! = 1 \cdot 2 \cdot 3 \cdot \ldots \cdot x$

- $\frac{x!}{(x-1)!} = x$

- $0! = 1$

H.1.6 Rules of Zero

Note that, in Chapter 28, there are some semi-exceptions to these rules introduced for hyperreal numbers (infinities and infinitesimals).

- $0 + x = x$

- $x + -x = 0$

- $0 \cdot x = 0$

- $\frac{0}{x} = 0$ if $x \neq 0$

- $x^0 = 1$

- $0^x = 0$

- $\frac{x}{0} = \infty$ (or undefined)

- $0! = 1$

- 0 is neither positive nor negative

- 0 is even

- 0 is not considered prime

H.1.7 Rules of One

- $1 \cdot x = x$

- $\frac{x}{1} = x$

- $\frac{x}{x} = 1$

- $x^1 = x$

- $1^x = 1$

- $1! = 1$

- 1 is not considered prime

H.1.8 Polynomial Rules

Quadratic Formula
For an equation of the form $ax^2 + bx + c = 0$, we can solve for x as follows:

$x = \frac{-b \pm \sqrt{b^2 - 4ac}}{2a}$

Vertex Formula
For an equation of the form $y = ax^2 + bx + c$, the x value for the vertex of the parabola can be given by the following formula:

$x = \frac{-b}{2a}$

The y value can be found by substituting the given x back in the equation.

Two-Term Binomial Theorem
$(F + S)^2 = F^2 + 2FS + S^2$

Three-Term Binomial Theorem
$(F + S)^3 = F^3 + 3F^2 S + 3FS^2 + S^3$

General Binomial Theorem

$$(F + S)^n = \sum_{k=0}^{n} \frac{n!}{k!(n-k)!} F^{n-k} S^k$$

Difference of Squares

$$F^2 - S^2 = (F - S)(F + S)$$

Difference of Cubes

$$F^3 - S^3 = (F - S)(F^2 + FS + S^2)$$

H.2 Complex Numbers

Complex numbers act similar to real numbers with the addition of the complex unit i. A complex number has a *real* part, which is just a real number, and an *imaginary* part, which is a real number multiplied by i. To a large extent, you can just treat i as a variable whose square also happens to equal -1. Thus, most of the existing rules of algebraic manipulation already apply.

The additional ones are:

- $i^2 = -1$
- $\sqrt{-1} = i$

Two complex numbers $a + bi$ and $c + di$ are added by simply adding up their real part and their imaginary part:

$$(a + bi) + (c + di) = (a + c) + (b + d)i$$

Two complex numbers $a + bi$ and $c + di$ are multipled just like any two-term multiplication, except that i^2 is simplified to -1:

$$(a + bi)(c + di) = ac + adi + bci + bdi^2 = ac + (ad + bc)i - bd = (ac - bd) + (ad + bc)i$$

The distance between two complex numbers $a + bi$ and $c + di$ is found using the distance formula:

$$\sqrt{(a - c)^2 + (b - d)^2}$$

H.3 Geometric Formulas

H.3.1 Area, Perimeter, and Volume Equations

a = area

l = length

h = height

v = volume

r = radius

b = base

w = width

Area of a Rectangle

area = lw

Perimeter of a Rectangle

perimeter = $2l + 2w$

Volume of a Rectangular Prism

volume = lwh

Surface Area of a Rectangular Prism

area = $2lw + 2lh + 2wh$

Area of a Circle

area = πr^2

Circumference of a Circle
circumference $= 2\pi r$

Volume of a Cylinder
volume $= \pi r^2 h$

Volume of a Sphere
volume $= \frac{4}{3}\pi r^3$

Surface Area of a Cylinder
area $= 2\pi r h + 2\pi r^2$

Surface Area of a Sphere
area $= 4\pi r^2$

Area of a Triangle
area $= \frac{1}{2}bh$

H.3.2   Other Geometry Formulas

Equation of a Line

A line with a slope of m that intersects the y axis at $x = b$ has the following equation:

$$y = mx + b$$

Equation of a Circle

A circle centered around the point (a, b) with a radius of r has the following equation:

$$(x - a)^2 + (y - b)^2 = r^2$$

Pythagorean Theorem

For a right triangle with sides A, B, and a hypotenuse C, the lengths of each side obey the following relationship:

$$A^2 + B^2 = C^2$$

Distance Formula

Given two points, (x_0, y_0) and (x_1, y_1), the distance between these two points is given by the following formula:

$$\text{distance} = \sqrt{(x_1 - x_0)^2 + (y_1 - y_0)^2}$$

Note that this formula is essentially what you get when you solve for the length of the hypotenuse from the Pythagorean Theorem.

The formula continues for any number of dimensions. For three dimensions, the equation is:

$$\text{distance} = \sqrt{(x_1 - x_0)^2 + (y_1 - y_0)^2 + (z_1 - z_0)^2}$$

H.3.3   Polar Coordinates

Polar coordinates are merely a different way of defining the same 2D coordinate plane. Instead of specifying the location in the plane by x and y coordinates (i.e., the Cartesian/rectangular coordinate system), in the polar coordinate system the location is specified by the rotation, θ, and the distance (radius) from the center, r.

Conversion from Polar to Rectangular Coordinates

$x = r \cos(\theta)$, $y = r \sin(\theta)$

Conversion from Rectangular to Polar Coordinates
$r = \sqrt{x^2 + y^2}$, $\theta = \text{atan2}(y, x)$

Note that function $\text{atan2}(y, x)$ is a modification of the $\arctan(\frac{y}{x})$ (inverse tangent) function which takes into consideration the quadrant that the coordinate is found in. Without this function, you would start with $\theta = \arctan(\frac{y}{x})$ and then add a multiple of $\frac{\pi}{2}$ radians (i.e., 90 degrees) to θ based on which quadrant the result was in.

H.4 Constants

Constant	Value	Name	Usage
π	$3.14159\ldots$	Pi (Archimede's constant)	used for geometry of circles
e	$2.71828\ldots$	Euler's Constant	often used in self-referential relationships
i	$\sqrt{-1}$	The imaginary unit	used for two-dimensional (complex) numbers
τ	$6.283185\ldots$	The turn constant	One full turn of a circle in radians; this is often used as a replacement for 2π to simplify formulas

H.5 Table of Trigonometric Identities

Basic Identities for Triangles

$\sin(\theta) = \frac{\text{opposite}}{\text{hypotenuse}}$ $\qquad\qquad$ $\csc(\theta) = \frac{\text{hypotenuse}}{\text{opposite}}$

$\cos(\theta) = \frac{\text{adjacent}}{\text{hypotenuse}}$ $\qquad\qquad$ $\sec(\theta) = \frac{\text{hypotenuse}}{\text{adjacent}}$

$\tan(\theta) = \frac{\text{opposite}}{\text{adjacent}}$ $\qquad\qquad$ $\cot(\theta) = \frac{\text{adjacent}}{\text{opposite}}$

Cofunction Identities

$\sin(\frac{\pi}{2} - u) = \cos(u)$ $\qquad\qquad$ $\cos(\frac{\pi}{2} - u) = \sin(u)$

$\tan(\frac{\pi}{2} - u) = \cot(u)$ $\qquad\qquad$ $\cot(\frac{\pi}{2} - u) = \tan(u)$

$\sec(\frac{\pi}{2} - u) = \csc(u)$ $\qquad\qquad$ $\csc(\frac{\pi}{2} - u) = \sec(u)$

Quotient Identifies

$\tan(u) = \frac{\sin(u)}{\cos(u)}$ $\qquad\qquad$ $\cot(u) = \frac{\cos(u)}{\sin(u)}$

Pythagorean Identities

$\sin^2(u) + \cos^2(u) = 1$ $\qquad\qquad$ $1 + \tan^2(u) = \sec^2(u)$

$1 + \cot^2(u) = \csc^2(u)$

Angle Addition and Subtraction Identities

$\sin(u + v) = \sin(u)\cos(v) + \cos(u)\sin(v)$ $\qquad$ $\sin(u - v) = \sin(u)\cos(v) - \cos(u)\sin(v)$

$\cos(u + v) = \cos(u)\cos(v) - \sin(u)\sin(v)$ $\qquad$ $\cos(u - v) = \cos(u)\cos(v) + \sin(u)\sin(v)$

$\tan(u + v) = \frac{\tan(u)+\tan(v)}{1-\tan(u)\tan(v)}$ $\qquad\qquad$ $\tan(u - v) = \frac{\tan(u)-\tan(v)}{1+\tan(u)\tan(v)}$

Power-Reducing Identities

$\sin^2(u) = \frac{1-\cos(2u)}{2}$ $\qquad\qquad$ $\cos^2(u) = \frac{1+\cos(2u)}{2}$

$\tan^2(u) = \frac{1-\cos(2u)}{1+\cos(2u)}$

Sum-to-Product Identities

$\sin(u) + \sin(v) = 2\sin(\frac{u+v}{2})\cos(\frac{u-v}{2})$ $\qquad$ $\sin(u) - \sin(v) = 2\cos(\frac{u+v}{2})\sin(\frac{u-v}{2})$

$\cos(u) + \cos(v) = 2\cos(\frac{u+v}{2})\cos(\frac{u-v}{2})$ $\qquad$ $\cos(u) - \cos(v) = -2\sin(\frac{u+v}{2})\sin(\frac{u-v}{2})$

Product-to-Sum Identities

$\sin(u)\sin(v) = \frac{\cos(u-v)-\cos(u+v)}{2}$ $\qquad\qquad$ $\cos(u)\cos(v) = \frac{\cos(u-v)+\cos(u+v)}{2}$

$\sin(u)\cos(v) = \frac{\sin(u+v)+\sin(u-v)}{2}$

H.6   Table of Differentials

In these tables, u and v can be either variables or functions of variables. n, and C always refers to constant values. These rules are only valid where the given functions exist and are continuous. For example, the differential $d(u^v)$ only works where $u > 0$ and the differential $d(\log_u(v))$ only work where $u > 0$ and $u \neq 1$.

Differentials of Basic Functions

$d(C) = 0$

$d(u) = du$

$d(n\,u) = n\,du$

$d(u^n) = n\,u^{n-1}du$

$d(u + v) = du + dv$

$d(u - v) = du - dv$

$d(u\,v) = u\,dv + v\,du$

$d\left(\frac{u}{v}\right) = \frac{v\,du - u\,dv}{v^2}$

$d(\ln(u)) = \frac{du}{u}$

$d(\log_n(u)) = \frac{du}{u\,\ln(n)}$

$d(\ln(|u|)) = \frac{du}{u}$

$d(\log_n(|u|)) = \frac{du}{u\,\ln(n)}$

$d(e^u) = e^u\,du$

$d(n^u) = \ln(n)\,n^u\,du \quad (\text{where } n > 0)$

$d(u^v) = v\,u^{v-1}du + \ln(u)\,u^v, dv$

$d(\log_u(v)) = \frac{dv}{v\,\ln(u)} - \frac{\log_u(v)\,du}{u\,\ln(u)}$ or $\frac{dv}{v\,\ln(u)} - \frac{\ln(v)\,du}{u\,(\ln(u))^2}$

Differentials of Trigonometric Functions

$d(\sin(u)) = \cos(u)du$

$d(\cos(u)) = -\sin(u)du$

$d(\tan(u)) = \sec^2(u)du$

$d(\cot(u)) = -\csc^2(u)du$

$d(\sec(u)) = \sec(u)\tan(u)du$

$d(\csc(u)) = -\csc(u)\cot(u)du$

Differentials of Inverse Trigonometric Functions

$d\left(\arcsin\left(\frac{u}{n}\right)\right) = \frac{du}{\sqrt{n^2 - u^2}}$

$d\left(\arccos\left(\frac{u}{n}\right)\right) = \frac{-du}{\sqrt{n^2 - u^2}}$

$d\left(\arctan\left(\frac{u}{n}\right)\right) = \frac{n\,du}{n^2 + u^2}$

$d\left(\text{arccot}\left(\frac{u}{n}\right)\right) = \frac{-n\,du}{n^2 + u^2}$

$d\left(\text{arcsec}\left(\frac{u}{n}\right)\right) = \frac{n\,du}{u\sqrt{u^2 - n^2}}$

$d\left(\text{arccsc}\left(\frac{u}{n}\right)\right) = \frac{-n\,du}{u\sqrt{u^2 - n^2}}$

Other Equivalencies

$d^2u = d(du)$

$\frac{d}{dv}(u) = \frac{du}{dv}$

$D_v(u) = D_v^1(u) = \frac{du}{dv}$

$D_v^n(u) = \frac{d(D_v^{n-1}(u))}{dv}$

$D_v^2(u) = \frac{d^2u}{dv^2} - \frac{du}{dv}\frac{d^2v}{dv^2}$

$D_v^2(u) = -D_u^2(v)\left(\frac{1}{D_u(v)}\right)^3$

If u is an independent variable, then $d^2u = 0$.

H.7   Table of Integrals

Integrals of Basic Functions

$\int 0 = C$	$\int du = u + C$
$\int n\,du = n \int du$	$\int u^n\,du = \frac{u^{n+1}}{n+1} + C$
$\int (du + dv) = \int du + \int dv$	$\int (du - dv) = \int du - \int dv$
$\int (u\,dv + v\,du) = u\,v$	$\int u\,dv = u\,v - \int v\,du$
$\int \frac{du}{u} = \ln(|u|) + C$	$\int \ln(u) = u \ln(u) - u + C$
$\int e^u\,du = e^u + C$	$\int n^u\,du = \frac{n^u}{\ln(n)} + C$ (where $n > 0$)

Integrals of Trigonometric Functions

$\int \cos(u)du = \sin(u) + C$	$\int \sin(u)du = -\cos(u) + C$
$\int \tan(u)du = -\ln(|\cos(u)|) + C$	$\int \sec(u)du = \ln(|\sec(u) + \tan(u)|) + C$
$\int \csc(u)du = \ln(|\tan\frac{u}{2}|) + C$	$\int \arctan(u)du = u\arctan(u) - \frac{1}{2}\ln(1 + u^2) + C$
$\int \arcsin(u)du = u\arcsin(u) + \sqrt{1 - u^2} + C$	$\int \arccos(u)du = u\arccos(u) - \sqrt{1 - u^2} + C$
$\int \sec^2(u)\,du = \tan(u) + C$	$\int \csc^2(u)\,du = -\cot(u) + C$

Integrals with Trigonometric Results

$\int \frac{1}{n^2 + u^2}du = \frac{1}{n}\arctan(\frac{u}{n}) + C$	$\int \frac{1}{\sqrt{n^2 - u^2}}du = \arcsin(\frac{u}{n}) + C$
$\int \frac{1}{u\sqrt{u^2 - 1}}du = \text{arcsec}(u) + C$	

H.8   Integration Formulas

H.8.1   Geometric Formulas

The formulas below presume a standard Cartesian xy plane, with y as a true function of x (i.e., each x value has at most 1 y result). Standard calculus assumptions apply (i.e., smooth and continuous function). The limits of integration will be the starting and ending x values.

- **The Area Under the Curve**
  (when the curve is below the x axis this will yield a negative area)

$$\int y\,dx$$

  This is based on the equation for the area of a rectangle that is y high and dx wide.

- **The Length of a Curve**

$$\int \sqrt{dx^2 + dy^2}$$

  This is based on the distance formula (i.e., solving the Pythagorean theorem for C), where A and B are dx and dy.

- **The Volume of Rotation Around the x-Axis**

$$\int \pi y^2\,dx$$

  This is based on the volume of a cylinder, $\pi r^2 h$, where y is the radius and dx is the height. Remember that the cylinder is on its side.

- **The Volume of Rotation Around the y-Axis**
  (on parts of the graph where x and y have opposite signs this will yield a negative volume)

$$\int 2\pi xy\,dx$$

  This is based on the volume of an extremely thin (dx thick) box wrapped around the y axis. Since it is wrapped around the y axis, its length is the circumference of the circle at x, or $2\pi x$, and its height is simply the y value.

Shapes involving the boundaries of two curves can usually be found by subtracting the results of applying the formula to one curve from the other. The rules for generating equations such as these using integrals is given in Chapter 20.

H.8.2   Other Formulas

- **Average Value Formula**
  The average y value on a curve from $x = a$ to $x = b$ can be given by:

$$\text{average}(y) = \frac{\int_a^b y\,dx}{b - a}$$

CPSIA information can be obtained
at www.ICGtesting.com
Printed in the USA
BVHW01*0046200618
519330BV00039BA/665/P